D1064577

IMPROVEMENT OF LIVESTOCK

THE MACMILLAN COMPANY
NEW YORK · CHICAGO
DALLAS · ATLANTA · SAN FRANCISCO
LONDON · MANILA

IN CANADA
BRETT-MACMILLAN LTD.
GALT, ONTARIO

IMPROVEMENT OF LIVESTOCK

by RALPH BOGART

Professor of Animal Husbandry, Oregon State College
and Animal Husbandman, Oregon Agricultural Experiment Station

THE MACMILLAN COMPANY · NEW YORK

PREFACE

The increase in population which is taking place brings with it the problem of providing food. Meats and other animal products contribute to a better state of human health and are desired by most Americans. In order for the average person to have the meat he likes and needs, it becomes more important for the producer to improve the over-all efficiency of his production. One area in which the producer may improve his production is through breeding. The improvement of livestock through breeding is mainly dependent on the application of genetic principles.

Most meat and other animal products are produced in commercial operations rather than in purebred herds and flocks. The problems of the purebred breeder and of the commercial producer are quite different, although it is axiomatic that the responsibility of the purebred breeder is largely that of improving his livestock for those traits which are important economically to the commercial breeder. In addition to this he needs to fix those traits through a breeding system so that animals from his herd will continually transmit those desirable traits in as high a degree as possible. It is the responsibility of the commercial breeder to exploit the genetic material from the purebred herds in a way which will give maximum production of a desirable product at as low a cost as possible. This fact has been given careful consideration in developing certain sections of this book. One section is devoted entirely to commercial herd improvement, of which the practical characteristics have been stressed.

In a field such as livestock improvement it is natural that I would draw heavily from my own experience in teaching and research. It follows, too, that in the discussion of the problems of animal improvement, I would express my own ideas and philosophies. Without doing these things, little or no contribution to the knowledge of animal improvement could be made by any practitioner in the field.

This book has been prepared for the student who has some knowledge of biology. It is based on the assumption that the student needs to review some of the basic genetic principles before applying them to the improvement of livestock. However, an attempt has been made to simplify the material so that readers with less biological and statistical background can also understand the concepts. Many of our farmers and ranchers are anxious to learn and to apply the basic knowledge of breeding in the improvement of their own herd and flocks, and therefore it is hoped that this book will contribute to their understanding of the principles of livestock improvement so that they will use more effective breeding programs.

In some cases management is so closely related to the improvement made possible through breeding that some of these management practices have been discussed in the text. However, the greater emphasis is placed on genetic improvement, on the assumption that optimum management is already in effect.

Many teachers use other books as references to complement the required text. For this reason material relative to the historical background of genetics has not been included, since other authors have expertly and fully provided many reference sources for this information.

I have had help and encouragement in preparing this book from many friends. To each of them I am very grateful. Some individuals deserve special thanks. Dr. R. T. Clark, Coordinator of The Western Regional Beef Cattle Breeding Research, has made office and other facilities available to me. I have drawn heavily on references provided by him and by Dr. Carl Roubicek, University of Arizona. The manuscript has been read and suggestions for improvement offered by Dr. Carl Roubicek and Dr. Hugo Krueger, Oregon State College, Dr. C. D. Squiers, Alabama Polytechnic Institute, and Dr. E. P. Warren, University of Georgia. Photographs and other material, including table data and charts, have been provided by Dr. Paul W. Gregory, University of California, Davis, California; Dr. C. E. Terrill, U. S. Sheep Breeding Station, Dubois, Idaho; Dr. Paul E. Bernier, Dr. J. E. Oldfield, Dr. D. W. Hedrick, Prof. A. W. Oliver, and Mr. Paul Rutland, Oregon State College; Dr. Paul O. Stratton, University of Wyoming; Prof. Walter H. Smith and the late Dr. H. L. Ibsen, Kansas State College; Dr. W. A. Craft, Regional Swine Breeding Laboratory, Ames, Iowa; Dr. Paul B. Sawin, Roscoe B. Jackson Memorial Laboratory, Bar Harbor, Maine; and Mr. Tom Lasater, Matheson, Colorado, breeder of Beefmaster cattle.

I have also drawn heavily on reports from the research done by various workers in the regional laboratories on beef cattle, sheep, swine, and poultry. I am especially indebted to my colleagues and graduate students, past and present, for their many contributions. Some of these persons have aided materially in the final preparations of this manuscript. I am especially indebted to Earl Ray, G. I. Alexander, Robert deBaca, Gordon Jessup, Floyd Stout, Mr. and Mrs. Lewis Brandt, and Robert Manning. I am particularly appreciative of material supplied by the American Berkshire Association, Springfield, Illinois; Chester White Record Association, Rochester, Indiana; the Hampshire Swine Registry, Peoria, Illinois; and Mr. Harry G. Hurlein of The Rockland Farms, New City, N. Y.

I am indebted to Mrs. Charles Pease, Robert Mason and to Elizabeth Bogart for assistance in checking the reference material.

Although every effort has been made by my colleagues who have read the manuscript, and by myself, to prevent any error from appearing in this book, I accept full responsibility for any that may have been made.

RALPH BOGART

Oregon State College
Corvallis, Oregon

TABLE OF CONTENTS

LIST OF FIGURES

LIST OF TABLES

ONE PAIR OF GENES—THE SIX FUNDAMENTAL TYPES OF MATING

The principles of genetics are based on the knowledge that the genes are in the *chromosomes* (bodies in the nucleus which have an affinity for chrome dyes) and that the distribution of the chromosomes in gamete production and fertilization governs the distribution of the genes. Thus the genes, which control the manner in which characters develop, are transmitted from parents to offspring by the passing of the chromosomes from the parents to the offspring.

When only one pair of alleles is taken into consideration, only three kinds of zygotes are possible. This is the case in the example of coat color in cattle (where B = black and b = red) in which the three kinds of zygote are (1) the homozygous dominant, BB, (2) the heterozygotes, Bb, and (3) the recessive, bb. With one pair of alleles, and using various combinations of the three kinds of zygote, there are six types of mating possible. These six fundamental types of mating, in which only one pair of alleles are involved, are called monohybrid (mono = one) matings. The same genes previously used will serve for illustration. The chromosome carrying the gene is shown with the segment in the chromosome indicated as the gene locus by a short cross line.

HOMOZYGOUS DOMINANT × HOMOZYGOUS DOMINANT

It can be seen (Fig. 1) that homozygous dominants × homozygous dominants produce all homozygous dominants. Each of the homozygous dominant individuals produces only the one kind of gamete.

HOMOZYGOUS DOMINANT × HETEROZYGOTE

The homozygous dominant produces only one kind of gamete, whereas the heterozygote produces two kinds in equal numbers; one carrying the domi-

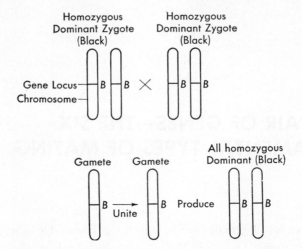

Fig. 1. Mating of homozygous dominant × homozygous dominant. Matings are shown as one individual × another individual.

nant gene while the other carries the recessive gene (Fig. 2). There is equal chance for the gamete produced by the homozygous dominant individual to unite with either of the gametes produced by the heterozygote. This type of mating gives homozygous and heterozygous dominants in approximately equal numbers, but all of them look alike; they are in this case all black. Because of the chance in gametic union, the exact ratio of 1:1 would not occur in actual practice.

HOMOZYGOUS DOMINANT × HOMOZYGOUS RECESSIVE

Both the homozygous dominant and the homozygous recessive individual will produce only one kind of gamete, since they are both pure, but naturally the one produces gametes carrying the dominant, *B,* while the other produces gametes carrying the recessive, *b,* gene (Fig. 3). This kind of mating gives all heterozygotes, all of which will be dominant in appearance.

It can be seen that when a homozygous dominant is used for breeding, all its offspring will show the dominant character, regardless of the kind of animal with which it is mated, i.e., another homozygous dominant, a heterozygote, or a homozygous recessive. This must be contrasted with the results obtained when a heterozygote is mated to another heterozygote or to a recessive, in which case, as will be shown, the offspring are not all alike in appearance. It is this difference in kind of offspring produced that distinguishes homozygous from heterozygous dominant individuals.

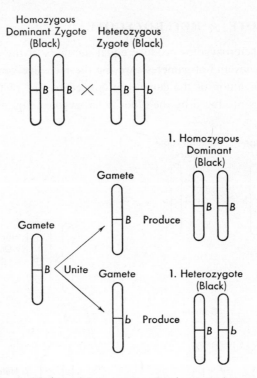

Fig. 2. Mating of homozygous dominant × heterozygote.

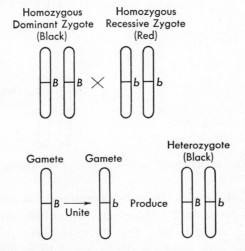

Fig. 3. Mating of homozygous dominant × homozygous recessive.

HETEROZYGOTE × HETEROZYGOTE

Each of the heterozygotes produce equal numbers of the gametes carrying the dominant genes and of gametes carrying the recessive genes. There is also equal chance for union of the gametes produced by one of the heterozygotes with the gametes produced by the other heterozygote (Fig. 4).

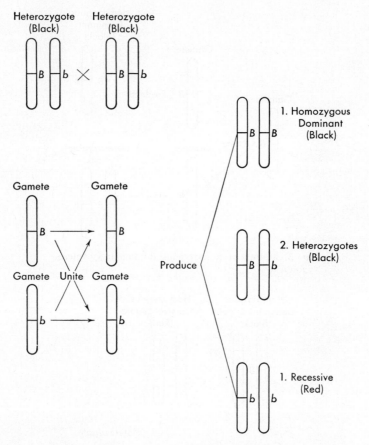

Fig. 4. Mating of heterozygote × heterozygote.

A ratio of 3 black:1 red is shown by appearance, but genetically the ratio is 1 homozygous dominant:2 heterozygotes:1 recessive. Any group of animals looking alike would be placed in the same phenotype. Any group of animals having the same genetic make-up would be in the same genotype. These ratios, both genotypic and phenotypic, will be only approximately correct with small numbers because of chance in gametic union.

HETEROZYGOTE × HOMOZYGOUS RECESSIVE

In this mating the phenotypic and genotypic ratios are both 1:1 (Fig. 5), i.e., the phenotypic ratio is 1 black:1 red, and the genotypic ratio is 1 hetero-zygote:1 recessive.

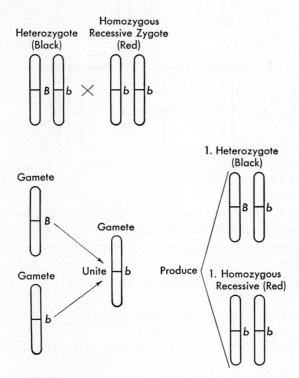

Fig. 5. Mating of heterozygote × homozygous re-cessive.

RECESSIVE × RECESSIVE

Since recessives must be homozygous, it follows that they will breed true when mated (Fig. 6).

If one learns these six types of mating, he will be in a position to understand the more complicated genetics in which more than one pair of genes is involved.

In the early work on genetics it was usual to mate the homozygous dominant to the recessive, producing offspring which were all heterozygous. These heterozygotes were then mated to produce a phenotypic ratio of 3 dominant:1 recessive. The first generation in which the pure dominant is mated to the

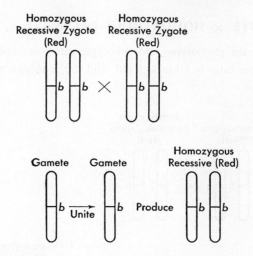

Fig. 6. Mating of homozygous recessive × homozygous recessive.

recessive is called the *First Parental* (P_1) generation. The heterozygous offspring produced by this mating are the *First Filial* (F_1) generation. The offspring produced when the heterozygotes are mated are called the *Second Filial* (F_2) generation. The gametes produced by the P_1 and F_1 individuals are called the P_1 gametes and F_1 gametes, respectively.

$$BB \quad \times \quad bb \longleftarrow P_1 \text{ zygotes}$$
$$B \longrightarrow b \longleftarrow P_1 \text{ gametes} \quad = Bb \longleftarrow F_1 \text{ zygote}$$
$$Bb \quad \times \quad Bb \longleftarrow F_1 \text{ zygotes (heterozygotes)}$$

$$\left. \begin{array}{c} B \longrightarrow B \\ \nearrow \\ b \longrightarrow b \end{array} \right\} F_1 \text{ gametes} \quad = \left. \begin{array}{c} 1\ BB \\ 2\ Bb \\ 1\ bb \end{array} \right\} \longleftarrow F_2 \text{ zygotes}$$

One can illustrate the production of gametes by the heterozygotes and the chance combination of these gametes by coin tossing. If one considers a coin having "head" on one side and "tail" on the other, it can be thought of as a heterozygote. If this coin were tossed several times, it should come up "heads" and "tails" with approximately equal frequency. If a heterozygous individual is producing gametes, they will be produced in approximately equal numbers of those carrying the dominant and of those carrying the recessive gene. If we make "heads" dominant and "tails" recessive, this could be illustrated with a coin being of the "genotype" *Hh*. If two such coins are tossed at the same time and a record is made of how the two came up at each toss, there will be an approximate ratio of 1 with both heads:2 with one coin showing head and one showing tail:1 with both tails. The ratio will not be exactly like this, and certainly with only four tosses one would not be likely to get a 1:2:1 ratio, even though the possibility exists. If one tossed these coins 100 times, the ratio would be very close to 1:2:1. The same is true when two heterozygous individuals are mated. With only four offspring it would not be likely that a ratio of 1:2:1 would be obtained even though such a ratio is possible. If 100 offspring were produced by mating heterozygotes, the ratio would be very close to 1 homozygous dominant:2 heterozygotes:1 recessive.

It can be seen from the material presented that recessive individuals are always pure for the character but that dominant individuals may be either homozygous or heterozygous. It is sometimes very important to test an animal showing the dominant character to determine if it is pure for the dominant or not. The simplest test, when possible, is to mate the dominant in question to the recessive. If it is pure, all its offspring will show the dominant character. If it is heterozygous, one-half the offspring should be dominant and one-half recessive.

PROBABILITIES IN GENETIC TESTING

A heterozygous individual would be expected one-half of the time to produce the gamete carrying the recessive gene. Thus, with two offspring, when this heterozygote is mated to the recessive, the expectancy is that one of the offspring will be recessive. If one uses this as a basic concept, it is evident that $(\frac{1}{2})^7 = \frac{1}{128}$, or with seven offspring in which a dominant is tested by mating to a recessive and none of the offspring are showing the dominant, the odds of this occurring by chance alone are less than 1 in 100. When a dominant animal produces a recessive offspring, it shows clearly that the dominant animal is heterozygous. It would be impossible for a homozygous dominant to produce any recessive offspring.

Sometimes it is impossible to mate the dominant animal to the recessive because the recessive type may be sterile, lethal (nonviable), etc. In such cases one can take as test animals any of the dominants that have produced the recessive, since they have proved themselves to be heterozygous by producing a recessive offspring. If these known heterozygotes are mated to the dominant in question, and any recessive offspring are produced, it proves that the dominant animal being tested carries the recessive gene (is heterozygous). One can expect 3 dominant:1 recessive if the dominant under test is heterozygous and is tested by mating to known heterozygotes. It will take at least 10 to 11 offspring with no recessives produced to be reasonably sure (odds of 19 to 1) that the dominant animal under test is homozygous, but only one recessive offspring is needed to prove that this animal is heterozygous. If one wants odds of 99:1 that the dominant individual under test is homozygous, it will require 16 offspring with none showing the dominant when the animal under test is mated to known heterozygotes. This is determined by raising ¾ to the power necessary to give the odds desired.

A second method may be used for testing a dominant male for homozygosity when it is impossible to mate him to the recessive. This is done by mating the sire back to its offspring. In this case one may assume that the male is mated to homozygous females. If a bull, for example, is homozygous for the dominant, all his offspring will be dominant even though he is mated back to his daughters. If he is heterozygous he should sire equal numbers of homozygous and heterozygous daughters if mated to homozygous females. When he is mated back to his daughters, those that are homozygous would produce only the dominant offspring, while those that are heterozygous would be expected to produce 3 dominant:1 recessive. Since the homozygous and heterozygous daughters should be equal in number if the dams are homozygous, a male that is heterozygous should produce 7 dominant:1 recessive when mated back to his daughters.

$$
\begin{aligned}
\text{Male } Dd \times \text{ females } \quad & DD = 1 \ DD{:}1 \ Dd \\
\times \text{ daughters } \ & DD = \text{all dominant} \\
\times \text{ daughters } \ & Dd = 3 \text{ dominant:1 recessive}
\end{aligned}
$$

To balance, one would make the *DD* daughters equal to the *Dd* ones, and there would be:

4—all dominant from the *DD* daughters
3—dominant:1 recessive from the *Dd* daughters
———
and for all matings 7 dominant:1 recessive

To determine the number of offspring necessary when the sire is mated to his daughters, one raises ⅞ to the power necessary to give the odds desired. The power to which ⅞ is raised to give odds approximately 19:1 or 99:1 is the number of offspring necessary when a sire is mated to his daughters and none of the offspring shows the recessive. Obviously, one recessive offspring proves that the sire is heterozygous for that character, but it would take 23 to 24 offspring (all showing the dominant) to give odds of 19:1, and it would take 34 to 35 offspring (all showing the dominant) to give odds of 99:1 that the sire is homozygous for the dominant.

The percentage of the time one can expect heterozygous animals to produce offspring of which all show the dominant can be shown. This percentage of the time is presented in tests for heterozygosity by mating to a recessive, by mating to known heterozygotes and by mating a sire to his daughters (Table 1).

Table 1. THE PERCENTAGE OF TIME ONE WOULD EXPECT HETEROZYGOUS ANIMALS TO PRODUCE OFFSPRING ALL OF WHICH SHOW THE DOMINANT ACCORDING TO NUMBER OF OFFSPRING AND TYPE OF TEST MATING.

Number of Offspring	Mating to Recessives	Mating to Known Heterozygotes	Mating a Sire to His Daughters
1	50.00	75.00	87.50
2	25.00	56.25	76.56
3	12.50	42.19	69.99
4	6.25	31.64	58.62
5	3.13	23.73	51.29
6	1.57	17.18	44.88
7	0.79	12.89	39.27
8	0.40	9.67	34.36
9		7.25	30.07
10		5.44	26.31
11		4.08	23.02
12		3.06	20.14
13		2.30	17.62
14		1.73	15.42
15		1.30	13.49
16		0.99	11.80
17		0.74	10.33
18		0.56	9.04
19		0.42	7.91
20		0.32	6.92
21			6.06
22			5.30
23			4.64
24			4.06
25			3.55
26			3.11
27			2.72
28			2.38
29			2.08
30			1.82
31			1.59
32			1.39
33			1.22
34			1.07
35			0.94

EXERCISES

1. Define or explain by diagram or some other method the following:

alleles	recessive
heterozygous	phenotypic ratio

dominant P_1 zygote
identical genes   homologous chromosome
homozygous F_1 gamete
genotypic ratio

2. A black guinea pig was mated to a chocolate guinea pig and produced
   A, a black male
   B, a black female
   C, a chocolate male
   D, a chocolate female

When male A was mated to female B, they produced eight black and three chocolate offspring. When male A was mated to female D, they produced five black and
five chocolate offspring. When male C was mated to female B, they produced seven
black and seven chocolate offspring. When male C was mated to female D, they
produced 17 chocolate offspring. Deduce the mode of inheritance.

3. In cattle, B = black and b = red. A Guernsey breeder (cattle are red
or bb) has filed suit against the man from whom he purchased a purebred Guernsey bull because this bull allegedly sired a black-and-white spotted calf. You are
asked to render a decision on this case to determine if the purchaser has grounds
for judgment against the seller of the bull.

2

MORE THAN ONE PAIR OF GENES—
INDEPENDENT INHERITANCE

If more than one pair of genes is considered at the same time, it would be possible for all to be in the same pair of chromosomes or for each pair of alleles to be in a different pair of chromosomes. If more than one pair of genes is in the same pair of homologous chromosomes, the genes are linked by the mere fact that they are in the same chromosomes. For the time being, we shall consider genes that are not linked. Since they are present in different pairs of chromosomes, the segregation and recombination of one pair of alleles is completely independent of how another pair of alleles may segregate or combine.

TWO PAIRS OF GENES

With two pairs of genes and one pair of alleles in each of two pairs of homologous chromosomes, there can be nine different kinds of zygote. The following example in cattle may be used to illustrate:

B = black	P = polled (naturally hornless)
b = red	p = horned

1. *BBPP*	6. *Bbpp*
2. *BBPp*	7. *bbPP*
3. *BBpp*	8. *bbPp*
4. *BbPP*	9. *bbpp*
5. *BbPp*	

With this variety of zygotes it would be possible to have 45 different crosses. No attempt will be made to show all of these crosses. It can be noted that four of the nine zygotes are double homozygotes and that one is a double heterozygote. One of the double homozygous individuals (number 9) is also known as a double recessive.

Double homozygous zygotes can produce only one kind of gamete. It should be kept in mind that the zygote with the genetic makeup of *Bb* would be expected to produce in approximately equal numbers those gametes carrying the *B* gene and those carrying the *b* gene. An individual heterozygous *Pp* would be expected to produce in approximately equal numbers those gametes carrying the *P* gene and those carrying the *p* gene. When the same individual is heterozygous, *Bb Pp,* the gamete production would be:

$$1B \begin{cases} 1P = 1Bp \\ 1p = 1Bp \end{cases}$$
$$1b \begin{cases} 1P = 1bP \\ 1p = 1bp \end{cases}$$

If two double heterozygotes, *Bp Pp,* are mated, one has several methods of calculating what kinds of offspring will be produced. It is possible to show it by arrows:

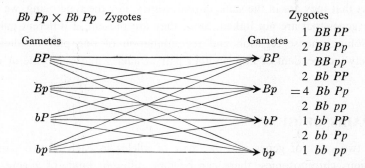

This is rather cumbersome and the inexperienced person might make errors when using this method. Some people prefer to use the checkerboard method:

	BP	Bp	bP	bp
BP	BB PP	BB Pp	Bb PP	Bb Pp
Bp	BB Pp	BB pp	Bb Pp	Bb pp
bP	Bb PP	Bb Pp	bb PP	bb Pp
bp	Bb Pp	Bb pp	bb Pp	bb pp

1 *BB PP*
2 *BB Pp*
1 *BB pp*
2 *Bb PP*
= 4 *Bb Pp*
2 *Bb pp*
1 *bb PP*
2 *bb Pp*
1 *bb pp*

The big difficulties with this method are that (1) it is a definite problem to determine the genotypic ratios after the checkerboard is completed, and (2) one has no way of using the checkerboard for working out the cross phenotypically.

A much better method than either of the ones listed above is that known as the *bracket* method. It is based on the assumption that one knows the genotypic and/or phenotypic ratio that would result in any one of the six fundamental types of mating in which one pair of genes is involved.

If one uses the bracket method of working the cross genotypically when two double heterozygotes are mated, it will be quite simple and accurate.

Bb Pp × *Bb Pp* produces:

$$1 \ BB \begin{cases} 1 \ PP = 1 \ BB \ PP \\ 2 \ Pp = 2 \ BB \ Pp \\ 1 \ pp = 1 \ BB \ pp \end{cases}$$

$$2 \ Bb \begin{cases} 1 \ PP = 2 \ Bb \ PP \\ 2 \ Pp = 4 \ Bb \ Pp \\ 1 \ pp = 2 \ Bb \ pp \end{cases}$$

$$1 \ bb \begin{cases} 1 \ PP = 1 \ bb \ PP \\ 2 \ Pp = 2 \ bb \ Pp \\ 1 \ pp = 1 \ bb \ pp \end{cases}$$

The number before the letters in the left-hand column must be multiplied by those before the letters in the right-hand column in order to get the proper ratio.

To work this cross phenotypically, the bracket method can also be used. It is both rapid and accurate for obtaining either the genotypic or phenotypic ratio.

Bb Pp × *Bb Pp* produces:

$$3 \ \text{black} \begin{cases} 3 \ \text{polled} = 9 \ \text{black polled} \\ 1 \ \text{horned} = 3 \ \text{black horned} \end{cases}$$

$$1 \ \text{red} \begin{cases} 3 \ \text{polled} = 3 \ \text{red polled} \\ 1 \ \text{horned} = 1 \ \text{red horned} \end{cases}$$

The number before the phenotypes in the left-hand column must be multiplied by the number before the phenotypes in the right-hand column to obtain the proper ratio.

Generally, problems will arise in which both parents are not double heterozygotes. Also, many times there may be three or four pairs of genes involved instead of only two pairs. The bracket method of working out either genotypic or phenotypic ratios when crosses are made in which several pairs of genes are involved never becomes complicated, but it does require more writing than if only two pairs of genes were involved.

THREE PAIRS OF GENES

When three pairs of genes are considered, it is possible to have a triple homozygote, heterozygote, or recessive. It may be quite difficult to differentiate a triple heterozygote from a triple homozygous dominant. Triple recessives can be located by inspection and triple heterozygotes can be produced by mating an animal showing all three dominant genes to a triple recessive, and then using from this cross the offspring which shows all three dominants. This individual would have to be a triple heterozygote.

By using the three pairs of genes in cattle, we can see what ratio would be obtained when two triple heterozygotes are mated if we were to use enough of this kind of female to get sufficient offspring, where

S = solid color　　　　　B = black　　　　P = polled
s = white spotted　　　　b = red　　　　　p = horned

Phenotypically:
Ss Bb Pp ♂ × *Ss Bb Pp* ♀♀ produces:

3 solid	3 black	3 polled = 27 solid black polled
		1 horned = 9 solid black polled
	1 red	3 polled = 9 solid red polled
		1 horned = 3 solid red horned
1 white spotted	3 black	3 polled = 9 black and white polled
		1 horned = 3 black and white horned
	1 red	3 polled = 3 red and white polled
		1 horned = 1 red and white horned

64, total, as the minimum number for expression of the phenotypic ratio

The group in which there are 27 shows all three dominants. The groups in which there are 9 show two dominants and one recessive. The groups in which there are 3 show one dominant and two recessives. There is only 1 in which all three recessives show. One must remember that this ratio of 27:9:9:9:3: 3:3:1 would be closely approximated only when large numbers are produced. With only 64 individuals, the minimum number, some of the classes might not be represented.

Genotypically:

$Ss\,Bb\,Pp\ \male \times Ss\,Bb\,Pp\ \female\,\female$ produces:

$$
1\,SS
\begin{cases}
1\,BB
\begin{cases}
1\,PP = 1\,SS\,BB\,PP \\
2\,Pp = 2\,SS\,BB\,Pp \\
1\,pp = 1\,SS\,BB\,pp
\end{cases} \\[2ex]
2\,Bb
\begin{cases}
1\,PP = 2\,SS\,Bb\,PP \\
2\,Pp = 4\,SS\,Bb\,Pp \\
1\,pp = 2\,SS\,Bb\,pp
\end{cases} \\[2ex]
1\,bb
\begin{cases}
1\,PP = 1\,SS\,bb\,PP \\
2\,Pp = 2\,SS\,bb\,Pp \\
1\,pp = 1\,SS\,bb\,pp
\end{cases}
\end{cases}
$$

$$
2\,Ss
\begin{cases}
1\,BB
\begin{cases}
1\,PP = 2\,Ss\,BB\,PP \\
2\,Pp = 4\,Ss\,BB\,Pp \\
1\,pp = 2\,Ss\,BB\,pp
\end{cases} \\[2ex]
2\,Bb
\begin{cases}
1\,PP = 4\,Ss\,Bb\,PP \\
2\,Pp = 8\,Ss\,Bb\,Pp \\
1\,pp = 4\,Ss\,Bb\,pp
\end{cases} \\[2ex]
1\,bb
\begin{cases}
1\,PP = 2\,Ss\,bb\,PP \\
2\,Pp = 4\,Ss\,bb\,Pp \\
1\,pp = 2\,Ss\,bb\,pp
\end{cases}
\end{cases}
$$

$$
1\,ss
\begin{cases}
1\,BB
\begin{cases}
1\,PP = 1\,ss\,BB\,PP \\
2\,Pp = 2\,ss\,BB\,Pp \\
1\,pp = 1\,ss\,BB\,pp
\end{cases} \\[2ex]
2\,Bb
\begin{cases}
1\,PP = 2\,ss\,Bb\,PP \\
2\,Pp = 4\,ss\,Bb\,Pp \\
1\,pp = 2\,ss\,Bb\,pp
\end{cases} \\[2ex]
1\,bb
\begin{cases}
1\,PP = 1\,ss\,bb\,PP \\
2\,Pp = 2\,ss\,bb\,Pp \\
1\,pp = 1\,ss\,bb\,pp
\end{cases}
\end{cases}
$$

It can be noted that there are eight kinds of homozygotes produced, with one individual in each case. Those homozygous for two pairs of genes and heterozygous for the third pair are in the groups in which there are two. Those homozygous for one pair of genes and heterozygous for the other two pairs are the groups in which there are four. The individuals of the one group of eight are heterozygous for all three pairs of genes.

PHENOTYPIC AND GENOTYPIC PREDICTIONS IN THE F_2 GENERATION

Since the results for mono- (one pair of alleles), di- (two pairs of alleles), and trihybrid (three pairs of alleles) crosses have been shown, it should be possible to make predictions based on crosses involving any number of pairs of alleles (polyhybrid crosses). The predictions that will be presented here will be only for the F_2 generation. It has been shown that 4 individuals are the minimum necessary in order to obtain the correct genotypic or phenotypic ratio in a monohybrid mating (both individuals are heterozygous for the one pair of alleles); 16, or $(4)^2$, for the dihybrid (both individuals used in the mating are heterozygous for 2 pairs of alleles); and 64, or $(4)^3$, for a trihybrid (both individuals used in the mating are heterozygous for 3 of the alleles). Therefore, for crosses involving any number (n) of pairs of alleles, the total number of individuals necessary to obtain the correct genotypic or phenotypic ratio would be at least $(4)^n$. For example, if the cross involves 10 pairs of alleles, $(4)^{10}$, or 1,048,576, individuals will be necessary to obtain the genotypic or phenotypic ratio in the F_2 generation, where each of the animals used in the cross is heterozygous for all 10 pairs of alleles.

It can be seen that a breeder of cattle who raises 1,000 calves per year, and this would be considered a large herd, would have to breed cattle for 1,000 years in order to obtain the complete genotypic or phenotypic ratio if 10 traits, each determined by one pair of genes, were in the heterozygous state. If one trait is conditioned by only four pairs of genes, a small breeder producing only 85 calves per year would need three calf crops in order to obtain the genotypic or phenotypic ratios when multiple heterozygotes are mated.

In a monohybrid cross three different genotypes are produced in the F_2 generation; in a dihybrid cross, 9, or $(3)^2$; and in a trihybrid cross, 27, or $(3)^3$. Therefore, in a cross involving 10 pairs of alleles, there would be $(3)^{10}$, or 59,049, genotypes in the F_2 generation. It becomes evident that with most of our farm animals there is little possibility of all F_2 genotypes being produced in crosses involving many pairs of alleles, since we usually have small numbers, particularly in beef cattle.

The possibility of a breeder obtaining a particular genotype when many genes are involved is very remote. Even if such an animal were obtained, the possibility of obtaining a mate of the opposite sex which would be identical in genotype would be extremely improbable.

The number of possible factor combinations (phenotypes) can also be calculated. When dominance is complete, the number of phenotypes is 2 in the F_2 generation of a monohybrid cross; 4, or $(2)^2$, in a dihybrid cross; and 8, or $(2)^3$, in a trihybrid cross. It is apparent then that for n pairs of alleles, the number of phenotypes is $(2)^n$. If 10 pairs of alleles are concerned, there will be $(2)^{10}$, or 1,024, phenotypes (factor combinations) in the F_2 generation (Ibsen, 1951). Obviously, the number of phenotypes will depend upon whether or not dominance is complete for all the pairs of alleles. If dominance is incomplete (i.e., the heterozygote has a phenotype different from either homozygote) for some of the alleles, the number of phenotypes will be correspondingly increased and will approach the number of genotypes.

Since the factor combinations (phenotypes) are much fewer than the genotypic groups, it is obvious that many genotypes are included in the same phenotypes. With 10 pairs of genes involved in the heterozygous condition the number of phenotypes is only 1,024 when there is complete dominance, whereas the number of genotypes is 59,049. This would almost preclude genotypic selection by use of phenotypic expression of the characters.

DETERMINING THE GENOTYPE OF ANIMALS

So far, the discussion has been concerned with determining what kind of offspring would be expected when animals of known genotype are mated. More often the livestock breeder is concerned with determining the genotype of certain animals. A great deal may be learned from the appearance of an animal, particularly if it is showing the recessive character, since one always recognizes the genotype of the animal with the recessive character.

The first step in determining the genotype of an animal is to write down what can be deduced from the appearance. One can then look at either the parents or the offspring of the animal, or both, for further information. In some cases it may not be possible to determine the genotype of an animal except by mating it to specific tester animals. An example in horses illustrates how one may approach the problem. In horses:

G = gray	B = black	S = white spotted
g = nongray	b = chestnut	s = solid color

A black, gray, and white spotted stallion was bred to a herd of solid chestnut mares and produced the following foals:

9 black, gray-and-white spotted
10 solid black-gray
10 black-and-white spotted
9 solid black

The first step is to look at the stallion and the mares and record what is known.

Stallion is B_____ S_____ G_____, but appearance does not reveal whether or not he is pure for each of these.

The mares are *bb ss gg*, since they are recessive for all three characters. By inspection of the offspring we see that even when the stallion is bred to mares that are recessive (chestnut), all the offspring produced are black. We are justified in assuming that the stallion is pure (homozygous) for black or *BB* in genotype.

Now, considering white spotting, we find that the white-spotted stallion has sired some solid-colored foals. It proves that he is impure (heterozygous) for white spotting, or is *Ss* in genotype. The other pair of genes is that for gray. Again, the stallion has sired some nongray foals and thus proves himself to be heterozygous for gray, or *Gg* in genotype. We can now write down the complete genotype of the stallion and the mares:

Stallion BB Ss Gg × mares bb ss gg

It is always desirable to check results by working the cross phenotypically to make sure that no mistake has been made. When one checks by this method to show that the animals with the genotypes as determined will produce offspring in the same phenotypic ratio observed in the actual mating, there can be no question but that the genotypic determination is correct.

BB Ss Gg × *bb ss gg* produces:

All black	1 white-spotted	1 gray = 1 black-gray-and-white spotted
		1 nongray = 1 black-and-white spotted
	1 solid	1 gray = solid black-gray
		1 nongray = 1 solid black

If this ratio of 1:1:1:1 is multiplied by nine, the product is 9:9:9:9, which is very close to the 9:10:10:9 ratio actually produced.

It may be that one would also like to know the genotype of the foals that were produced. It so happens that the genotype of each of the foals can be determined by its appearance and by knowing the genotypes of its parents. The procedure for determining the genotypes of the foals is similar to that used in the preceding example. First, one puts down what he knows about the genotype of the foal by its appearance:

Black-gray-and-white spotted	= B_____ G_____ S_____
Solid black-gray	= B_____ G_____ *ss*
Black-and-white spotted	= B_____ *gg* S_____
Solid black	= B_____ *gg ss*

It can be seen immediately that when each of the foals shows the dominant character, it must be heterozygous, since the mare which is the mother in each case is recessive. Thus, with all mares of the genotypes *bb, gg, ss,* it is certain that the genotypes of the foals are:

$$Bb \quad Gg \quad Ss$$
$$Bb \quad Gg \quad ss$$
$$Bb \quad gg \quad Ss$$
$$Bb \quad gg \quad ss$$

Suppose that a black-gray-and-white spotted stallion had been mated to a black-gray-and-white spotted mare, and one foal, a solid chestnut, was produced. This one foal is sufficient to tell us, along with the appearance of the stallion and the mare, what their genotypes are. The following is known about the genotype of the stallion and the mare from their appearances:

$$\text{Stallion } B\text{\_\_\_\_\_ } G\text{\_\_\_\_\_ } S\text{\_\_\_\_\_}$$
$$\text{Mare } \quad B\text{\_\_\_\_\_ } G\text{\_\_\_\_\_ } S\text{\_\_\_\_\_}$$

The appearance is not sufficient to tell us whether they are homozygous or heterozygous for each of the characters. The foal, which is recessive *bb gg ss,* tells us immediately that both the stallion and the mare had to be heterozygous for all three pairs of genes. Then one can be certain that the stallion is *Bb Gg Ss* and the mare also is *Bb Gg Ss* in genotype.

EXERCISES

1. In cattle:

P = polled	S = solid color	B = black
p = horned	s = white spotted	b = red

　　Pp Ss bb ♂ × *Pp ss BB* ♀♀
   (a) Give the appearance of the ♂ and ♀♀.
   (b) Work the cross phenotypically.
   (c) Work the cross genotypically.

2. Use the same genes as given in Exercise 1. A solid black, polled bull × a solid black, polled cow produced a horned, red and white calf. What are the genotypes of the bull, cow, and calf?

3. How could you eliminate an undesirable dominant gene from your herd or flock?

4. How could you get a strain of animals which breed true for a desirable dominant character?

5. Use the same genes as given in Exercise 1 and work each cross phenotypically and genotypically.

    (a) *BB Ss Pp* × *bb Ss pp*
    (b) *Bb Ss Pp* × *Bb ss pp*
    (c) *bb Ss Pp* × *BB Ss Pp*
    (d) *Bb Ss Pp* × *Bb Ss Pp*
    (e) *Bb Ss Pp* × *bb ss pp*

6. In horses:

G = gray	*B* = black
g = nongray	*b* = chestnut

    A black, gray stallion was bred to a group of black, gray mares that were sired by a nongray chestnut stallion and produced:

                16 black, gray
                  4 chestnut gray

    (a) What do you know about the genotype of mares used in this mating?

    (b) What do you know about the genotype of the stallion to which these mares were bred?

7. In cattle:

B = black	*P* = polled	*S* = solid color
b = red	*p* = horned	*s* = white spotted

D = normal
d = dwarf

dd Bb pp SS ♂ × *DD Bb Pp ss* ♀♀

    (a) Give the appearance of the male and females.

    (b) Work the cross phenotypically.

    (c) Work the cross genotypically.

3

GENE INTERACTIONS

The material presented so far has not taken into consideration the interaction of genes, except for pointing out that some genes are dominant over others. It is important to consider all the interactions of genes because the animals we see are the result of genes interacting with other genes, with the cytoplasm, and with the environment under which genes bring about the expression of the characters.

GENES INTERACT WITH OTHER GENES

Allelic Interaction—Dominance

Dominance may be complete, incomplete, or totally lacking, or there may be overdominance. We do have the interaction of alleles with each other, since one of the genes in the allelic pair may be acting to cause the development of the character in one way, while the other gene of the allelic pair may be acting to cause the development of the character in an entirely different way. The final outcome in the development of the character depends on how strong the dominance may be. An example of complete dominance is found in black (*B*) and red (*b*) coat color inheritance in cattle.

The different types of dominance are diagrammed to give a clear understanding of each.

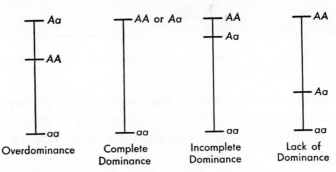

Overdominance   Complete Dominance   Incomplete Dominance   Lack of Dominance

The lines represent total maximum differences between genotypes. In over-dominance the heterozygote is superior to either of the two homozygotes. In complete dominance the homozygous and heterozygous dominants are equal. Where dominance is incomplete, the heterozygote is inferior to, but approaches, the homozygous dominant. The lack of dominance is represented by the heterozygote which is halfway between the two homozygotes. Actually it might be difficult to prove that the incomplete dominance and the lack of dominance are not degrees of the same kind of dominance.

An example in which dominance is not complete is that of the dominant bulldog calf. In this species the homozygous normal animal differs markedly from the animal that is heterozygous. The latter is short-legged and quite small, and the homozygous bulldog is a complete monstrosity (Fig. 7), and dies before birth.

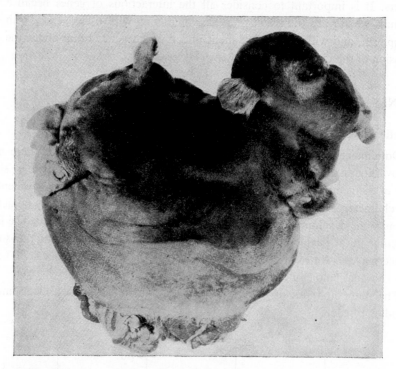

Fig. 7. Bulldog calf (dominant). *(From Mead, Gregory, and Regan,* J. Hered., *37:185, 1946.)*

An example of lack of dominance is found in the roaning character of Shorthorn cattle. The roan color is due to an interspersion of white hair with the colored hairs, which in the case of the Shorthorn are red (Fig. 9). An animal that is pure for the roan gene is white, with a few colored hairs on the inside of the ears (Fig. 8). The heterozygote is roan (Fig. 9), and the homozygous

Fig. 8. White Shorthorn bull, Calrossie Evening News. *(Courtesy American Shorthorn Breeders' Association.)*

animal for the Shorthorn nonroan is red (Fig. 10). There are other kinds of roan besides the red roan because the roan gene does nothing more than intersperse white hairs with the colored hairs.

There is some evidence to indicate that the traits in which complete dominance exists may be slightly different in the homozygous and heterozygous dominant. The concept proposes that complete dominance may exist only because we have been unable to distinguish the two. There is also evidence that the complete and incomplete dominance, and the condition where dominance is lacking, all represent degrees of gene expression and that the categories do not exist as separate entities.

The F_2 ratio of 9:3:3:1 will be modified if one pair of the alleles lacks dominance while there is complete dominance in the other pair. Since neither roan nor nonroan can be considered dominant, it becomes more difficult to apply symbols to the genes. We may, for the time being, let R = roan and N = nonroan. If black and red are used along with the roaning, the ratio comes out considerably different than it would be in the case of complete dominance. Suppose that two double heterozygous black roans are mated.

Fig. 9. Roan Shorthorn female, Lynwood Patience II. *(Courtesy American Shorthorn Breeders' Association.)*

Bb RN × *Bb RN* produces:

$$3 \text{ black} \begin{cases} 1 \text{ white} & = 3 \text{ white; black hairs inner side of ears} \\ 2 \text{ roan} & = 6 \text{ black roan} \\ 1 \text{ nonroan} & = 3 \text{ black} \end{cases}$$

$$1 \text{ red} \begin{cases} 1 \text{ white} & = 1 \text{ white; red hairs inner side of ears} \\ 2 \text{ roan} & = 2 \text{ red roan} \\ 1 \text{ nonroan} & = 1 \text{ red} \end{cases}$$

If there is a lack of dominance in both pairs of alleles of a dihybrid cross, the phenotypic and genotypic ratios will be the same, i.e., 1:2:1:2:4:2:1:2:1.

Overdominance is a condition in which the heterozygous state, *Aa,* produces a greater over-all effect than either of the homozygous conditions, *AA* or *aa.* It is assumed that the allelic interaction accounts for this greater effect of the genes than when they are identical. Let us assume that size is one character which shows the effect of overdominance. If *A* stands for rapid growth and *a*

Fig. 10. Red Shorthorn bull, Scotsdale Jupiter. *(Courtesy American Shornhort Breeders' Association.)*

for an extended growing period, then *Aa* individuals could grow rapidly for a long period of time. Animals that are *AA* would grow rapidly but not for long, and those that are *aa* would grow for a long time but not at a rapid rate. This supposition is purely theoretical, but it is used to show how allelic genes might interact to give overdominance.

There are other possibilities that gene *A* might react favorably under one environment while gene *a* would react favorably under a different environment. As the environment shifted, the *Aa* animal could continue to grow, whereas the *AA* animal would respond favorably only at the time the environment favored it and not when the environment was better for the *aa* animal. Also, the *aa* animal would respond well only when the environment was favoring it and not when the environment changed to the condition in which *AA* is favored.

It is possible that overdominance is the result of linkage of desirable with undesirable genes. If no crossing-over occurred, the two genes would act as one. The only condition in which superior performance for the trait could be obtained would be in the heterozygous state. There is also the possibility of chemical reactions in the Aa animal that could not exist in the AA or aa animal.

Nonallelic Interaction—Epistatic Interaction

Some genes may cover up the expression of other genes to which they are not allelic. This modifies the expected phenotypic ratio but has no influence on the genotypic ratio. When a gene covers up the expression (acts dominant) of a gene to which it is not allelic, it is called *epistatic*. The gene that is not permitted to express itself because of the dominating effect of the epistatic gene is called *hypostatic*. Either dominant or recessive genes may be epistatic to other genes, but to be epistatic the recessive gene must be homozygous, whereas a dominant gene in either the homozygous or heterozygous state may be epistatic to other genes.

In a dihybrid mating in which there is no epistasis (accent on second syllable), the phenotypic ratio is 9 showing both dominants:3 showing one dominant and one recessive character:3 (the opposite to the other group of 3) showing one dominant and one recessive character:1 showing both recessives. This can be illustrated by taking an example in cattle:

$$B = \text{black} \qquad P = \text{polled}$$
$$b = \text{red} \qquad p = \text{horned}$$

$Bb\ Pp \times Bb\ Pp$ produces:

9 B (B or b) P (P or p)	black polled
3 B (B or b) pp	black horned
3 bb P (P or p)	red polled
1 bb pp	red horned

In every dihybrid cross, the ratio in the F_2 generation is 9:3:3:1 as given in the preceding illustration. However, epistatic genes may make it impossible to distinguish some of these groups. This means that individuals belonging to two or more of the factor combinations look alike and are therefore included in the same phenotype.

The case of one dominant gene which is epistatic can be found in cattle and will be used to illustrate what happens to the expected 9:3:3:1 ratio of a dihybrid cross.

In cattle:

B = black (found in Angus) (epistatic to Bs)
b = red (present in Guernseys, Herefords, and Shorthorns)
Bs^* = blackish (found in Jerseys, Ayrshires, and Brown Swiss)
bs = nonblackish

---

* Two letters are used for one gene. These two letters are always paired since they are the symbol for only one gene.

Two double heterozygous black animals, when mated ($Bb\ Bs\ bs \times Bb\ Bs\ bs$), would produce:

$$
\begin{array}{l}
3\ \text{black} \\
B\ (B\ \text{or}\ b)
\end{array}
\left\{
\begin{array}{ll}
3\ \text{blackish} & \\
Bs\ (Bs\ \text{or}\ bs) & \\
1\ \text{nonblackish} & \\
bs\ bs &
\end{array}
\right\} = 12\ \text{black}
$$

$$
\begin{array}{l}
1\ \text{red} \\
bb
\end{array}
\left\{
\begin{array}{ll}
3\ \text{blackish} & = 3\ \text{blackish} \\
Bs\ (Bs\ \text{or}\ bs) & \\
\\
1\ \text{nonblackish} & = 1\ \text{red} \\
bs\ bs &
\end{array}
\right.
$$

Blackish color can show only in the bb animal because in the B animal the black will cover up its expression. This epistatic relation acted such as to put the group of 9 and one of the groups of 3 into the same phenotype. The resulting ratio is 12 black:3 blackish:1 red.

A recessive gene may be epistatic because it may cover up the expression of the other genes to which it is not allelic. To act epistatically, however, it must be in the homozygous state. A good example of a recessive that is epistatic is that of albinism. Although there may be many color genes, an albino is a pink-eyed white.

In rabbits:

C = color B = black
c = albino; epistatic b = chocolate
     to all colors

$Cc\ Bb\ \male \times Cc\ Bb\ \female$ produce:

$$
\begin{array}{l}
3\ \text{colored} \\
C\ (C\ \text{or}\ c)
\end{array}
\left\{
\begin{array}{ll}
3\ \text{black} & = 9\ \text{black} \\
B\ (B\ \text{or}\ b) & \\
1\ \text{chocolate} & = 3\ \text{chocolate} \\
bb &
\end{array}
\right.
$$

$$
\begin{array}{l}
1\ \text{albino} \\
cc
\end{array}
\left\{
\begin{array}{ll}
3\ \text{black} & \\
B\ (B\ \text{or}\ b) & \\
1\ \text{chocolate} & \\
bb &
\end{array}
\right\} = 4\ \text{albino}
$$

In the case of a single recessive epistatic relation, the ratio is 9:3:4, since one of the groups of 3 and the 1 have the same appearance and, consequently, go into the same phenotype.

The case of both a dominant and a recessive epistatic relation can best be shown by using an example of poultry.

In chickens:

I = inhibition of color; white (epistatic to any color)
i = noninhibition of color
W = colored
w = white; White Rock type of white (epistatic to all colors)

When two double heterozygous white chickens of the genotype below are mated, the phenotypic ratio is 13 white:3 colored.

$Ii\,Ww\;\male \times Ii\,Ww\;\female$ produces:

3 inhibited	3 colored	
I (I or i)	W (W or w)	
	1 White Rock	= 13 white
	ww	
1 noninhibited	3 colored	
(colored)	W (W or w)	
ii	1 White Rock	= 3 colored
	ww	

In this case the group of 9, one group of 3, and the 1 are all indistinguishable and, consequently, appear in the same phenotype making a total of 13 white.

Duplicate recessive epistasis is also found in chickens. In this relationship the recessive (in the homozygous state) of one pair of alleles covers up the expression of the dominant of the other pair of alleles.

In chickens:

C = color
c = albino (epistatic to all colors)
W = color
w = white; found in White Rocks (epistatic to all colors)

An albino has no pigment even in the eyes. Therefore the eyes appear pink as a result of the vascularity of the retina. An albino of the genotype $cc\,WW$ × a White Rock of the genotype $CC\,ww$ will give all colored offspring in the F_1 with the genotype $Cc\,Ww$. When two of these colored double heterozygotes are mated, there will be only two phenotypes produced.

As the following diagram shows, the genes are segregating and recombining in the same manner as when no epistatic relations are involved. Epistatic relations simply prevent certain genotypes from being differentiated from other genotypes. It should be apparent that epistatic relations would interfere with selection.

$$
3 \text{ colored} \atop C \ (C \text{ or } c) \left\{ \begin{array}{l} 3 \text{ colored} \\ W \ (W \text{ or } w) \\ 1 \text{ White Rock} \\ ww \end{array} \right\} = 9 \text{ colored}
$$

$$
1 \text{ albino} \atop cc \left\{ \begin{array}{l} 3 \text{ colored} \\ W \ (W \text{ or } w) \\ 1 \text{ White Rock} \\ ww \end{array} \right\} = 7 \text{ white}
$$

In this case the two groups of 3 and the 1 are all white, so they go into one phenotype. It might be possible to distinguish three of the whites from the other four because of the absence of eye pigment in the four that are *cc*.

True examples of duplicate dominant epistasis are found in plants in which there is polyploidy (doubling of chromosomes). It can be seen that a tetraploid would have all of its genes doubled. Such characters as color that result in a 3:1 ratio when heterozygotes are mated would come out 15:1 if double heterozygotes in tetraploids were mated. The duplication of whole sets of genes as a result of polyploidy is not known in farm animals. It is not impossible for such to exist because numerous plants are quite normal as polyploids. A triploid pig has been reported, but no genetic information regarding it has been made available. By the use of such materials as colchicine, a drug which purportedly causes the chromosomes to stick together, it may be possible to produce polyploidy (a duplication of chromosomes) in our farm animals. Melander (1950) and Haggqvist and Bane (1950) produced what they assumed to be a triploid rabbit by treating eggs with colchicine. The size of the erythrocytes and of the young were much larger than normal. Fishberg and Beatty (1951 and 1952), Beatty and Fishberg (1949 and 1951), and Pincus and Waddington (1939) have reported polyploid mouse and rabbit eggs in the precleavage and up to the blastula stage which resulted from temperature and ether treatments. One would expect that tetraploids (double the chromosome number) would survive and be fertile. This would give duplicate genes in animals as in plants.

If one ignores the differences in shade, several examples of a 15:1 ratio can be found in plants. Chaff color in wheat was reported by Nilsson-Ehle to be due to incompletely dominant and incompletely epistatic genes in which each dominant gene increased the intensity of color. Double heterozygous plants of the genotype *Bb B'b'* (where *B* is brown and *b* is white, and *B'* is brown and *b'* is white) would result in a ratio of 15 colored:1 white. There would be more than one intensity of color, however. Similar relations, but with three pairs of duplicate genes, were also reported by Nilsson-Ehle in kernel color of wheat. The triple heterozygote, when self-fertilized, produced 63 colored:1 white. Here, again, there was more than one intensity of kernel color.

Shepherd's Purse is an example of duplicate genes in which dominance and epistasis are both complete. The pure plants, F, or flattened capsules, were $FF\ F'F'$, and when crossed with plants having round capsules, f, of the genotype $ff\ f'f'$, the F_1 had all flattened capsules. The F_2 plants gave a ratio of 15 flattened capsules:1 round capsule because of complete dominance and complete epistasis.

So far, the discussion has dealt only with the dihybrid. It would be possible to have epistasis in trihybrid crosses, but it is perhaps desirable to keep the discussion simple rather than discuss trihybrid crosses in which there is epistasis. There are several epistatic genes in cattle, and one which generally concerns cattle breeders is that in which black, blackish, and brindling are involved. The relation of brindling and blackish will be discussed first before these two are considered together with black.
In cattle:

Bs = blackish Br = brindle; acts only on Bs to produce brindle
bs = nonblackish br = nonbrindle

Jersey cows are generally $Bs\ Bs\ br\ br$. Most of them breed true for blackish, but they are recessive for brindle, since none of them show it. Herefords are $bs\ bs$, since they show no blackish but may carry brindling genes, although the latter would not show because there is no Bs gene with which the Br gene might interact to produce a brindle. If we assume that the Hereford is $bs\ bs$ $Br\ Br$, and the Jersey is $Bs\ Bs\ br\ br$, then a cross of these would give $Bs\ bs$ $Br\ br$, which would be brindle. If these brindle animals were mated, the ratio would be 9 brindle:3 blackish:4 red.

$$
\begin{array}{llll}
 & & \text{3 brindle} & = 9 \text{ brindle} \\
\text{3 blackish} & & Br\ (Br \text{ or } br) & \\
Bs\ (Bs \text{ or } bs) & & \text{1 nonbrindle} & = 3 \text{ blackish} \\
 & & br\ br & \\[2ex]
 & & \text{3 brindle} & \\
\text{1 nonblackish} & & Br\ (Br \text{ or } br) & \\
bs\ bs & & & = 4 \text{ red} \\
 & & \text{1 nonbrindle} & \\
 & & br\ br &
\end{array}
$$

If we recall that black is epistatic to both blackish and brindling, we see that it is possible to have a trihybrid cross in which there is nonallelic gene interaction.

Bb Bs bs Br br × *Bb Bs bs Br br* produces:

$$
\text{1 red } bb
\begin{cases}
\text{3 black} \\
B \ (B \text{ or } b)
\begin{cases}
\text{3 blackish} \\
Bs \ (Bs \text{ or } bs)
\begin{cases}
\text{3 brindle} & = 27 \\
Br \ (Br \text{ or } br) \\
\text{1 nonbrindle} & = 9 \\
br \ br
\end{cases} \\
\text{1 nonblackish} \\
bs \ bs
\begin{cases}
\text{3 brindle} & = 9 \\
Br \ (Br \text{ or } br) \\
\text{1 nonbrindle} & = 3 \\
br \ br
\end{cases}
\end{cases} \\
\underline{\qquad\qquad\qquad} \\
48 \ \text{black}
\end{cases}
$$

3 black
B (B or b)

3 blackish
Bs (Bs or bs)

3 brindle
Br (Br or br)   = 27

1 nonbrindle
br br   = 9

1 nonblackish
bs bs

3 brindle
Br (Br or br)   = 9

1 nonbrindle
br br   = 3

48 black

1 red
bb

3 blackish
Bs (Bs or bs)

3 brindle
Br (Br or br)   = 9 brindle

1 nonbrindle
br br   = 3 blackish

1 nonblackish
bs bs

3 brindle
Br (Br or br)

1 nonbrindle
br br   = 4 red

Epistatic genes are very important to livestock breeders. One undesirable epistatic gene may cover up the expression of numerous desirable genes. Since it is so easy to eliminate undesirable dominant genes by selection or culling, it is generally the undesirable recessive epistatic genes that cause breeders so much trouble. It is apparent that, since one undesirable gene which is epistatic to a large number of desirable genes will lower the desirability of the animals, a breeder may eliminate very valuable inheritance by culling such animals. As will be seen later, these epistatic genes are not manipulated in a selection program in the same way as additive genes. The only way that one can retain desirable genes which are suppressed by undesirable epistatic genes is to judge the performance of the offspring produced by males when mated to females unrelated to these undesirable males. If the offspring produced by mating these animals to unrelated animals perform quite satisfactorily, it is proof that good genes were covered up by undesirable epistatic genes. Mediocre performance of the offspring produced when less desirable animals are bred to unrelated stock is proof of generally poor genetic constitution.

Linear Interaction of Genes

Genes not only interact with alleles, and in some cases with genes in other chromosomes (nonallelic genes), but there is also evidence that they undergo linear interaction in the same chromosome. A given gene may have different phenotypic effects, which are related to its location in the chromosome. Such changes in the effect of a gene due to changes in its location in the chromosome are called *position effects*.

In Drosophilia, the fruit fly, the bar-eye character is due to a small duplication rather than to a point mutation. The normal-eyed fly would be represented by a chromosome with one segment (a) in which the bar gene, *B,* is

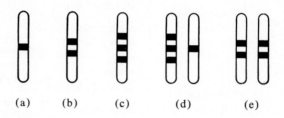

located. When this segment is duplicated, it results in the bar-eye, and it would be represented by showing the chromosome with two segments (b). If the segment is in triplicate, it causes further reduction in eye size and brings about ultrabar. This would be shown by three segments in the chromosome (c).

One would expect that a fly having three such segments in one chromosome and one in the other (d) would have the same phenotypic expression as a fly with two segments in each of the chromosomes (e), since in each fly there is a total of four segments and, thus, of four genes for bar-eye. The two kinds of flies have quite different appearances. The one which has three bars in one chromosome and one in the other has only 45 facets to each compound eye, whereas the fly which has two bars in each chromosome has 68 facets to each compound eye. Thus, the effect of the bar-eye gene is quite different, due to its location.

There have been some other indications that the action of the gene is dependent upon its location in relation to other genes. Such examples are found in translocations and inversions, but there may be some question as to whether these effects are due to the location of a particular gene or to the fact that more material than the gene under study has been carried along in the change.

However, it is evident from the example, i.e., that the effect of the bar-eye gene differs in different locations, that genes are interacting with other genes according to their location.

GENES INTERACT WITH THE CYTOPLASM

The expression of the characters, although fundamentally under the control of the genes, is generally the result of gene-cytoplasm interaction. Clear-cut evidence of gene-cytoplasm interaction in our farm animals is more difficult to obtain than its presence in plants, and particularly in the lower forms of life.

Sonneborn (1951) summarizes the role of genes in cytoplasmic inheritance into five categories. The first is the induction of cytoplasmic mutation. Genes have been reported to induce plastids to change to a form incapable of producing chlorophyll. Also, genes have caused changes to occur in mitochondria. There is reason to believe that changes in many of the granular structures in the cytoplasm may be brought about by the nuclear genes.

The second role of the genes interacting with the cytoplasm is that in which the genes control the intracellular concentration of cytoplasmic self-duplicating material. The best evidence for this is the concentration of kappa particles in killer paramecia. Other evidence for this is found in the cytoplasmic factor in maize which causes male sterility. Here, again, is clear-cut evidence of gene-cytoplasmic interaction.

The third role of genes interacting with the cytoplasm is their action as selective agents acting upon self-duplicating cytoplasmic entities. Where there are alternative self-duplicating structures occurring in the cytoplasm, the intracellular selection of one of these over the other may be gene-controlled. This type of interaction is shown by Drosophilia, in which more than one form of sigma (the cytoplasmic basis of sensitivity to CO_2) is present. Evidence of this type of interaction will also be found in plants of diverse types of plastid. The selection of alternative, cytoplasmic, self-duplicating particles that are under gene interaction is also postulated in Oenothera. It is indicative that the evolution of diverse genomes, now characteristic of different species of Oenothera, has been accompanied by the evolution of diverse types of plastid.

The fourth role of the genes is to cooperate with the cytoplasmic material in the control of hereditary traits. Thus, the character cannot be attributed entirely to a nuclear gene or to cytoplasmic action. If certain gene complexes that have a specific effect in one cytoplasm are transferred into a different cytoplasm, their action is entirely different. There are many instances in which genes act differently in different cytoplasms. Also the same cytoplasm may react differently with different gene complexes.

The fifth role of the genes in their interaction with the cytoplasm is that in which different genes in the same nucleus may be capable of determining two or more alternative, mutually exclusive traits, only one of which can come to full phenotypic expression. The decision of which action the nuclear gene may take is dictated by the cytoplasmic material. The genes govern the possibilities that the cytoplasm may dictate, but the cytoplasm dictates which of the alternative genetic possibilities will be developed. There are three main features of the relation between the genes and the cytoplasm in the control of hereditary traits: (1) The cell may contain genes for alternative and mutually exclusive traits so that only one of them can come to expression at any one time. (2) The cytoplasm of the cell embodies mechanisms that perpetuate for certain periods the particular alternative trait which happens to have developed. (3) Environmental conditions can bring about shifts from one gene-controlled alternative trait to another.

There is some evidence that the cytoplasm may exert great influence upon the genes. Such examples as the influence on gene mutability by the cytoplasm and the acceptance or rejection of certain chromosomes by the cytoplasm will suffice to show that the gene-cytoplasm interaction is not the entire genic influence on cytoplasmic particles.

As stated earlier, it is difficult to obtain clear-cut evidence of gene-cytoplasm interaction in farm animals. One example that may be indicative is that in which horses of small and large sizes were used in reciprocal crosses. The foal that was produced by the larger breed of mares grew more rapidly and reached a larger adult size than the foal produced by the small breed of mares. This may be entirely a matter of differences in uterine environment and, consequently, not an example of gene-cytoplasm interaction. To determine if this difference in growth rate and adult body size of crossbred foals is due to uterine environment or to gene-cytoplasm interaction would require egg transfer. If the reciprocal crosses were made, and then eggs produced by the small mare and eggs produced by the large mare were both developed in mares of the same breed, one could determine how much gene-cytoplasmic interaction existed. It is logical to assume that, with as much evidence for this type of interaction as there is in plants and in the lower animals, it is likely that the interaction of genes and cytoplasm also exists in farm animals. Certainly, there is no logical reason for believing that gene-cytoplasm interaction does not occur in farm animals.

GENES INTERACT WITH THE ENVIRONMENT

Every livestock breeder is aware of the importance of good environment in making possible the complete expression of desirable genes. One of the most important examples of a condition that may prevent desirable genes from expressing themselves is the amount and kind of feed the animals receive. The high potential milking ability of a Holstein could never be realized on a desert range without supplemental feed. In some areas where animals receive so little from the pastures that growth is materially retarded, a permanent effect on adult body size results. This does not change the genetic constitution of the animal, but it does impose a natural selection process on the animals different from that existing where feed conditions are adequate for optimum growth. Under adverse conditions the animals are faced primarily with the problem of survival. Actually, high production under these conditions might be a detriment, since this might interfere with survival.

The general concept is to make the environment such that genes deemed desirable by man find it possible to express themselves. It would be unwise to try to make the environment so desirable that animals of all genetic constitutions could perform satisfactorily. We must not overlook the possibility of exploiting the desirable genes to the extent that animals will survive in an undesirable environment which cannot be improved and which can produce only the minimum essentials for existence. Even when the environment is generally satisfactory and reasonably constant, we find that for such traits as growth rate, fertility, milking ability, and feed efficiency, some of the variation is attributable to nongenetic causes. Thus the environment influences greatly the performance of animals, and because of it, rapid progress through selection is hampered.

The interaction of genes with the environment may create the necessity for developing breeding stock whose selection is determined by the conditions under which the animals are to perform commercially. If a breeding program is conducted under one set of conditions, breeding stock from such a herd may or may not show superior performance under a different set of conditions. Until one knows how much interaction of this nature exists, it is best to secure animals bred under conditions similar to those in which they are to produce young.

EXERCISES

1. What is meant by epistatic genes?
2. Clearly differentiate partial dominance, complete dominance, and overdominance.
3. List the types of gene interactions which may exist.
4. In cattle:

B = black	Bs = blackish	Br = brindle
b = red	bs = nonblackish	br = nonbrindle

Black is epistatic to blackish and brindle. The brindling gene acts only on blackish to produce a brindle.

$Bb\ Bs\ bs\ br\ br\ \male \times bb\ Bs\ bs\ Br\ br\ \female$.

(a) Give the appearance of the $\male$ and $\female$.

(b) Work the cross phenotypically.

(c) Work the cross genotypically.

Does epistasis influence the genotypic ratio? The phenotypic ratio?

    5. In chickens:

I = inhibition of pigment W = colored

i = no pigment inhibition w = White Rock

I is epistatic to W, and ww acts epistatically to ii.

       $Ii\ Ww$ ♂ $\times$ $Ii\ Ww$ ♀.

    (a) What is appearance of the ♂ and ♀?

    (b) Work the cross phenotypically.

    6. In chickens:

W = colored C = colored

w = White Rock c = albino

ww acts epistatically to C, and cc acts epistatically to W.

       $Ww\ Cc$ ♂ $\times$ $Ww\ Cc$ ♀.

    Work the cross phenotypically.

MULTIPLE FACTORS—QUANTITATIVE CHARACTERS

4

So far, the material presented has considered such superficial traits as color and horns. These characters are clearly understood because one has no difficulty in seeing whether a cow has horns or is polled, or whether she is black or red. Characters such as we have been dealing with are known as *discontinuous* because horns do not grade into polled and black does not grade into red. They are separate characters, clearly distinguishable, with no intermediate classes.

Let us now consider some characters that are continuous, i.e., where the expression of the character may range from one extreme to the other, with no separate and definable natural classes. Characters such as body size, growth rate, efficiency with which feed is converted into body gains, and milking ability are examples of continuous characters.

We speak of the discontinuous types, those for which sharp and separate classes are the rule, as *qualitative* characters. An animal either has the character or it does not, and all animals that show it have the same (or approximately the same) amount of it. Thus we seldom concern ourselves with a shade of color (such as, which cow is "blacker" than the other), but we do want to know the dominant color, i.e., whether the cow is black or red.

The continuous characters in which animals vary from one extreme to the other, with no sharply defined classes, are called *quantitative* characters. The quantitative or continuous characters are due to many genes, (each having a small effect) rather than to one or two genes (each with a large effect), as is the case in qualitative or discontinuous characters. Because of the variation from one extreme to the other quantitative characters cannot be expressed in clear-cut ratios. The F_1 will generally be intermediate, between the two parents; the F_2 will show all grades from that of one parent to that of the other, if sufficient offspring are produced.

We speak of the genes which control quantitative characters as *multiple factors* or multiple genes. In general the multiple factors governing quantitative characters do not show complete dominance. Let us take a theoretical example, using length of ears in rabbits. A rabbit with ears 10 in. long may be used to represent the "long-eared" rabbit, while one with ears 2 in. long may be used to represent the "short-eared" rabbit. With dominance lacking, the F_1 of this cross would have ears that were uniformly 6 in. in length. If these F_1 were interbred to produce the F_2, we should get an F_2 population of rabbits with ears ranging from 2 to 10 in. in length, if sufficient animals were produced in the F_2. How many pairs of genes would be involved in determining ear length in rabbits might be ascertained by inspection of the F_2 rabbits. Suppose that one animal out of every 64 had 10-in. ears and one out of every 64 had 2-in. ears. It would be evident then that three pairs of genes were involved in ear length inheritance.

PROPORTION OF F_2 SHOWING PARENTAL EXTREMES

It is perhaps advisable to show the proportion of the F_2 which would have the extreme of each parent when based on the hypothesis of multiple factor inheritance (Table 2).

Table 2. PROPORTION OF THE F_2 WHICH IS THE EXTREME OF EACH PARENTAL TYPE FOR DIFFERENT NUMBERS OF GENE PAIRS

Number of Pairs of Genes Involved	*Proportion of* F_2 *Which Is the Extreme of Either Parental Types*
1	1:4
2	1:16
3	1:64
4	1:256
5	1:1,024
10	1:1,048,576
20	1:1,099,511,627,776

It is apparent that in cases where very many pairs of genes were involved, one would never obtain in the F_2 the extremes of the parents which were used to produce the F_1.

There is every reason to believe that in most of the quantitative characters we deal with in farm animals, the number of pairs of genes is very large.

Suppose that in the preceding example of the rabbit cross the F_1 were intermated and produced 1,500 offspring, six of which had 10-in. ears and six of which had 2-in. ears. How do we proceed to determine the number of pairs of genes involved? If 1,500 is divided by 6, the number in one of the extremes, the result is 250. This equals the 256 in Table 2 more closely than it does either the 64 or the 1,024. We would conclude, then, that four pairs of genes are involved.

Suppose that the F_1, having ears 6 in. long, were intermated and produced not only some offspring with ears 10 in. and some with ears 2 in. long, but also a few with ears 12 in. long and a few with ears 1 in. long. This type of result has been termed *transgressive variation*. It would be explained on the basis that not only did the rabbit with 10-in. ears have genes for long ears but that it also had some genes for short ears. Also, the rabbit with 2-in. ears not only had genes for short ears, but it also had some genes for long ears. The example can be illustrated as follows: Long-eared rabbit *AA BB CC dd* $\times$ short-eared rabbit *aa bb cc DD* produced the F_1 with intermediate ear length, *Aa Bb Cc Dd*. When the F_1 were mated to produce the F_2, some of them had the genotype *AA BB CC DD*; hence, they had ears longer than the long-eared parent. Some offspring had the genotype *aa bb cc dd* and therefore had ears shorter than the short-eared parent.

Most quantitative characters in farm animals are not only governed by a large number of pairs of genes but also are influenced by the environment. Thus individuals belonging to the same genotype might be quite unlike in phenotype. This would make it almost impossible to separate the F_2 into distinct classes based on genetic composition. The result is that when the F_2 is shown graphically, it will usually present a fairly smooth and symmetrical frequency curve. The two ends of the curve will be the grand-parental types while the intermediates will be found in the modal part of the curve.

SELECTION OF QUANTITATIVE TRAITS

Where large numbers of genes are involved, and we are dealing with small numbers of animals, only a small segment of the possible F_2 will be obtained. This will give an F_2 population which resembles very closely the F_1 population. The desired genes for quantitative characters may show some dominance because selection would tend to eliminate the dominant genes that were not desired. We must not overlook the fact, however, that some desirable genes affecting quantitative characters may be recessive. If we have some desirable recessive genes affecting a quantitative character, it will be possible to obtain intermediate F_1 when two extremes are crossed, even though complete dominance existed. The objective in manipulating genes affecting quantitative characters is to substitute the desirable genes for the less desirable genes so that more of the desirable genes are accumulated at the expense of the less desirable ones.

There are three views on how this substitution of the desirable gene may affect production. One view is that as we increase the desirable genes, their effects are simply added. If we take three pairs of genes with the desirable ones having 6, 5, and 4 units of value and their alleles 3, 2, and 1, respectively, the intermediate would have the genetic composition of

$$6 + 3$$
$$5 + 2$$
$$4 + 1$$

or a total productive value of 21. If we substitute the desirable genes for the undesirable ones, the genetic composition would be

$$6 + 6$$
$$5 + 5$$
$$4 + 4$$

or a total productive value of 30.

Another view is that, since the desirable genes in one locus may make it possible for the genes in another locus to express themselves more efficiently, the effects are not additive but multiplicative.

The third view is that as we substitute more desirable genes, they become less important. According to this concept, there are large numbers of genes affecting quantitative inheritance, and there is an interaction of the genes so that as the more effective genes are accumulated, the less effective the addition of another desirable gene will be. Certainly stockmen will agree that the more closely we approach the ideal in our farm animals, the more difficult it is to make further improvement through selection. Of course one of the reasons for this difficulty is our inability to find animals which are of sufficient merit to improve an already good herd or flock.

MATHEMATICAL DESCRIPTION OF POPULATIONS—
STATISTICS

There are several ways of describing two parental populations and their F_1 and F_2 generations when quantitative characters such as size are considered. The first and most simple method is to give the average weight of each group. This may or may not be very descriptive, since we could have three rabbits which average 4,500 gm. with each of the three weighing 4,500 gm. Or, there might be three rabbits averaging 4,500 gm. with one weighing 4,000; one, 4,500; and one, 5,000 gm. Therefore we must find some way of describing the variation, as well as knowing the average. A statistic known as the *standard deviation* is used to describe variation. If it is known how much each animal's weight differs from the average weight of his group of animals, each difference can be squared, the squares added, and the total divided by the number of animals less one in the group, and the square root extracted. This gives the standard deviation, or *mean squared deviation*. Let us assume that the Polish, a breed of small rabbits, averages 1.3 kg. each, while the Flemish Giant, a breed of very large rabbits, averages 7 kg. The two parental populations and the F_1 and F_2 generations are represented by ten rabbits each (Table 3).

Table 3. BODY WEIGHTS WITH DEVIATIONS FROM THE MEANS FOR POLISH, FLEMISH GIANTS, F_1 AND F_2 RABBITS.

Polish	(d)*	(d²)	Flemish Giants	(d)*	(d²)	F_1	(d)*	(d²)	F_2	(d)*	(d²)
1.2	−0.1	0.01	7.3	+0.3	0.09	4.0	−0.2	0.04	3.6	−0.8	0.64
1.3	0	0	7.0	0	0	4.2	0	0	3.7	−0.7	0.49
1.4	+0.1	0.01	6.7	−0.3	0.09	4.4	+0.2	0.04	5.0	+0.6	0.36
1.3	0	0	6.8	−0.2	0.04	4.2	0	0	5.3	+0.9	0.81
1.2	−0.1	0.01	6.9	−0.1	0.01	4.0	−0.2	0.04	4.0	−0.4	0.16
1.3	0	0	7.0	0	0	4.1	−0.1	0.01	4.6	+0.2	0.04
1.5	+0.2	0.04	7.1	+0.1	0.01	4.3	+0.1	0.01	5.1	+0.7	0.49
1.4	+0.1	0.01	7.2	+0.2	0.04	4.3	+0.1	0.01	3.9	−0.5	0.25
1.3	0	0	7.1	+0.1	0.01	4.3	+0.1	0.01	4.0	−0.4	0.16
1.1	−0.2	0.04	6.9	−0.1	0.01	4.2	0	0	4.8	+0.4	0.16
Av. 1.3	0	0.12	7.0	0	0.30	4.2	0	0.16	4.4	0	3.46

* d = deviation from the mean.

To calculate the standard deviation take the sum of the squared deviations, divide by $n-1$ (9), and extract the square root. The Polish is $\sqrt{0.12} \div 9 = 0.11532$ for the standard deviation; the Flemish Giant is $\sqrt{0.30} \div 9 = 0.18$ for the standard deviation; the F_1 generation is $\sqrt{0.16} \div 9 = 0.13$ for the standard deviation; and the F_2 generation is $\sqrt{3.46} \div 9 = 0.62$ for the standard deviation. The number of pairs of genes in this cross can be calculated by

$$N = \frac{D^2}{8 \left(s^2_{F_2} - s^2_{F_1} \right)}$$

where N is the number of pairs of genes, D is the difference in the mean (average) of the Flemish Giant and Polish rabbits, $s^2_{F_2}$ is the variance of the F_2, and $s^2_{F_1}$ is the variance of the F_1. If we substitute our figures into this equation,

$$N = \frac{(7.0 - 1.3)^2}{8 (0.3844 - 0.0177)} = \frac{32.49}{2.9336} = 11$$

or approximately 11 pairs of genes involved. It is obvious from the data that the numbers used in these examples are not large, but the examples serve to illustrate the method which can be used from Parental, F_1 and F_2, generation figures to estimate the number of genes controlling a quantitative character.

To estimate how near to the true averages is the 1.3 kg. for the weight of the Polish, the 7.0 kg. for the weight of the Flemish Giants, the 4.2 kg. for the weight of the F_1, or the 4.4 kg. for the weight of the F_2 generation, using our sample of 10 rabbits, we may divide the standard deviation by the sqaure root of N. This would be $\sqrt{10}$, or 3.16228, in each case. If we multiply this figure by 3 (taken to be the *standard error* of estimate) the product tells us that if we were to draw samples of 10 from the population for 100 times, the averages of these samples would, in 99 of the 100 samples, fall somewhere between our average, plus or minus three times the standard error. Thus, samples of Polish rabbits, if taken from the group in this example, should average 1.3 $\pm$ 0.11 kg. That is, one could expect these sample averages to vary from 1.2 to 1.4 kg. Similarly, the sample averages taken from the population of Flemish Giants used in the example should vary from 6.8 to 7.2 kg.

In the calculation of variance we usually assume a mean of zero. In this way all observations are squared and a correction is applied later. This facilitates machine calculation. Also, it may be necessary to determine or to remove the variance attributable to certain variables. From the within-variance and the variance due to the variables of treatments imposed, etc., one can determine the probability that these differences between treatments were real or were due to chance. A simple example may make the concept more understandable. Two sires at the Oregon Station were used within the same line to sire calves in the same season. The effects of sires and of sex of calves on rate of gain were studied; the rates of gain of the calves are shown in Table 4.

Table 4. RATES OF GAINS FOR BULLS AND HEIFERS SIRED BY TWO DIFFERENT BULLS

	Sire A		*Sire B*	
	Male	*Female*	*Male*	*Female*
	3.3	2.6	2.8	1.9
	3.7	2.3	2.8	2.1
	3.3	2.5	2.3	2.2
	3.5	2.4	2.8	2.3
	3.1	2.2	3.2	2.3
Total	16.9	12.0	13.9	10.8
Average	3.38	2.40	2.78	2.16

The analysis of variance, where the variances due to sex of calf and sire have been removed, is shown in Table 5.

Table 5. ANALYSIS OF VARIANCE

Source of Variation	D/F	s^2	s	F Ratio
Total	19	5.072	0.267	..
Between groups	3	4.244	1.415	27*
Between sires	1	0.882	0.882	17*
Between sexes	1	3.200	3.210	62*
Sire × Sex (interaction)	1	0.162	0.152	3
Remainder	16	0.828	0.052	..

* Significant at the 1 per cent level. The odds are less than one in one hundred that this difference is due to chance.

It is clear from the analysis of variance that there was a difference between bulls and heifers in rate of gain, with the bulls gaining more rapidly than the heifers. It is also clear that the two bulls differed in their ability to sire rapidly gaining calves. The calves sired by one bull gained 0.42 lb. per day more than those sired by the other bull; this difference is highly significant.

EXERCISES

1. What is meant by the terms quantitative and qualitative characters?
2. How would you distinguish between continuous and discontinuous variation? Which type of characters show continuous variation?
3. A rabbit with ears 2 in. long was mated to one with ears 10 in. long.

(a) When the F_1 were intermated, they produced 1,087 young, with four showing 10-in. and four showing 2-in. ears. How many pairs of genes are involved?

(b) When the F_1 were intermated, they produced 9,762 offspring. Three rabbits had ears 12 in. long and four had ears 1 in. long. Explain.

5

MULTIPLE ALLELES—GENE MUTATIONS

Multiple factors must not be confused with multiple alleles. One characteristic may be controlled by many genes, known as *multiple factors. Multiple alleles,* on the other hand, all involve a particular locus but are due to more than one mutation or gene change. The same individual may have many pairs of multiple factors, but only one pair of alleles in a multiple allelic series is ever present in any one individual. Thus multiple factors may be in many pairs of homologous chromosomes; for example,

Aa in chromosome I
Bb in chromosome II
Cc in chromosome III

Multiple alleles, or an allelic series, is a term used to describe the fact that in a particular locus more than one mutation has occurred making the possibilities greater at this locus for effects different from those resulting when only one mutation, or none, has occurred. A mutation is a change in the effect of the gene.

MUTATION—THE BASIS FOR ALLELES

Let us assume that all the original cattle were of solid color. The genotype for cattle with this character in these circumstances would be *SS,* and they would all breed true for solid color. In this case we would not even be aware that there was a gene governing coat color distribution because there would be no segregation. Now, if some type of agent induced the *S* gene to mutate to *s,* there would eventually be some *Ss* individuals mated, and hence some white spotted cattle would appear. From then on, we would be aware of this character and we would have a pair of alleles to study. It so happens that the genes in this locus have mutated more than once; so we now have not one pair of alleles but several other possibilities. We know that alleles occupy corresponding loci in the homologous chromosomes, and therefore it is easy to see that no individual will have more than one pair of genes of an allelic series affecting the character, and that no one gamete will carry more than one gene of the multiple allelic series.

Studies of coat color in cattle have established that the following genes are in the multiple allelic series:

$$S^C = \text{color-sided}$$
$$S^D = \text{Dutch belt}$$
$$S^H = \text{Hereford pattern}$$
$$S \ \ = \text{solid color}$$
$$s \ \ = \text{white-spotted}$$

We know that the Hereford pattern is incompletely dominant over solid color because when Herefords (white face, etc.) are mated to Angus (entirely pigmented), a white-faced animal is produced which does not have all the markings of the Hereford, i.e., much less white is present (Figs. 11, 12, 13).

Although the Hereford pattern is also dominant over white-spotted coat color, two results may be obtained when these two are crossed. There may be

Fig. 11. Hereford bull, OSCA21—Oregon David Domino, showing $S^H S^H$, Hereford pattern. (*Courtesy Oregon State College.*)

Fig. 12. Angus heifer showing *S*, solid color. *(Courtesy Oregon State College.)*

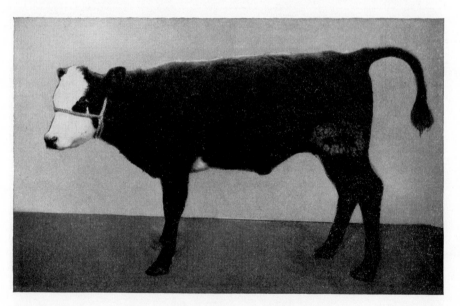

Fig. 13. Crossbred Hereford Angus calf, showing white-face pattern dominant over solid color. *(Courtesy Oregon State College.)*

broken areas with small white spots appearing in some regions where the Hereford is normally pigmented. In addition, some of the white-spotted animals may carry a modifying gene (to be discussed later) which causes pigmented spots to appear in the face of the crossbred. This is known as *brockle face* (Fig. 14).

Fig. 14. Brockle face and broken areas in the $S^H s$ animal due to modifier gene and interaction of alleles. *(Courtesy Oregon State College.)*

Color-sided is dominant over solid color and to white-spotted coats. Solid color is completely dominant over white-spotted. Dutch belt is apparently dominant over both solid color and white-spotted. It is not known how Hereford pattern, Dutch belt, and color-sided act in crosses because the breeds in which color-sided and Dutch-belt patterns exist are not common to America, and also because no records of combining breeds possessing these patterns have been recorded.

The white-spotted pattern varies, due to modifying genes, from almost entirely white to almost entirely pigmented. All Guernseys, Ayrshires, and Holsteins are white-spotted, and some Jerseys and Shorthorns are also white-spotted, but certainly many of the Jerseys are solid-colored. In order that the reader may visualize all five of the patterns in this multiple allelic series, photographs of white-spotted, Dutch-belted, and color-sided animals are shown (Figs. 15, 16, 17).

Fig. 15. An Ayrshire heifer showing *ss*, white-spotting. *(Courtesy Oregon State College.)*

Fig. 16. Dutch belt. *(Courtesy Oregon State College.)*

Fig. 17. Color-sided. *(Courtesy S. Berge, The Agricultural College of Norway, Volle-bekk, Norway.)*

It is more easily understood that these alleles are transmitted in the same way as other alleles if we take some examples and make some crosses. A (Hereford × Angus) crossbred, S^HS, × an (Angus × Guernsey) crossbred, Ss, when mated

$$S^HS \times Ss, \text{ zygotes}$$

$$\left.\begin{array}{c} S^H \longrightarrow S \\ S \longrightarrow s \end{array}\right\} \text{gametes}$$

gives the following ratio:

$$
\begin{aligned}
&1\ S^HS = \text{white face} \\
&1\ S^Hs = \text{Hereford; may show slight spotting} \\
&\left.\begin{array}{c} 1\ SS \\ 1\ Ss \end{array}\right\} \text{solid color}
\end{aligned}
$$

Notice that in each individual there was only one pair of alleles and that each gamete contained only one gene. The effect of multiple alleles is to provide more possibilities as to which gene will be in a particular locus.

In the multiple allelic series S^C, S^D, S^H, S, and s, the following kinds of genotype are possible:

$S^C S^C$	$S^D S^D$	$S^H S$
$S^C S^D$	$S^D S^H$	$S^H s$
$S^C S^H$	$S^D S$	SS
$S^C S$	$S^D s$	Ss
$S^C s$	$S^H S^H$	ss

One can see how many kinds of mating would be possible.

BASIC PRINCIPLES REGARDING MUTATIONS

Recently it has been found that such agents as X-ray and other radiations and some chemical substances stimulate gene mutations. It is generally agreed from these and from other studies that mutations occur quite readily in certain loci and only rarely in others. In different loci in the same species the mutation rate may vary from 10 or less to 80 or more per million gametes. Considering the rate of reproduction in most of our large farm animals, one would not expect to see many mutations.

Genes that have mutated may revert to the type of gene from which they mutated, or they may mutate to entirely new genes. The fact that certain loci are labile and may mutate more frequently, makes it more likely that multiple alleles will be present at this locus.

There are two major concepts regarding mutations: (1) The rate of spontaneous mutation is constant for a particular locus but varies from one locus to the next. (2) Mutations may be reversible but the rates of mutation in the two directions may differ.

Most mutations are not desirable, either from the standpoint of what the breeder wants or what is best for the species. If one is thinking of producing desirable mutations by use of such methods as radiation, he must realize two things: (1) no desirable mutations may occur, and (2) fertility may be materially reduced by the radiation. Thus, a breeder attempting to create desirable mutation must be in a position to stand great losses.

Ionizing radiations, the alpha, beta, and gamma radiation of radioactive substances, and X-rays, all induce mutations. The rate of induction of mutation by X-ray is related to the dose. Intensity and time of exposure govern the dosage, since low intensity for long periods is as effective as high intensity for a short time if the dosage of the two is the same. Ultraviolet rays may be absorbed by tissues in sufficient quantities to cause mutations. In addition, such agents as high temperatures and many chemical substances are mutagenic.

As stated previously, a breeder should not expect to induce mutations and come out with a large number of desirable mutants. He would be aiming in the dark and might get no mutations at all or might get mutations that were quite undesirable. The conclusion may be drawn that all mutations are bad, but this is not the case. Mutations are both good and bad in nature, and it is only through natural or artificial selection which preserves the desirable and eliminates the undesirable mutations that evolution, the change in animals, occurs.

EXERCISES

1. What is the difference between multiple factors and multiple alleles?
2. Show by diagram what is meant by multiple alleles.
3. Work the following crosses phenotypically and genotypically:
   (a) $S^H S$ ♂ × Ss ♀.
   (b) $S^D S$ ♂ × SS ♀.
   (c) $S^H S$ ♂ × $S^H S$ ♀.
   (d) $S^H s$ ♂ × Ss ♀.

6

LINKAGE—GENES IN THE SAME CHROMOSOME

In all the previous discussions the assumption was that the various alleles were in different pairs of chromosomes and that the segregation and recombination involving one pair of genes is entirely independent of the segregation and recombination of other alleles. Thus, if a double heterozygote, *Bb Pp,* is mated to a double recessive, *bb pp,* the results genotypically and phenotypically are 1:1:1:1, as shown below where

$$B = \text{black} \qquad\qquad P = \text{polled}$$
$$b = \text{red} \qquad\qquad p = \text{horned}$$

Bb Pp × *bb pp* produces:

$$1 \; Bb \begin{cases} 1 \; Pp = 1 \; Bb \; Pp, \text{ black polled} \\ 1 \; pp = 1 \; Bb \; pp, \text{ black horned} \end{cases}$$

$$1 \; bb \begin{cases} 1 \; Pp = 1 \; bb \; Pp, \text{ red polled} \\ 1 \; pp = 1 \; bb \; pp, \text{ red horned} \end{cases}$$

If the *B* and *b* genes were in the same chromosome as the *P* and *p* genes, there would be a definite tendency for the distribution of genes in one pair of alleles to be associated with the way the other pair of alleles segregated.

In animals having relatively large and only a few pairs of chromosomes, such as Drosophilia, we readily find several genes in the same chromosome. In our farm animals the chromosomes are relatively very small but they are quite numerous. Thus, recognized linkage groups (more than one pair of alleles in the same pair of chromosomes) are rare in farm animals. Another reason why very few linkage groups are known in farm animals is that we work with a small number of animals. In poultry several linkage groups are known. One common group is dominant white (found in white Leghorns) and frizzle plumage (dominant over the normal plumage).

In chickens:

I = white (pigment inhibited) F = frizzle plumage
i = colored f = normal plumage

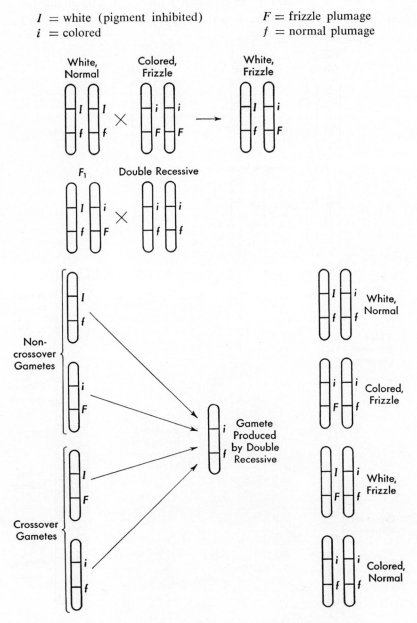

Fig. 18. Linkage and crossing-over in the "repulsion" phase.

THE REPULSION PHASE OF LINKAGE

Hutt (1933) crossed colored, frizzle × white, normal to produce F_1, white, frizzle. The F_1 were mated to the double recessive, *ii ff*. The production of the F_1 and the mating of the F_1 back to the double recessive are shown in Fig. 18.

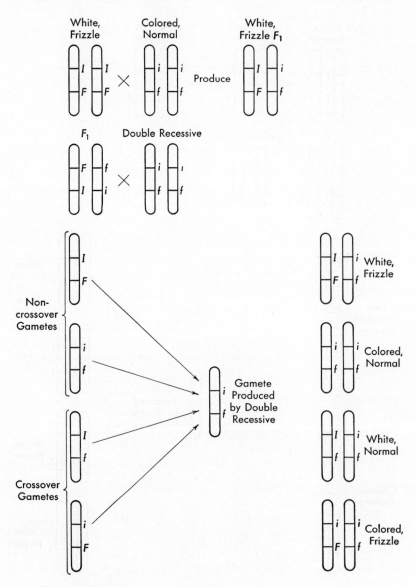

Fig. 19. Linkage and crossing-over in the "coupling" phase.

THE COUPLING PHASE OF LINKAGE

In a second cross in which the white, frizzle F_1 were produced from crossing white frizzle $\times$ colored, normal, the results of mating these F_1 back to the double recessive are shown in Fig. 19. We can see at a glance that the two homologous chromosomes could part, one member going to one gamete while the other member goes to another gamete. This would be quite easy, and consequently these two kinds of gamete are produced in the greatest number. However, there could be crossing-over; in this case, using the first example

(Fig. 20), the chromosomes may break, and part of one will join a part of the other so that two gametes *IF* and *if* are produced. These are called *cross-over gametes* to distinguish them from the gametes resulting from one member of a pair of

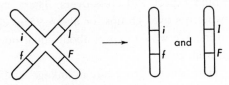

Fig. 20. Crossing-over.

homologous chromosomes going to one gamete while the other member goes to another gamete, the noncross-over gametes.

In the second cross we notice that the two dominant genes, *I* and *F*, tend to stay together because *IF* and *if* are the noncross-over gametes produced. This type of inheritance is known as *coupling* (Fig. 19). However, in the first mating *I* and *F* tend to keep apart because the *If* and *iF* are the noncross-over types of gamete, and the only point at which they come together is when crossing-over occurs. Since *I* and *F*, the two dominant genes, tend to stay apart, this condition is called *repulsion* (Fig. 18).

It is evident that the only difference between coupling and repulsion is in the composition of the F_1. If the two dominants are in one chromosome of the F_1, and the two recessives in the other, we have coupling. If the F_1 has one dominant and one recessive in each chromosome, we have repulsion.

We can calculate the percentage of crossing-over by dividing the sum of the cross-overs by the total sum and multiplying by 100.

Hutt (1933) obtained in the first case:

> 63 noncross-over (colored, frizzle)
> 63 noncross-over (white, normal)
> 18 cross-over (white, frizzle) $\left.\right\}$ = 31, sum of cross-overs
> 13 cross-over (colored, normal)
>
> ——
> 157 total

$$31 \div 157 \times 100 = 19.7 \text{ per cent crossing over}$$

In the second instance,

  15 noncross-over (white, frizzle)
  12 noncross-over (colored, normal)
   4 cross-over (white, normal) ⎫
   2 cross-over (colored, frizzle)⎬ = 6 cross-overs
  ──
  33 total

$$6 \div 33 \times 100 = 18.2 \text{ per cent crossing-over}$$

If 1,000 birds were produced and there were 19 per cent crossing-over, we would expect 190 cross-overs. There should be about equal numbers in the two cross-over groups, or about 95 in each. This would leave 810 noncross-overs. We would expect about equal numbers in each group of these, or 405 in each group.

The general procedure in linkage studies with animals is to mate the double heterozygous animal back to the double recessive. The reasons for doing this are that fewer numbers are needed to get reliable results and animals cannot be self-fertilized. In plants it may be simpler to self-fertilize the double heterozygotes and obtain F_2 in large numbers than it is to mate the F_1 back to the double recessive. In the case of plants, tables have been calculated so that crossing over percentages are easily obtained when the F_1 individuals are selfed. Since this method of mating heterozygotes is never used in animal linkage studies, the reader is referred to a book on plant genetics for a discussion of this method.

LINKAGE MAPS—SINGLE AND DOUBLE CROSSING-OVER

Suppose we had tested two genes, A and B, and found that there was a 10 per cent crossing-over between them. We would say that these two genes were 10 units apart. Now, if it is also found that B and C are 15 units apart (15 per cent crossing-over between B and C), we would not know in which order the genes were, i.e., whether they were ABC or CAB. To determine this, it would be necessary also by test to determine how much crossing-over occurred between A and C. If A and C show only 5 per cent crossing-over, we know the order to be CAB. If A and C are about 25 units apart, then we know the order to be ABC.

To show the linear order of the genes, we construct a chromosome map diagram as follows:

Assuming that we have a triple heterozygote with the arrangement of the genes in the chromosome as

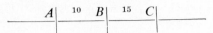

we mate this triple heterozygote to a triple recessive. Our first guess would be that we would get 10 per cent of crossing-over between *A* and *B*, 15 per cent of crossing-over between *B* and *C*, and 25 per cent of crossing-over between *A* and *C*. However, we would not only have the single crossing-over (Fig. 21)

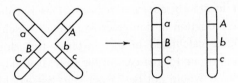

Fig. 21. Single crossing-over.

and the other type of single crossing-over (Fig. 22)

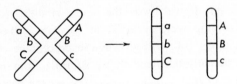

Fig. 22. Single crossing-over.

but we might also have double crossing-over (Fig. 23)

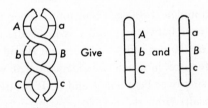

Fig. 23. Double crossing-over.

which, as far as *A* and *C* are concerned, would result in an effect the same as though no crossing-over had occurred. Thus, double crossing-over between two genes would result in reducing the crossing-over between them.

INTERFERENCE AND COINCIDENCE

With the genes in the order:

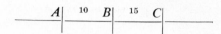

in which *A* and *B* are 10 units apart, and *B* and *C* are 15 units apart, one would expect that 10 per cent of 15 per cent of the time (or 1.5 per cent) double crossing-over would occur. This would always be the case if it were not for the fact that crossing-over in one region of the chromosome interferes with crossing-over in closely adjacent regions. This is called *interference*; it is measured by the reduction in double crossing-over which calculations show as possible. We have calculated in this instance that double crossing-over would be expected to occur 1.5 per cent of the time. If it did, then the crossing-over between *A* and *C* would not be 25 per cent but would be 25 — 1.5, or 23.5 per cent. Suppose that we tested the crossing-over between *A* and *C* and found that it was 24 per cent. We see that the double crossing-over is 1 per cent (25 — 24 = 1), rather than the 1.5 per cent expected when *A* and *B* are 10 units apart and when *B* and *C* are 15 units apart (10 per cent of 15 per cent = 1.5 per cent). If we divide the actual double crossing-over by the expected double crossing-over, we arrive at 1.0/1.5 = 0.66, which is called *coincidence*. This, times 100, will give us the percentage of expected double crossing-over that actually occurred. If we subtract from 100 the percentage of double crossing-over that actually occurs, we get the percentage of interference taking place. Thus, for 34 per cent of the time, crossing-over between *A* and *B* interfered with simultaneous crossing-over between *B* and *C,* or crossing-over between *B* and *C* interfered with simultaneous crossing-over between *A* and *B.*

If interference is complete (100 per cent interference and a coincidence of zero), then crossing-over between *A* and *C* will be the sum of the crossing-over between *A* and *B* (10 per cent) and between *B* and *C* (15 per cent), or 25 per cent. No interference, in which coincidence is 1.0, would give 25 — 1.5, or 23.5 per cent crossing-over between *A* and *C*. It is obvious that in order to obtain dependable results from the double crossing-over between two genes, particularly where these two genes are not very far apart, we shall require large numbers. We would probably never have a sufficient quantity of animals for this purpose from our larger farm animals, but enough certainly could be obtained from poultry.

The question may well arise as to how we can obtain double or triple heterozygotes and know that they are such. It is not necessary to have a double or triple homozygote in order to produce known double or triple heterozygotes. An animal showing the two or three dominant genes can be mated to the double or triple recessive. The F_1, which shows the two dominants, is a double heterozygote, or the one showing the three dominants is a triple heterozygote. These animals can then be used for mating to the multiple recessive for linkage studies.

It has been stated that linkage groups are uncommon in farm animals. However, there is some evidence of gene-block inheritance (whole small chromosomes segregating) in farm animals, which could be a type of linkage. Since the chromosomes are small and because the effect of each gene controlling quantitative characters is so small, we can presume that groups of genes may be transmitted because they are all in one chromosome in such a way that they are practically one gene. However, crossing-over can take place, and then a different kind of gene-block occurs. Sometimes, in selection for quantitative characters, a breeder may raise two or three generations without making any noticeable progress, and then a large increase in the direction desired may be realized. From this we can assume that there has been a break in a gene-block, so that the offspring develop more of the genes favoring the direction in which selection pressure has been applied.

It would be extremely difficult to differentiate complete linkage of two genes from manifold effects of one gene, a condition called *pleotropy*. An example of this is found in the yellow mouse, which is always in the heterozygous state. When yellow mice are mated they produce 2 yellow:1 non yellow. It has been shown that about one-fourth of the embryos die in the uterus. It has not been established that the yellow color gene also causes fatness in the heterozygous state and acts as a lethal when homozygous, or that a lethal gene is closely linked with the yellow color gene. One might explain all cases of pleotropy as close linkage of two or more genes, rather than two or more effects of one gene. However, until we obtain crossing-over by breeding to demonstrate that more than one gene is involved, it will be impossible to disprove the concept that one gene may have more than one effect.

Two genes that are so closely linked that no crossing-over occurs will segregate as one gene. If a desirable gene were closely linked with an undesirable gene, only the heterozygous state would show the desired trait. This could give the same effect as overdominance, in which the heterozygote is superior to either of the homozygotes. In investigations in progress now, researchers are studying blood groups and the chemical constituents of the blood in an attempt to find something which may be linked with production characteristics. If such linkages can be located, the blood groups or the chemical constituents of the blood could be used as a basis of selection to obtain the desired production characteristic. In addition to this, a knowledge of inherited differences in blood constituents might give more information about the action of genes.

EXERCISES

1. What is meant by linkage?
2. In chickens:

$$I = \text{inhibition of pigment (white)}$$
$$i = \text{noninhibition (colored)}$$

$$F = \text{frizzle}$$
$$f = \text{normal}$$

A pure white, frizzle, was mated to a colored, normal. The F_1 were back-crossed to the colored, normal.

Work the crosses, showing the genes in the chromosomes. Label the cross-over and noncross-over gametes produced by the F_1.

If you had 20 per cent crossing over and 800 birds produced when the F_1 were back-crossed to the colored, normal, how many would be in each phenotype?

Suppose you produced by this mating:

180 white, frizzle
20 white, normal
20 colored, frizzle
180 colored, normal

What is the crossing-over percentage? Is this an example of coupling or repulsion?

3. What effect does double crossing-over have on the cross-over percentage between the genes which are farther apart?

4. What are coincidence, interference?

5. Genes A, B, and C are located in that order; the distance between A and B is 12 units, and distance between B and C is 20 units. How much double crossing-over would be expected?

If the expected double crossing-over were obtained, how much crossing-over would there be between A and C?

If the crossing-over between A and C upon test is 30 per cent, what is the percentage of double crossing-over? What is the coincidence? How much interference is there?

7

INHERITANCE ASSOCIATED WITH SEX

Certain genes may be associated with sex because they are in the sex chromosome; these genes are called *sex-linked* genes. Other genes may be associated with sex because the sex hormones influence the way in which the heterozygous condition will be expressed; these genes are called *sex-influenced* genes. Still other genes may be associated with sex because they can be expressed only in one sex. Such genes as those controlling cryptorchidism, the retention of one or both testes in the abdomen, can be expressed only in the male, even though the female also may carry genes for this trait. Others, like the genes affecting egg production or milk production, are expressed only in the female, although the male can carry and transmit such genes. These are called *sex-limited* genes.

SEX DETERMINATION

The chromosomes in farm animals are in homologous pairs with the exception of the sex chromosomes. We speak of the chromosomes which are homologous as the *autosomes*. The genes in these chromosomes are called *autosomal* genes, and it is with them that all the discussion so far has been concerned. The sex chromosomes are homologous in one sex but not in the other sex. In mammals, the sex chromosomes are in homologous pairs in the female, but those in the male differ. The sex in which the sex chromosomes are paired is called the *homogametic sex* (female in mammals and males in poultry). The sex in which the sex chromosomes differ is called the *heterogametic* sex (male in mammals and female in poultry). The chromosomes that are paired in the homogametic sex but unlike in the heterogametic sex are known as the *sex-chromosomes*. We speak of the sex chromosomes in the homogametic sex as xx and those in the heterogametic sex as xy. In most instances the x chromosome carries genes which have no alleles in the y chromosome, since the latter is almost entirely lacking in genes.

There are a number of theories relative to sex determination but most of them agree that sex is the result of a balance of genes for maleness and for femaleness. Bridges (1932), working with Drosophilia, assumes that the genes for femaleness are located in the x chromosome and that genes for maleness are located in the autosomes. Thus an individual that is $xx + 2A$, where $2A$ means two sets of autosomes, would be a female because the genes for femaleness in the two x chromosomes are sufficient to overpower the genes for maleness in the two sets of autosomes. The individual that is $1x + 2A$, on the other hand, has more genetic effect for maleness in the two sets of autosomes than for femaleness in the (1) x chromosome. This would be a male. Keep in mind that for all practical purposes we may consider the y as being without genes.

With this mechanism, which is assumed to exist in all mammalian farm animals, sex can be determined as shown in Fig. 24. This determination gives

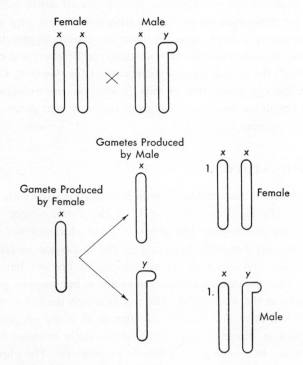

Fig. 24. Chromosomal basis for sex determination in mammals.

a sex ratio of one female to one male. There are several unexplained facts regarding sex ratios using this type of explanation.

In most species many more males are conceived than females. Death rate is always higher in the male than in the female, particularly in prenatal and early post-natal periods. Greater death losses of males can be explained by sex-linked lethals (to be considered later), but the greater number of males than females that are conceived has led to many speculations. Many theories have been advanced for explaining why the egg should be fertilized preferably by the y-bearing sperm rather than by the x-bearing sperm. One theory considered that the x-bearing sperm, having the added weight of the x chromosome, would travel with greater difficulty, and that the y-bearing sperm, being lighter, would win the race to the egg more often. Attempts by centrifuging to separate the x-bearing from the y-bearing sperm have been unsuccessful. This does not necessarily mean that the theory is without basis because our methods of centrifuging may not possess the precision and sensitivity necessary for making such separations.

Another concept is that the electric charges on the x-bearing sperm are the same as those on the egg, while the charges on the y-bearing sperm are opposite. It is known that opposite charges attract each other, whereas like charges repel each other. In an experiment based on this premise, rabbit semen was placed in the center of a tube in which an electrolyte diluter was present, through which a current was passed. After the current passed through the tube, samples for insemination were taken from the two ends and from the center. A large percentage of males resulted from semen taken from the cathode, while a large percentage of females resulted from semen taken from the anode. The ratio of male to female offspring was approximately 1 when semen for insemination was taken from the center of the tube. So far, no confirmation of this theory has been reported.

Still another concept suggested that acidity and alkalinity of the female tract differentially affected the x-bearing and the y-bearing sperm. Roberts (1940) reported that alkaline douches before mating gave more male offspring and that acidic douches before mating gave more females, resulting in a great spread in sex ratio. It appeared from this that perhaps the female tract might generally favor the y-bearing sperm and that this inclination could explain the greater number of males conceived. Later work by Roberts and by other workers (Casida and Murphree, 1942) failed to show any relation of alkalinity or acidity to sex ratio.

It is still a mystery why more males are conceived than females, but for the present, in order to simplify subsequent material, we shall base our discussion on the supposition that males and females are produced in equal numbers.

If we return now to the Drosophilia studies of Bridges (1932), we find considerable evidence supporting his theory of a balance of genes in the x chromosome for femaleness, with genes in the autosomes for maleness. He was able to produce flies that were

$$x + 3A = \text{super males}$$
$$x + 2A = \male$$
$$xx + 3A = \text{intersex; showing } \male \text{ and } \female \text{ characteristics}$$
$$xx + 2A = \female$$
$$xxx + 2A = \text{super females}$$

(where $2A = 2$ sets of autosomes).

In the lower forms, sex is not so apparent as in farm animals. In fact, sex is often controlled by the interaction of the genes and the environment. Hence, all males or all females may be produced by severe alterations in the environment. In most of these forms there is no evidence for x and y chromosomes or genes in the x for femaleness and in the autosomes for maleness. The genes for the sexes are scattered throughout the chromosomes.

Goldschmidt (1942) worked with a moth in which the females are of the xy and the males are of the xx. He found that, in addition to the balance of the genes in the x chromosomes and autosomes, the cytoplasm also interacts in sex determination.

In the fish, *Lebistes reticulatus,* Winge (1934) found that the genes for maleness and femaleness are present in the x chromosome and in the autosomes, but, in addition, one powerful gene for maleness is located in the y chromosome. There are, however, more genes for maleness in the autosomes and more for femaleness in the x chromosome. An individual of the xx constitution would be female. Winge was able to produce xx males by crossing species. When this xx male was used on regular xx females, all the offspring produced were xx and females. It is apparent, then, that in these fishes the normal balance of male and female is very close and only when the y chromosome, which carries a strong gene for maleness, is involved is the balance between maleness and femaleness distinctly separate. Even intersexes produced in this species are fertile.

In wasps and bees the male is haploid while the female is diploid. In *Habrobracon juglandis,* a parasitic wasp, Whiting (1943) has found that there are nine genes which may control sex. Females are always heterozygous for these genes, whereas the male, being a haploid, is hemizygous and could never be heterozygous. However, diploid males have been produced which are the result of homozygosity for these sex genes. These males are very low in fertility as contrasted with the haploid males.

In poultry sex reversals may occur. The ovaries which are paired embryonically do not both develop. One, the left, becomes a functional ovary while the other, the right, remains indifferentiated. If something happens to the functional ovary (atrophy due to disease or surgical removal) the undifferentiated right ovary can develop into testicular tissue and produce testosterone instead of the estrogens which were formerly produced by ovarian function. This testosterone can change the plumage of the hen from that known as "henny plumage" to the cock type of plumage. In fact the comb will also develop, the animal will crow, and it will show the sex behavior of the male.

SEX-LINKED INHERITANCE

The best examples of sex-linked genes in animals, in which the female is xx and the male is xy, is found in humans.

To illustrate sex-linked inheritance in the human, let us consider the genes for color blindness.

$$C = \text{normal eyes}$$
$$c = \text{color blind}$$

A female, pure for normal eyes, $\times$ a male that is color blind produces offspring as shown in Fig. 25.

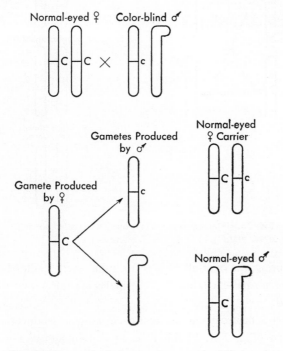

Fig. 25. Pure normal-eyed woman $\times$ color-blind man.

This type of mating is similar to ordinary inheritance in which a homozygous dominant $\times$ a recessive produces all dominant offspring phenotypically. It differs materially from autosomal inheritance genotypically. Let us see the results if individuals of the genotypes in the offspring shown in Fig. 25 should produce young (Fig. 26).

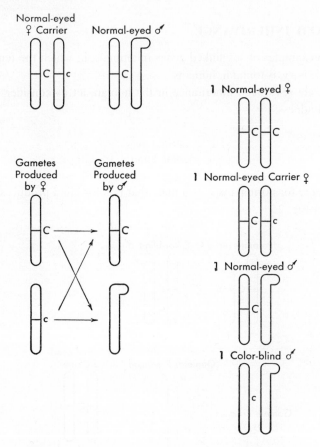

Fig. 26. Heterozygous normal-eyed woman $\times$ normal-eyed man.

For these offspring, the over-all ratio is 3 normal eyed:1 color blind, but both the females are normal-eyed, one-half the males are normal-eyed and one-half are color blind.

Suppose that a heterozygous normal-eyed woman produces children by a color-blind man (Fig. 27). In this case equal numbers of normal-eyed and color-blind within each sex are produced. This type of mating is similar

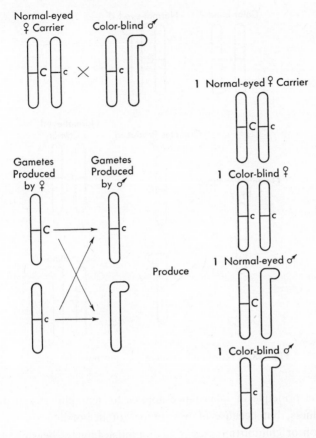

Fig. 27. Heterozygous normal-eyed woman × color-blind man.

phenotypically to autosomal inheritance, in which the heterozygous dominant is mated to the recessive.

Suppose a color-blind woman and a normal-eyed man produce children. The ratios shown in Fig. 28 are obtained.

Thus, although we started out with a color-blind female and a normal-eyed male, all the offspring are just the opposite; the males are all color blind and the females are all normal-eyed. This is called *criss-cross* inheritance. It is by this type of mating that sex-linked genes may be differentiated from autosomal genes, as will be explained later.

Another sex-linked gene in humans is that causing hemophilia, a defect in the blood-clotting mechanism that may lead to death from hemorrhage in the event of injury.

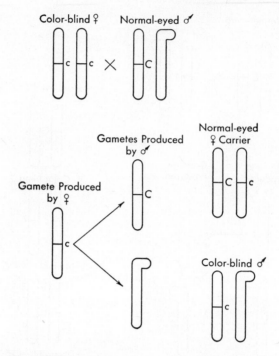

Fig. 28. Color-blind woman × normal-eyed man.

The same principle of inheritance applies to hemophilia as in the case of color blindness, but because of possibilities of hemorrhage in the female at menstruation or childbirth, cases of hemophiliac females bearing children are rare. It is because of this that the medical profession has considered sex-linked genes to be transmitted by the female but expressed only in the male. Therefore, when hemophiliac females are observed, they are called pseudohemophiliac because, according to definition by the medical profession, female hemophiliacs cannot occur. It is unfortunate that this error in concept developed.

A woman who carries the gene for hemophilia × a normal man would produce all normal females and one normal male:one hemophiliac male, where the genes H = normal and h = hemophilia (Fig. 29).

If a female who carries the gene for hemophilia bears children by a hemophiliac male, the offspring will be 1 normal:1 hemophiliac in both the males and the females (Fig. 30).

Although it would be very rare for a hemophiliac woman to produce offspring, the results that would be obtained if such a woman × a normal man were to produce offspring are shown in Fig. 31.

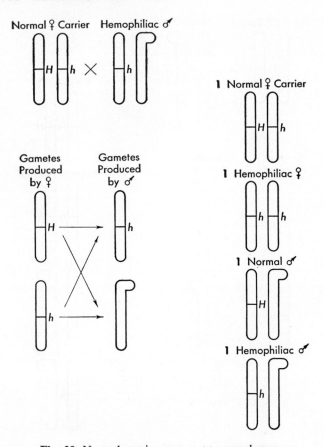

Fig. 29. Normal carrier woman × normal man.

In chickens the male is *xx* and the female is *xy,* which is just opposite to the situation in mammals, where the female is *xx* and the male is *xy* as we have previously shown.

Since the barred character is expressed at hatching by a small light spot on the head which is lacking in the nonbarred chicks at hatching, this gene could be used for sexing chicks at hatching by use of the criss-cross mating. Some difficulties are experienced with these genes in commercial broiler production, however, because black chickens are difficult to dress without the black pin feathers making the carcass quite unattractive.

Another pair of sex-linked genes in chickens is that of gold and silver, where *G* = silver and *g* = gold. This pair of genes also has been used for sexing chicks at hatching by bringing in the gold through the male and the silver through the female. In this cross the male offspring will all be silver and the female offspring will all be gold.

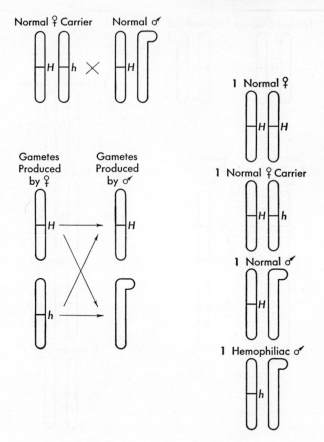

Fig. 30. Normal carrier woman × hemophiliac man.

A pair of sex-linked genes in chickens is *e* (early) and *E* (late) feathering. These genes attracted so much attention for use in sexing at hatching that one research worker put both genes into the same breed, although normally such breeds as Leghorns are early feathering, while most of the heavy breeds are late feathering. By combining males that were early feathering, *ee,* with hens that were late feathering, *Ey,* all the males were late-feathered and all the females were early-feathered. Within 24 hrs. after hatching, the early-feathered birds showed wing and tail feathers, while the late-feathered birds showed only down, even after 48 hrs.

This experiment showed that this pair of genes did not turn out so desirable an offspring as expected because males are used for broiler production and females are raised to maturity for egg production. In this case, the late-feathered males would be undesirable for carcasses because of bare backs,

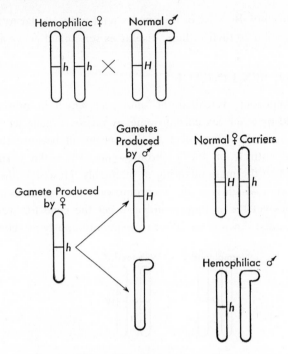

Fig. 31. Hemophilic woman × normal man.

which is also caused by the late-feathering gene. Even if kept somewhat longer, they would have troublesome pin feathers.

At present most chicks are sexed at hatching by inspection of the vent region, so that no genetic markers are needed. Good workers can sex chicks at hatching with better than 95 per cent accuracy, which appears adequate for practical purposes.

DIFFERENTIATING SEX-LINKED FROM AUTOSOMAL GENES

To determine whether genes are sex-linked or autosomal requires only one type of mating, assuming that the dominant and the recessive are known. A mating in which the homogametic parent is recessive and the heterogametic parent is dominant will give criss-cross inheritance if the genes are sex-linked. If the genes are autosomal, all the offspring will show the dominant, or there will be a ratio of one dominant:one recessive, dependent upon whether the individual that introduces the dominant gene is homozygous or heterozygous. The homogametic offspring always get one x chromosome from each of the parents. The heterogametic offspring gets its x chromosome from the homogametic parent only. Because of this, males tend to be similar to their mothers, and females similar to their fathers, insofar as sex-linked genes are concerned.

ALLOSOMAL SEX-LINKAGE

The *y* chromosome is called the *allosome*, which in present day usage means the odd or other sex chromosome. A recessive gene in the *y* chromosome would have the same effect as no gene at all because the segregation would depend entirely on the *x* chromosomes, since the *y* chromosome is always handed to the male offspring in mammals. However, there is a dominant gene in man which is in the *y* chromosome and which causes web toes. Since the males get the *y*, they would also get the gene for web toes; hence it would be handed down from father to son continuously as shown in Fig. 32.

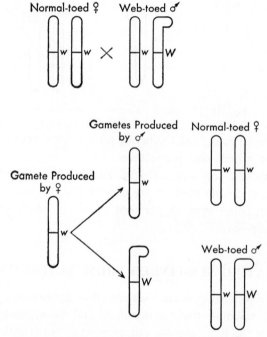

Fig. 32. Normal-toed woman × web-toed man.

Another example of an allosomal sex-linked gene is the one for maleness in the fish *Lebistes reticulatus*, which has already been mentioned. In fact, the *y* chromosome in this species is never empty. In Drosophilia there is a sex-linked lethal * which acts differently from ordinary sex-linked lethals. Ordinarily, the losses from a sex-linked lethal are only in the males, since the male

---

* A lethal gene is a gene that brings about death when certain genetic conditions are met. A complete discussion of lethals is given in Chap. 8.

cannot transmit the *x* chromosome containing a lethal gene to his female offspring; however, female, being homogametic, can transmit the *x* chromosome bearing the lethal to one-half her sons. Regardless, there is the case in which the dominant allele to the lethal is in the *y* chromosome. In this case, the male can transmit the *x* chromosome containing the lethal gene to his daughters. Since the viable female can have both the lethal gene and dominant gene to the lethal, the female can inherit the lethal in the homozygous condition, which causes death, whereas the male offspring cannot be affected because of the dominant allele in the *y* chromosome. Such a case is shown in Fig. 33, in which the sex ratio is 2 males:1 female.

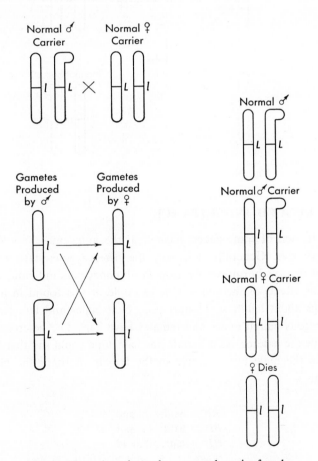

Fig. 33. Normal carrier male × normal carrier female.

A second example in Drosophilia is bobbed, *bb* (short hairs), which is found only in the females because the nonbobbed, *B,* is present in the *y* chromosome (Fig. 34).

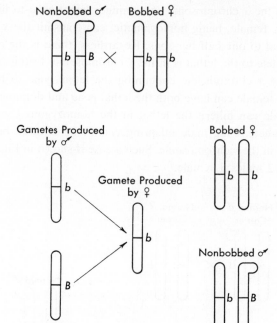

Fig. 34. Nonbobbed male × bobbed female.

SEX-INFLUENCED INHERITANCE

The expression of some genes, located in the autosomes, is influenced by the sex hormones. Generally it is only the heterozygous state which is influenced by the sex hormones because the homozygous individuals of either sex show the effects of the genes. One example of this found in man is that which brings about baldness. Homozygous bald males and females are bald, and homozygous haired males and females have hair. The heterozygous male is bald, while the heterozygous female has hair. One could say that baldness is dominant in the male but recessive in the female. Perhaps the best way to illustrate this is

$$BB = \text{bald, } \male \text{ and } \female$$
$$BH = \text{bald } \male, \text{ hair } \female$$
$$HH = \text{hair, } \male \text{ and } \female$$

If a heterozygous bald ♂, *BH,* mates with a heterozygous haired ♀, *BH,* the result (ignoring sex) is one bald to one haired. When the sexes are considered, one obtains a ratio of 3 bald:1 with hair in males and 3 with hair:1

bald in females. This case has been proven to be influenced by testosterone, the male sex hormone, because in cases where the heterozygous male has been castrated, recession of hair stops. The administration of the male hormone into such an individual causes hair recession to continue and baldness to develop.

A second example of sex influenced inheritance is found in cattle, but here the sex-influenced genes modify * the expression of another gene, the one causing blackish, Bs. Blackish animals, such as Jerseys, Brown Swiss, and Ayrshires, vary a great deal in intensity of the blackishness. Some are quite dark while others are much lighter. One notices that most bulls are dark and most cows are light blackish, although there are some light blackish bulls and some dark blackish cows. The heterozygous bull for this modifier is dark whereas the heterozygous cow is light blackish.

The reader may have raised the question: Is it not possible that the y chromosome instead of containing few or no genes has only recessive alleles to the ones in the x chromosome? There are three reasons for believing that it has very few genes: (1) Cytological examination of heterogametic tissue usually reveals a very small odd chromosome. (2) In some species there is no y chromosome, the species is xO instead of xy, and the same results are obtained with sex-linked genes as with the xy type. This would indicate that genes in the y chromosome are not necessary for the survival of the individual. (3) It would not be logical to assume that most of the mutations are recessive in the y chromosome but are both dominant and recessive in the x chromosome.

One other question may arise:—Why isn't there crossing-over between x and y chromosomes? Certainly if there is no chromosome material of the y, there could be nothing to cross over with the x. More fundamental than this is the fact that in some species, at least, there is no crossing-over in the male within any pair of homologous chromosomes.

SEX-LIMITED INHERITANCE

One type of sex-limited inheritance has been described: the allosomal sex-linked dominant in which all males show the gene but the females do not. Three other examples of sex-limited inheritance, in which the gene or genes are not in the y chromosome, are the autosomal genes affecting milk production, egg production, and cryptorchidism. The first two of these are expressed only in the female, while the third is expressed only in the male.

There are numerous genes affecting milk and egg production, although

* Modifying genes are fully discussed in Chap. 9.

attempts have been made to analyze the inheritance of each on the basis of three or more pairs of important genes. It seems more likely that we may have some individual pairs of genes, each with large effects, but that in addition to these we may have many multiple genes (polygenes), each with a small effect on both milk and egg production. These genes can be expressed only in the female, but the male has the same gene loci as the female for these genes and transmits them to his offspring just as the female does. For example, the daughters of a bull out of a strain of high-producing cattle when crossed with cows of mediocre production will produce a great deal more milk than their dams.

It has been postulated (McPhee and Buckley, 1934) that cryptorchidism, the retention of one or both testes in the abdomen, is conditioned by one or possibly two genes in swine. This is a clear-cut example of a character that the females never have but which they may transmit to their sons. Since it is definitely inherited, the breeder should certainly select against it. The sires and dams of cryptorchid males, as well as sisters of such males, should be considered for culling because they are likely to carry the genes for the character.

EXERCISES

1. What is meant by sex-linked genes?
2. How can you test to determine whether a gene is sex-linked or autosomal?
3. Suppose you have a sex-linked recessive lethal gene in cattle. Do you know the genotype of bulls for this gene? Why?
4. How could you eliminate a sex-linked lethal gene from a flock of chickens? Be specific and complete in your answer.
5. Distinguish sex-linkage from sex-influenced inheritance and allosomal sex-linked genes.
6. In man:

$$W = \text{web toes} \atop w = \text{normal toes} \Big\} \text{allosomal sex-linked} \qquad C = \text{normal eyes} \atop c = \text{color blind} \Big\} \text{sex-linked}$$

$$BB = \text{bald, } \male \text{ and } \female \atop BH = \text{bald } \male, \text{ hair } \female \atop HH = \text{hair, } \male \text{ and } \female \Big\} \text{sex-influenced}$$

A web-toed, bald, normal-eyed man whose father was color blind and had normal hair × a normal-toed, color-blind, normal-haired woman whose mother was bald. Assume unlimited reproduction and give the appearance of the children by sexes.

8

INHERITANCE OF LETHALS AND ABNORMALITIES IN FARM ANIMALS

There are two types of abnormal conditions in farm animals: one that is viable (lives) and may be able to reproduce, and one that is not viable (lethal). Lethal genes have been defined as those which cause death of the animal. We shall divide lethals into (1) true lethals, those which are expressed before or shortly after birth (such as bull dog in cattle); (2) delayed lethals, those which are expressed later in life (such as Huntington's chorea in man); and (3) partial lethals, those in which the animal inherits the character which becomes lethal only under certain conditions (hemophilia in swine, in which the character is lethal only when animals become injured and die from hemorrhage).

Lethal genes may also be classified as dominant and recessive, and as autosomal and sex-linked. Lethals that are expressed before or shortly after birth are all recessive, either autosomal or sex-linked, because a dominant lethal mutation will eliminate itself. Being a dominant mutation, it would have to express itself, and this would mean that it would die. Delayed and partial lethals may be dominant if the expression of the character does not always bring about death prior to the time the animal is capable of reproducing. These two kinds of lethals may also be, and in many instances are, recessive. Undesirable dominant genes are quite easily eliminated from a herd or flock because any time that the gene is present in either the homozygous or heterozygous condition, it will express itself and can be removed from the herd or flock.

Undesirable recessives are quite difficult to eliminate from the herd or flock. Simply culling those animals that show the character will not eliminate it because the gene can be carried in the herd or flock in the heterozygous condition. The viable, fertile type of undesirable can be eliminated from a herd or flock in which reproduction is at a high rate, such as chickens, pigs, and rabbits, but such a gene can never be eliminated from a herd of cattle or horses, or a

77

flock of sheep or goats. The incidence could be materially reduced if only tested males were used. Suppose that there exists in a herd of cattle an undesirable recessive, and also suppose that the undesirable is viable and fertile so that it can be used as a test animal. Desirable males could be tested by mating to several undesirable females, and only the males that proved not to carry this undesirable trait would be used for breeding in the regular herd. In this way no undesirable individuals for that trait would be produced and, unless there was a selective advantage for the carrier, the incidence of this undesirable gene would be reduced.

A question may arise as to whether or not it is sufficiently important to test sires, since it takes considerable time and money to make such tests. Just one male cannot be tested because if he were to prove to be a carrier of the undesirable gene, there would be nothing to do except to use an unknown male for that crop of calves. The number of offspring necessary to prove that a male mated to recessive tester females does not carry an undesirable gene may be debated. Certainly the larger the number of offspring, all of which are free of the undesirable trait when the male is being tested by mating to the undesirable females, the more accurate is the test. With a given number of females to use for testing a male, we are faced with the problem of which is more important, accuracy of the test on each male tested or number of males which can be tested. Suppose one could use a bull on 100 tester cows or he could use the same 100 tester cows for testing several bulls. Obviously, if five bulls are tested, the accuracy of the test on each is lower than if one bull were tested by using all the cows. However, it might be more important to have a less accurate test on the five bulls. There would be a good chance, if five bulls are tested, that one would be found that did not carry the undesirable gene under consideration. Generally, if a breeder can get 10 to 12 offspring from a mating of a desirable male with tester (undesirable) females, with none of the offspring showing the undesirable, he can consider the male has been proven not to carry the undesirable. Although there will be some error in this assumption, it will not be great.

To eliminate a recessive lethal gene from a herd or flock is even more difficult than to eliminate an undesirable viable character. One cannot use the lethal as a tester because it is dead. The only thing that can be done in this case is to reduce the incidence of the lethal in the herd or flock by testing and using males that have been proven not to carry the lethal. In cattle, sheep, hogs, and rabbits, this can be done by mating the males under consideration back to their daughters. This requires a great deal of time because one must breed females, wait until they produce young, then wait for these young to reach breeding age, breed them, and again wait until their young are dropped. One advantage in this type of test is that one can test for all lethals and undesirable recessives at the same time. That is, when a male is mated back to his daughters, any and all undesirable recessive genes will be involved in the test. For accuracy, at least 24 daughters would be required for mating back to the sire when testing for lethals due to one gene. This would be only about three times the 7:1 ratio which is expected in the offspring when the male that carries a lethal is mated to his daughters: $L =$ normal, $l =$ lethal.

Male Under Test		Females	
L (l)	$\times$	$LL = 1\ LL$	
		$1\ Ll$	

This male $\times$		daughters	
L (l)	$\times\ LL$		$= 4$, all normal
L (l)	$\times\ Ll$		$= 3$ normal:1 lethal
Total			$= 7$ normal:1 lethal

Of course any time a male sires a lethal offspring when he is mated to produce the daughters for further test, or when he is mated to his own daughters, it proves that he carries the lethal gene. The number of offspring given (24, or three times the 7:1 ratio), all of which are normal when a male is mated to his daughters, will not prove definitely that he does not carry the lethal, but it is a good indication. This number must be considered the minimum rather than the optimum necessary to produce a good indication. Also, it would be necessary to test several males, rather than one, in order to find one which does not carry the lethal or undesirable gene.

Undesirable sex-linked genes are less difficult to eliminate than undesirable autosomal genes, since the heterogametic individual which is desirable does not carry any undesirable sex-linked genes. If it did, these genes would express themselves, and therefore only the desirable homogametic individuals must be tested. In the case of our farm animals, such as hogs, sheep, and cattle, only the female would need to be tested for sex-linked undesirable recessive genes. This could be done in a regular breeding program because observation of her male offspring would indicate whether the female parent carried the undesirable gene. If a female carried an undesirable sex-linked recessive gene, one-half of her male offspring would show it and one-half would not.

Females (such as cattle, sheep, and hogs) that produce sex-linked undesirable male offspring prove themselves carriers and should be culled. Also, their female offspring should be culled because one-half of them will carry the undesirable sex-linked gene. The desirable males may be kept because they are hemizygous in genotype and cannot carry the sex-linked undesirable gene.

This same principle applies to sex-linked lethals. We know that the heterogametic individual does not carry any sex-linked lethal genes, but that the homogametic may carry lethals. The test in hogs, sheep, and cattle is to observe the male offspring. Any female that produces sex-linked lethal offspring carries the lethal gene and should be eliminated from the herd. Her normal male offspring will be satisfactory to keep, since they cannot carry the sex-linked lethal gene (or they are dead), but all her female offspring should be culled because one-half of them could be expected to carry the lethal gene.

In the case of poultry, it is the female that is heterogametic and cannot carry undesirable, recessive sex-linked genes without showing them or sex-linked recessive lethals without dying. It is only the male, the homogametic sex, in poultry which needs to be tested for sex-linked undesirable or lethal genes. He can be tested in a regular breeding program by observing his female offspring for these sex-linked lethals or undesirables. If he sires any, he should be eliminated along with his sons, since one-half of the sons would be expected to carry the sex-linked gene under consideration. All normal, desirable daughters would be satisfactory to keep, as far as sex-linked genes are concerned, because they cannot carry any sex-linked undesirable or lethal genes.

Abnormalities may be physiological (improper functioning) or anatomical (improper in structure), but many of the ones we observe as being an improper function may be actually abnormal structure of some gland or organ. Examples of physiological abnormalities are nervous disorders (spasms), blood disorders (anemia, hemophilia), and endocrine disfunctions (sterility, etc.). Anatomical disorders may involve any part of the body.

It is not the object in this chapter to review and list all the genetic abnormalities and lethals that have occurred and have been reported in farm and laboratory animals. Some of these will be listed along with a brief description, the mode of inheritance, and the investigator(s) describing the condition. For convenience of the reader, this material is presented for cattle, hogs, sheep, and horses. A complete coverage was not attempted, but some of the information is summarized so that one may appreciate the kinds of abnormality which have been reported. Obviously, many inherited abnormalities exist, but these have never been reported in the literature.

INHERITED LETHALS AND ABNORMALITIES IN CATTLE

Abnormality	Description	Mode of Inheritance	Investigators
1. Achondroplasia	Bulldog. Extremes are aborted at 3 and 8 months gestation. Delivery may be very difficult. Lethal. (Figs. 7, 35.)	Three kinds. One is incompletely dominant with the heterozygote smaller than normal and bulldog, a complete monstrosity as the lethal. One type is born alive. The other is simple recessive.	Gregory, et al; Hutt, Mead, et al; Johansson, Downs, Surrarrer, Berger and Innes, Carmichael, Brandt
2. Acroteriosis congenita (amputated)	Also called amputated. Eyes protrude. Ears short, lower jaw short, forelegs terminated at elbow and rear legs at hock, with ends of all four blunt, covered with skin. Lethal. (Fig. 36.)	Hereditary, but mode of inheritance unknown	Wriedt and Mohr
3. Agnathia	Short, lower jaw; lethal.	Simple recessive	Annett, et al; Fordyce, et al
4. Ankylosis	Legs rigidly bent due to bones of joints fusing. Some cases of jaw fusions noted. Lethal.	Probably recessive	Tuff; Mohr; Eaton
5. Brachygnathia	Short lower jaw. (Fig. 37.)	Probably recessive	Bogart (unpublished)
6. Bulldog head	Short, broad skull, orbits large, upper jaw short, impaired vision. (Fig. 38.)	Simple recessive	Becker and Dix
7. Bowed pasterns	Bowed outward. (Fig. 39.)	Probably recessive	Atkeson, et al
8. Cancer eye	Occurs mostly in white-eyed Hereford. Cancer develops in nictitating membrane. Usually occurs late in life. Results eventually in death. (Fig. 40.)	Hereditary, but mode of inheritance not determined. Seldom occurs in animals with pigmented eyelids.	Frank, Guilbert, et al; Woodward and Knapp; Anderson, et al; Anderson, et al
9. Cataract	Lens shows opaque body beneath cornea.	Simple recessive	Detlefson and Yapp; Gregory, et al
10. Cerebellar hypoplasia	Poor coordination. Cerebellum rudimentary, excessive fluid. Some walk like ballet dancers.	Probably simple recessive	Anderson and Davis; Saunders, et al
11. Curly hair	Hair in tight curls, viable. (Fig. 41.)	Simple dominant	Eldridge, et al

INHERITED LETHALS AND ABNORMALITIES IN CATTLE

Abnormality	Description	Mode of Inheritance	Investigators
12. Digital anomaly	One toe shorter, toes spread, animals lame. (Fig. 42.)	Simple recessive	Mead, et al
13. Double ears	Double ear is thin flap of cartilage parallel to main axis of ear and projecting out of back surface.	Simple dominant	Lush

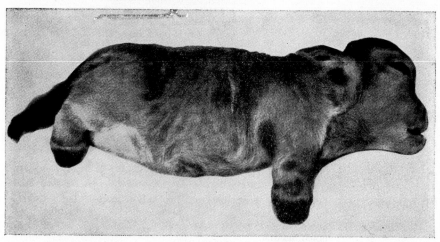

Fig. 35. Recessive Achondroplasia. *(From Brandt, J. Hered., 32:183, 1941.)*

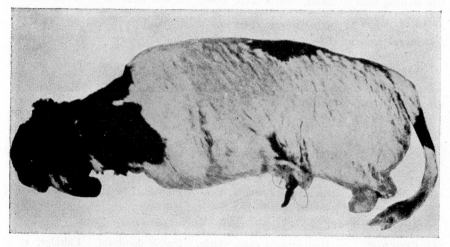

Fig. 36. Lethal amputated-acroteriosis congenita. *(From Hutt, Cornell Vet., 24:1, 1934.)*

Fig. 37. Brachygnathia or short lower jaw. (*From Bogart, unpublished, Courtesy Oregon State College.*)

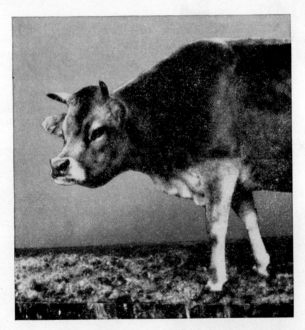

Fig. 38. Bulldog head in cattle. (*From Becker and Dix Arnold, J. Hered., 10:281, 1928.*)

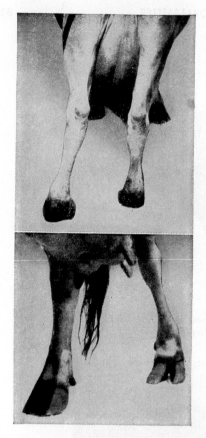

Fig. 39. (Left) Bowed pastern in cattle. *(From Atkeson, Eldridge, and Ihsen,* J. Hered., *34:25, 1943.)*

Fig. 40. (Below) Cancer eye. *(Courtesy Oregon State College.)*

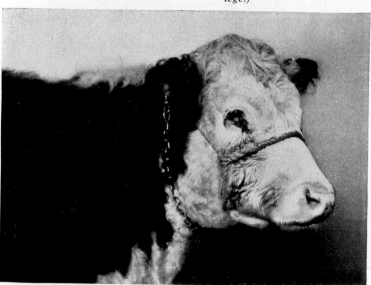

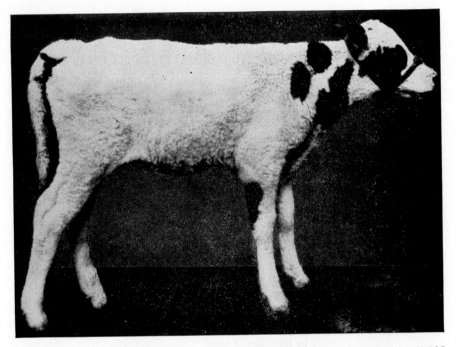

Fig. 41. Curly hair in cattle. *(From Eldridge, Atkeson, and Ihsen,* J. Hered., *40:205, 1949.)*

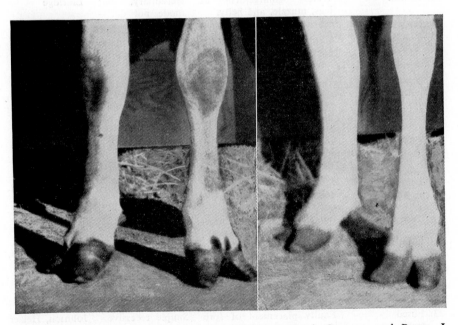

Fig. 42. Inherited digital anomaly in cattle. *(From Mead, Gregory, and Regan,* J. Hered., *40:151, 1949.)*

INHERITED LETHALS AND ABNORMALITIES IN CATTLE

Abnormality	Description	Mode of Inheritance	Investigators
14. Double muscle	Thighs deep, full, with deep groove. Homozygous is undesirable, but heterozygous has selective advantage. (Fig. 43.)	Incomplete recessive	Kidwell, et al; Weber and Ibsen
15. Dropsy	Degrees of dropsy expressed. Severe cases may cause loss of dam.	Simple recessive	Donald, et al
16. Duck-legged	Cattle very short-legged. (Fig. 44.)	Dominant	Lush
17. Dwarfism	Described in most major breeds of beef cattle. Several distinct kinds. Some appear normal except for being small. Some are cretins, short heads, wide through shoulders, breathing hard, etc. Cannot always be identified at birth. Some are long-headed. (Figs. 45, 46, 47.)	Recessive	Mead, et al; Johnson, et al; Baker, et al; Pahnish, et al; Gregory, et al; Carroll, et al; Gregory, et al; Lindley
18. Edema	Watery enlargement of legs, muzzle, and belly.	Hereditary, but mode not determined	Eldridge
19. Epileptic fits	Lowering of head, tongue chewing, foaming at the mouth, collapse into coma.	Simple dominant	Atkeson, et al
20. Epithelial defects	Defective formation of skin below knees, one or more claws undeveloped, deformed integument of muzzle and the mucous membranes of nostrils, tongue, palate, and cheek. Lethal. (Fig. 48.)	Simple recessive	Hadley and Cole; Hadley; Hutt and Frost
21. Female sterility	Sex-limited with only females showing it. Probably zygote abortion in late cleavage or early blastocyst.	Simple, sex-limited, recessive	Gregory, et al; Gregory, et al
22. Flexed pasterns	Usually with front legs. Toes may turn under in severe cases. Metatarsal inclination and bowed pasterns.	Simple recessive; hereditary, but mode not determined	Habel; Atkeson, et al
23. Fused teats	Faulty placement of fore and rear teats, fused in severe cases. (Fig. 49.)	Simple recessive	Johnson, Heizer

Fig. 43. Muscular hypertrophy in cattle. *(From Kidwell, Vernon, Crown, and Singletary, J. of Hered., 43:63, 1952.)*

Fig. 44. Duck-legged cattle. *(From Lush, J. Hered., 21:85, 1927.)*

Fig. 45. Long-headed dwarf. *(Courtesy P. W. Gregory, University of California.)*

Fig. 46. Dwarf cow and calf. Calf was delivered by Caesarean. *(Courtesy P. W. Gregory, University of California.)*

Fig. 47. Dwarf bull compared with normal bull at one year of age. *(Courtesy Oregon State College.)*

INHERITED LETHALS AND ABNORMALITIES IN CATTLE

Abnormality	Description	Mode of Inheritance	Investigators
24. Hairlessness	Born hairless or semihairless. Skin thick and shows cracks. Appears to be two kinds: one lethal, while the other lives but grows slowly and never has normal hair. (Fig. 50.)	Simple recessive	Regan, et al; Kidwell and Guilbert; Surrarrer; Ishikara; Hutt and Saunders
25. Hernia	Umbilical rupture. Appears in males 8 to 20 days of age. Disappears at 10 weeks to 7 months.	One or more pairs of recessive genes; sex-limited	Warren and Atkeson; Gilman and Stringham
26. Hydrocephalus	Water on the brain. Malgrowth of diencephalon with constriction of third ventricle to narrow channel. Hydrocephalus restricted to the two cavities of the olfactory bulbs. Lethal. (Figs. 51, 52.)	Not known; probably recessive	Houck; Godgluck; Cole; Gianotti

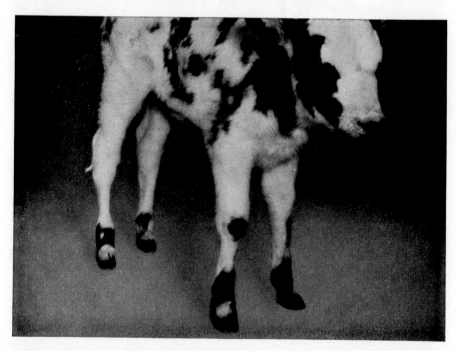

Fig. 48. Epithelial defects in cattle. (*From Hutt and Frost, J. Hered., 39:131, 1948.*)

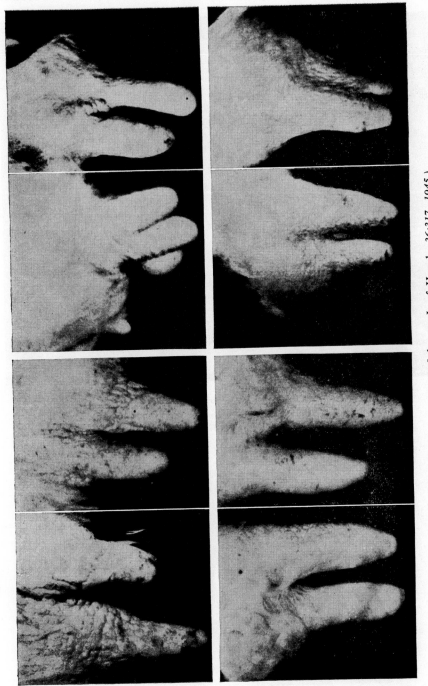

Fig. 49. Fused teats. *(From Johnson, J. of Hered., 36:317, 1945.)*

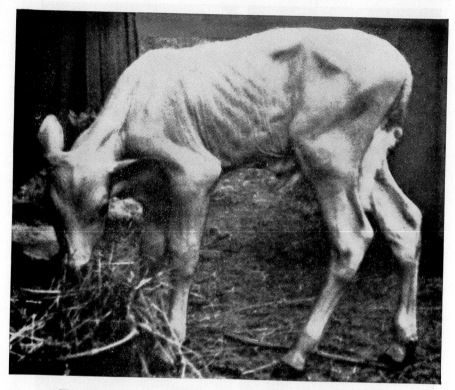

Fig. 50. Hairlessness. *(From Surrarrer, J. Hered., 34:175, 1943.)*

Fig. 51. Hydrocephalus. *(Courtesy Oregon State College.)*

INHERITED LETHALS AND ABNORMALITIES IN CATTLE

Abnormality	Description	Mode of Inheritance	Investigators
27. Hypoplasia	Epithelial layers of testes, tubules, and follicles underdeveloped. Sterile if bilateral.	Simple recessive	Eriksson
28. Impacted molars	Molars misplaced and deranged. Terrific stress on jaw which might cause break in bone. Lethal. (Fig. 53.)	Simple recessive	Heizer and Hervey
29. Imperforati anus	No exterior opening of the anus.	Recessive	Lerner
30. Lameness	Lameness in calves.	Not determined	Christensen and Christensen
31. Missing teat	Only one teat on left side.	Recessive	Shrode and Lush
32. Mummified fetus	Calves die at eighth month gestation but carried to term.	Apparently simple recessive	Loje
33. Muscle contracture	Calf born at full term with contracture of neck and limbs. May lead to death of cow at delivery. Lethal. (Fig. 54.)	Simple recessive	Hutt

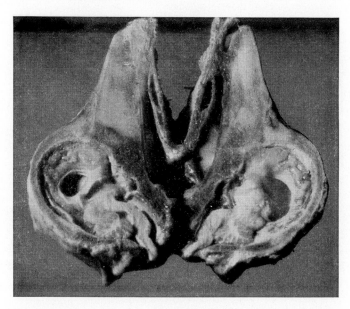

Fig. 52. Hydrocephalus in cattle. Note brain ventricle which has filled with fluid. (*Courtesy Oregon State College.*)

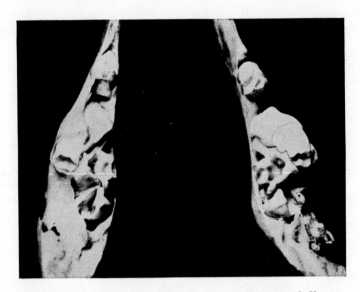

Fig. 53. Impacted molars in cattle. *(From Heizer and Hervey,* J. Hered., *28:123, 1937.)*

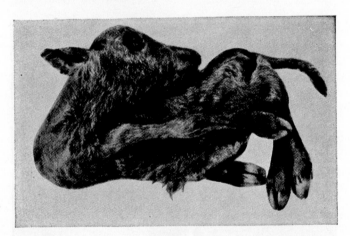

Fig. 54. Muscle contracture. *(From Hutt,* J. Hered., *25:41, 1934.)*

INHERITED LETHALS AND ABNORMALITIES IN CATTLE

Abnormality	Description	Mode of Inheritance	Investigators
34. Night blindness	Animals do not see well at night but have good vision during day.	Not determined	Craft
35. Paralysis	Posterior paralysis. May have muscular tremors and blindness. Dies shortly after birth. Lethal.	Simple recessive	Tuff; Cranek and Ralston
36. Polydactylism	Extra toes. Defect of front feet. Affected animals go lame.	Probably recessive	Morrill; Roberts; Shrode and Lush
37. Prolonged pregnancy	Pregnancies up to 403 days. Calves born dead.	Simple recessive	Ishihara
38. Screw tail	Distinct kinks in lower part of tail. (Fig. 55.)	Simple recessive	Knapp, et al
39. Short spine	Entire vertebral column is short but legs are normal length. (Fig. 56.)	Recessive	Mohr and Wriedt
40. Skull defect	Frontal opening in skull. Brain tissue protrudes.	Not determined	Shaw
41. Spasms	Animals appear normal at birth but in a short time go into spasms and die. Lethal.	Simple recessive	Shrode and Lush
42. Sterility	(a) Malformation and underdevelopment of sex organs. (b) Endocrine imbalance resulting in cystic ovaries, and aspermia. (c) Adolescent infertility. (d) Ovarian hypoplasia. (e) Absence of gonads. (f) Incompletely developed. (g) Testes hypoplasia. (h) Sigmoid flexure will not straighten.	Not determined; most of these are recessive	Lagerlof
43. Strabismus	Cross eyes. Not evident at birth but identified by 12 months of age.	Simple recessive	Regan, et al
44. Streaked-hairless	Streaks of hairlessness in perpendicular rows in cows. These cows produced a ratio of 2 heifers:1 bull calves.	Incomplete dominant; sex-linked	Elridge and Atkeson
45. Syndactylism	One toe on each front foot instead of two. (Fig. 57.)	Simple recessive	Elridge, et al
46. Tendon contracture	Tendons pulled rigidly. Calves either born dead or die shortly after birth.	Simple recessive	Dale and Moxley

Fig. 55. Screw tail in cattle. *(From Knapp, Emmel, and Ward,* J. Hered., *27:269, 1936.)*

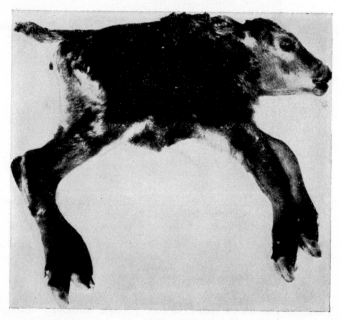

Fig. 56. Short spine, a recessive lethal in cattle. *(From Mohr and Wriedt,* J. Genetics, *22:279, 1930.)*

INHERITED LETHALS AND ABNORMALITIES IN CATTLE

Abnormality	Description	Mode of Inheritance	Investigators
47. White heifer disease	Persistent hymen or incomplete cervix. Horns of uterus become distended with fluid. Associated with white Shorthorn.	Probably recessive	Gilmore; Spriggs
48. Wry tail	Tail twisted to one side at tail head. Direction not genetic. (Fig. 58.)	Simple recessive	Atkeson, et al

INHERITED LETHALS AND ABNORMALITIES IN SHEEP

Abnormality	Description	Mode of Inheritance	Investigators
1. Amputated	Limbs are amputated at the fetlocks. Lethal.	Not determined	Lerner
2. Cryptorchidism	One or both testes retained in abdomen rather than descending into scrotum.	Recessive	Warwick
3. "Daft lamb"	Cortical cerebellar atrophy. Lambs born alive but usually do not walk because of poor balance. Lethal.	Recessive, but also modifying genes involved	Innes and MacNaughton

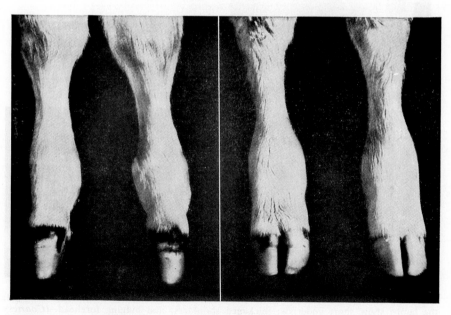

Fig. 57. Syndactylism in cattle. (*From Eldridge, Smith, and McLeod,* J. Hered., *42:241, 1933.*)

INHERITED LETHALS AND ABNORMALITIES IN SHEEP

Abnormality	Description	Mode of Inheritance	Investigators
4. Dwarf	Affected lambs are short-legged, particularly the front, and thick through shoulder. Thyroid disfunction. May live for a few weeks. Lethal. May be associated with short underjaw. (Fig. 59.)	Simple recessive	Bogart and Dyer
5. Earless and clef palate	Lambs born alive but die soon. May have extra toes.	Recessive	Lerner

Fig. 58. Wry tail. *(Courtesy Oregon State College.)*

Fig. 59. Dwarfism in sheep. On left is Southdown ewe and twin dwarf lambs. On right, the lambs show short underjaw, thickened shoulders, and bulging forehead. *(Courtesy University of Missouri.)*

INHERITED LETHALS AND ABNORMALITIES IN SHEEP

Abnormality	Description	Mode of Inheritance	Investigators
6. Earless	There are two kinds: (a) Reported in Karakul sheep. Affected animals have no ears or very short ears.	Incompletely dominant	Lush; Wriedt
	(b) Homozygous earless have no ears, heterozygotes have short ears and homozygous normals are not affected. (Fig. 60.)	Incompletely dominant	
7. Entropion	Turned-in eye lids. There appears to be the type in sheep having body folds where this affects eye. The other type occurs in smooth-bodied sheep. Lambs go blind if the condition is not corrected. Once recovered, the sheep is normal.	Not determined	Warwick
8. Lethal gray	Gray × gray gives 2 gray:1 nongray; assume that pure gray is early lethal.	Incompletely dominant	Eaton
9. Muscle contracture	Lambs born dead. Forelimbs, particularly, are very rigidly bent. (Fig. 61.)	Recessive	Roberts; Hutt
10. Naked	Lambs have only a few scattered hairs and no wool. Skin is shiny. Lambs grow normally but sensitive to temperature changes.	Recessive	Popova-Wasina
11. Paralysis	Rear legs are paralyzed. Lambs born alive but soon die because they cannot stand. Lethal.	Recessive	Eaton
12. Rigid fetlocks	Legs are bent and rigid at fetlock. Body is short and thick, claws compressed and short. Lethal.	Recessive	Eaton
13. Scurs	Occurs in hornless sheep. Loose, horny growth not firmly attached to head, and bone from head does not grow into it.	Incompletely dominant	Ibsen and Cox
14. Short ears	Differs from earless. Only short ears and normals are produced.	Recessive	Wriedt

Fig. 60. Earlessness in sheep. *(From Wriedt,* J. Hered., *12:56, 1921.)*

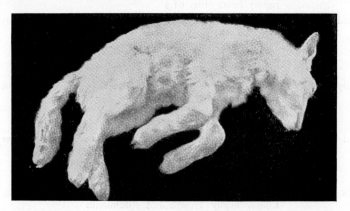

Fig. 61. Muscle contracture in sheep. *(From Hutt,* Cornell Vet., *24:1, 1934.)*

INHERITED LETHALS AND ABNORMALITIES IN SHEEP

Abnormality	Description	Mode of Inheritance	Investigators
15. Skeletal defect	Skeleton, including the skull, is deformed. May have hernia. Associated with short wool. Lethal.	Recessive	Lerner
16. Skin folds	Occurs in fine wool sheep. Makes the sheep more difficult to shear.	Not determined	Russel
17. Tailless	A desired abnormality because tailless sheep do not have to be docked.	Not determined	Wilson
18. Undershot and overshot jaws	Jaws do not match. Interferes with grazing. Parrot mouth refers to one with very short under jaw. Undershot means lower jaw is longer, so that teeth hit in front of dental pad. Overshot means the teeth hit behind the dental pad. (Fig. 62.)	Mode of inheritance complicated	Nordby, et al
19. Wattles	Skinlike projection hanging down from throat near jaw.	Recessive	Wassin
20. Yellow fat	Fat of carcass is yellow; considered quite objectionable.	Recessive	Castle

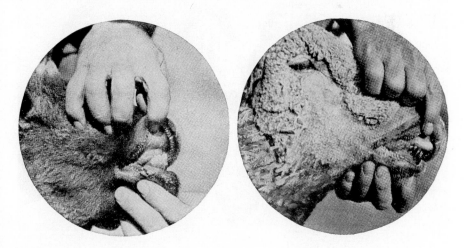

Fig. 62. Undershot (left) and overshot (right) jaws in sheep. *(From the originals of figures 3 and 5, J. E. Nordby, C. E. Terrill, L. N. Hazel and J. A. Stoehr,* Anatomical Record, *92:237, 1945.)*

INHERITANCE OF LETHALS AND ABNORMALITIES IN SWINE

Abnormality	Description	Mode of Inheritance	Investigators
1. Atresi ani	No anal opening; causes death in males, but feces are voided through vulva in females.	Not determined	Kinzelbach
2. Bent legs	Legs bent at right angle and stiff. Usually front legs, but rear legs may also be involved. Lethal.	Recessive	Hallquist
3. Blindness	Pigs born without eyeballs. Lethal.	Probably nutritional; genetic interrelation	Buchanan-Smith; Hale, et al
4. Brain hernia	Skull does not close along median line and allows brain to protrude with only a membrane covering. May be lethal.	Recessive	Hughes and Hart
5. Catlin mark	Incomplete development of the skull.	Recessive	Warwick
6. Cleft palate	Palate does not close during development. May be unilateral or bilateral and may even result in hare lip. Lethal. (Fig. 63.)	Recessive	McPhee, et al

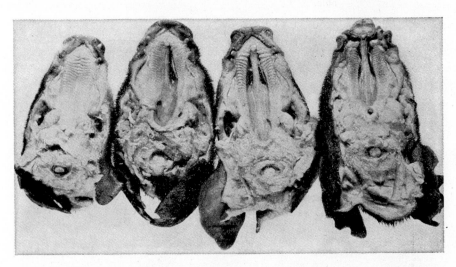

Fig. 63. Cleft palate and harelip in swine. From left to right are normal unilateral and bilateral cleft palate and harelip. *(From McPhee, et al., J. Hered., 22:400, 1931.)*

INHERITANCE OF LETHALS AND ABNORMALITIES IN SWINE

Abnormality	Description	Mode of Inheritance	Investigators
7. Cryptorchidism	One or both testes retained in abdomen instead of descending into scrotum. Sterile of bilateral. (Fig. 64.)	Recessive; sex-limited	McPhee and Buckley
8. Ear defect	Ears split. Lethal. Rear legs twisted.	Undetermined	Annett
9. Excessive fatness	Pigs become very fat at 70 to 150 lb. and die. Lethal.	Recessive	Eaton
10. Eyes absent	Partial lethal.	Probably recessive	Smith, et al
11. Fetal mortality	Born dead or are reabsorbed.	Recessive	Eaton
12. Hairless	Few hair follicles that are normal. May be inherited thyroid disfunction.	Two recessive genes	Roberts and Carroll

Fig. 64. Bilateral cryptorchidism in swine. *(From McPhee and Buckley*, J. Hered., *25:295, 1934.)*

INHERITANCE OF LETHALS AND ABNORMALITIES IN SWINE

Abnormality	Description	Mode of Inheritance	Investigators
13. Hemophilia	Animals normal in appearance but bleed to death from slight wounds. Condition not apparent at birth but progresses until full expression at 3 or 4 months of age. (Figs. 65, 66.)	Recessive	Bogart and Muhrer
14. Hernia	(a) Scrotal. Intestines come down large inguinal canal to scrotum.	Two recessive genes	Warwick, et al
	(b) Umbilical weakness of the belly wall at umbilicus allows intestines to protrude.	Dominant	

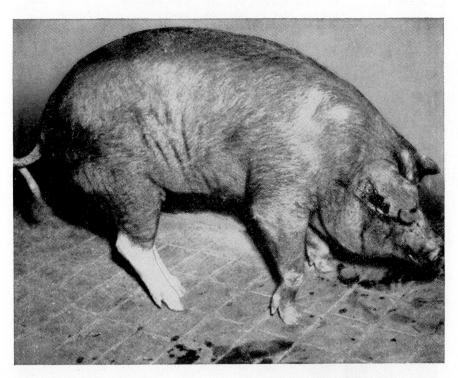

Fig. 65. Hemophilia in swine. Note profuse bleeding from ear. *(From Bogart and Muhrer,* J. Hered., *33:59, 1942.)*

INHERITANCE OF LETHALS AND ABNORMALITIES IN SWINE

Abnormality	Description	Mode of Inheritance	Investigators
15. Hydrocephalus	Water on the brain. Brain enlarged, with much fluid in skull cavity. Fluid interferes with bone growth of head. (Fig. 67 a and b.) Lethal.	Simple recessive	Blunn and Hughes
16. Inverted nipples	Teats turn in instead of protruding so that pigs can nurse. Nonfunctional. (Fig. 68.)	Undetermined	Weaver and Bogart

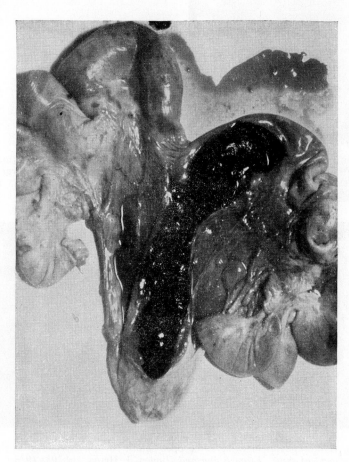

Fig. 66. Hemophilia in swine. Note hemorrhage in uterus of sow at time of farrow. The blood clots, but not rapidly. (*From Bogart and Muhrer, J. Hered., 33:59, 1942.*)

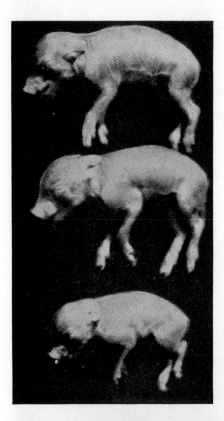

Fig. 67(a). Hydrocephalus in swine. Note enlarged forehead of pig in lower photo. *(From Blunn and Hughes,* J. Hered., *29:203, 1938.)*

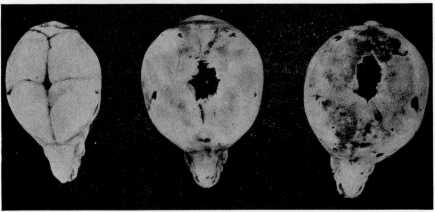

Fig. 67(b). Hydrocephalus in swine. Note open skulls, particularly in two at right, and also enlargement of skull. *(From Blunn and Hughes,* J. Hered., *29:203, 1938.)*

INHERITANCE OF LETHALS AND ABNORMALITIES IN SWINE

Abnormality	Description	Mode of Inheritance	Investigators
17. Kinky tail	Rigid angles in the tail. Shows at birth but more rigid with development.	Simple recessive	Nordby
18. Mastitis	Caked udders that may have to be removed to save life of sow. Susceptibility to mastitis. (Fig. 69.)	Not determined; occurs in certain strains	Weaver and Bogart
19. Melanotic tumors	Moles or skin tumors are small at birth of pig but enlarge. Very heavily pigmented and contain hair. All moles are not genetic.	Recessive	Nordby
20. Muscle contracture	Forelegs are stiff. Lethal.	Simple recessive	Hallqvist
21. Paralysis	Hind legs are paralyzed. Lethal.	Recessive	Mohr
22. Polydactyly	Extra toes on forefeet.	Undetermined	Hughes
23. "Streamlined"	Legless pigs; born alive but soon die. Lethal.	Simple recessive	Johnson
24. Stringhalt	Pigs lift leg with a jerk; sometimes the leg goes as high as the back.	More than one recessive	Warwick

Fig. 68. Inverted nipples in swine. Note that pigs nurse only the normal teats. This sow farrowed 13, but raised only five pigs because of inverted nipples. (*From Weaver and Bogart,* Mo. Agri. Exp. Sta. Bul. 461.)

INHERITANCE OF LETHALS AND ABNORMALITIES IN SWINE

Abnormality	Description	Mode of Inheritance	Investigators
25. Syndactyly	Mule foot. Only one toe instead of two. Idea, once prevalent, that they are resistant to cholera is untrue.	Dominant	McPhee and Hankins
26. Thickened forelimbs	Forelimbs greatly swollen, with gelatinous infiltration of connective tissue replacing muscle. Lethal. (Fig. 70.)	Simple recessive	Walther, et al
27. Wattles	Skinlike flaps hanging from throat near lower jaw.	Simple dominant	Kronacher
28. Whorls	Instead of hair going in one direction, it is in a whorl. There may be a number of whorls in one pig.	Two completely dominant genes	Nordby
29. Wooly	Kinky hair.	Simple dominant	Rhoad

INHERITANCE OF LETHALS AND ABNORMALITIES IN HORSES

Abnormality	Description	Mode of Inheritance	Investigators
1. Atresia coli	Foals born alive but soon show symptoms of colic and die within four days from closed colon. Swollen colon can be palpated from left flank. Lethal.	Simple recessive	Yamane
2. Bighead	Enlarged face and jaws.	Simple dominant	Gonzalez and Villegas
3. Horned	Horn located on lower border of ear. Firmly attached to skin and muscle.	Undetermined	Miller
4. Lethal white	Low fertility in white horses of Frederiksborg stud assumed due to lethal associated with gray.	Undetermined	Eaton
5. Stiff forelimbs	Forelegs stiff, with fetlock joint pulled and rigid. Can live only with special care. (Fig. 71.)	Recessive; partial lethal	Prawockenski

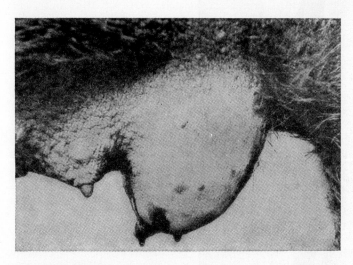

Fig. 69. Mastitis in swine. The large udder has mastitis. Suscepti-bility to mastitis appears to have a genetic control. *(From Weaver and Bogart, Mo. Agri. Exp. Sta. Bul. 461.)*

Fig. 70. Thickened forelimbs in swine. *(From Hutt, Cornell Vet., 24:1, 1934.)*

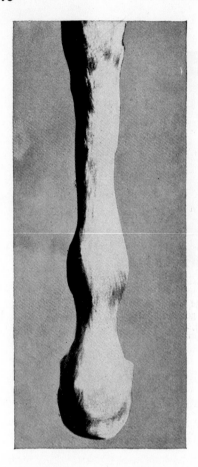

Fig. 71. Stiff forelimbs in horses. This condition involves a fusion of the bones at the joints. *(From Prawochenski, J. Hered., 27:411, 1936.)*

From the lethals and abnormalities listed, it may be deduced, that cattle and hogs, more than sheep, or particularly horses, are afflicted with such undesirable inheritance. Horses are not highly fertile, and the fact that many of them have been raised by men with a few mares bred to stallions which stand for service on some other farm, has made it difficult to study horse genetics. Swine reproduce at a higher rate and cattle have been studied more intensively, which perhaps accounts for the reason why more lethals and abnormalities have been reported for these two classes of livestock. Therefore, there is not sufficient evidence to show that any one species is afflicted more frequently than any other species.

Lethals and abnormals are often not observed or, if noticed, they are attributed to some other cause. Many times a farmer tries to explain how a certain case came about, using whatever information he has available, but in many cases he may have the wrong interpretation. One example is that of short spine in cattle, which at one time was believed by farmers to be the result of cows becoming pregnant by an elk. Many calves born dead are attributed to injury of the pregnant female. Such might occur, but it is very seldom. The pregnant female is much stronger an animal than most of us realize. An example of what pregnant sows may endure without loss of pigs occurred at the University of Missouri. Pregnant sows were being hauled in a truck from a farm to farrowing quarters. A bridge about 35 ft. above a creek, which had a solid rockbed, was placed so that a sharp turn was necessary to approach the bridge. The driver of the truck was in a hurry as evening approached and took this turn rapidly. The sows were forced to one side of the truck, which could not withstand the extra weight, so that the sows were dumped over the railing into the creek. These sows were injured, some of them rather severely, but not one aborted, farrowed early, or farrowed dead pigs.

When an animal gives birth to dead or abnormal young, there are three general factors which should be studied: (1) adequacy of diet; (2) presence of any infectious disease in this herd; and (3) providing that diet seems satisfactory and no disease is noted, the possibility that such dead or abnormal young may be the result of inheritance. There may be occasions when abnormal young are the result of nutrition-genetic interrelations. To be normal, certain genotypes may need a nutritional level higher than for other genotypes. Also, under rather rugged conditions certain strains will produce abnormal young, whereas other strains may perform quite satisfactorily.

There are two approaches to livestock improvement that differ a great deal. One approach is to develop some very outstanding individuals, the object being to establish outstanding records. The other approach is to eliminate the material which is genetically unfit and cannot exist properly under a normal environment. Either approach will raise the level of production of a herd a great deal. The first approach (outstanding individuals) is the one generally taken by stock growers. It is possible that more progress could be made by eliminating the lethals and abnormals.

When well over 40 known lethal and abnormal conditions exist in a species, it is possible that one herd may have a dozen or more of these undesirable characters. Even if the incidence were low for each lethal and the loss from each not more than 2 per cent per year, with several of these undesirables in the herd or flock a breeder could lose as high as one-fourth or more of the young resulting from inheritance of such characters. In one flock of Southdown sheep, for which records were kept over a 3-year period, losses from the dwarf gene alone amounted to 22 per cent. Before records were kept, the man in charge of this flock stated that the character was not of any consequence.

Sometimes stock growers do not want to admit that they have an abnormality or lethal character in their herd or flock. They think that the sale of breeding stock may be affected if potential buyers become aware of the difficulty. This is erroneous reasoning, for hiding such things is the best way to make it spread in the herd and into other owners' herds. A purebred breeder who hides such things, rather than making an effort to eliminate them from his herd or flock, is certainly not showing the honesty that one in his important position should show.

It has been estimated that if lethals and undesirables which are not capable of doing well under a normal environment could be eliminated, stockgrowers could produce 120 per cent of the meat and animal products that are now being produced, with the same amount of feed and labor.

Lethal genes sometimes modify expected ratios. For example, yellow mice when intermated will produce 2 yellow:1 nonyellow. Studies by Kirkham (1917) and Ibsen and Stiegleder (1917) have shown that the yellow mouse is a heterozygote, and when two such animals are mated, one-fourth of the young die during gestation. Pregnant yellow mice, experimentally expended, showed many more dead embryos when impregnated by a yellow male rather than by a nonyellow male. Three explanations can be offered for this lethal condition. One theory assumes that the gene which acts dominant for yellow color also acts as a recessive lethal. On this assumption, one gene has two separate and distinct effects. This could be called *manifold effects* (or pleiotropic effects) of a gene. The other explanation could be based on the assumption that a lethal gene, l, is linked so closely with yellow, Y, that the two never cross over. Such a situation would have the same effect as if it were one gene. We know that each gene has more than one effect because we have seen that genes may interact with each other. In the case of the yellow mouse, it is known that the heterozygotes differ from nonyellows in that they become very fat. Thus, this gene not only brings about the expression of color but it also affects metabolism. This in itself is an example of more than one effect of a gene.

It is also postulated that farm animals express characters which are caused by many genes being in a block as a result of small chromosomes which show little crossing-over. Thus, either explanation of the yellow mouse, manifold effects of the y gene, or linkage of a lethal with the y gene in which no crossing-over occurs, could be possible. The occurrence of obesity and the lethal effects, separate from the yellow color which behaves without lethality, would be all that are needed to show that crossing-over had occurred. Until such occurs, one cannot be sure which of these three explanations is correct.

Other color genes, such as genes for white spotting, have also been found to have a lethal effect (or to be associated closely with the lethal gene). For example, W = white spotting, patchy small spots; w = self-colored; S = self-colored; s = white spotting. The two white-spotting genes are cumulative, and when together (Ww ss), the animals are "black-eyed whites." When two black-eyed whites are mated, they produce 2 black-eyed whites:1 piebald (white-spotted but showing large pigmented areas).

$$Ww\ ss \times Ww\ ss = \text{All }\ ss \begin{cases} 1\ WW = 1\ ss\ WW \text{ (dies)} \\ 2\ Ww = 2\ ss\ Ww = 2 \text{ black-eyed white} \\ 1\ ww\ = 1\ ss\ ww\ = 1 \text{ piebald} \end{cases}$$

The WW embryos produced by black-eyed white females remain alive until birth but develop anemia about a week before birth. They die within a few days after birth (de Aberle, 1925).

It has also been shown that sex-linked lethals can result in altering the sex ratio, since the homogametic parent can transmit these to heterogametic offspring in which the gene expresses itself and brings about death.

EXERCISES

1. What is meant by lethal, partial lethal, delayed lethal?
2. How could you eliminate a simple recessive lethal gene from your herd or flock?
3. How could you test a bull to determine if he carries lethal genes?
4. How could you eliminate from your herd a simple recessive undesirable gene that does not interfere with fertility? Be specific.
5. A farmer has had losses from dead calves at birth. How can you determine which of the three causes—improper nutrition, a disease condition, or an inherited lethal—is the most likely cause of these losses?

9

MODIFYING GENES

We may have a character which is determined by one or more pairs of genes, but the expression of this character may be modified by one or more pairs of genes. The gene or genes which bring about the expression of the character are called the *main* genes, while those which modify the expression of the main genes are called *modifying* genes.

There are two principal types of modifying genes: those that modify a character such as milk production, which is determined by a large number of gene pairs; and those that modify the expression of one pair of genes. The former type of modifying gene is a *general modifier,* while the latter is a *specific modifier.* Sometimes specific modifying genes are reserved to designate those which modify the expression of one allele.

In cattle, white spotting is caused by the genes s in the homozygous condition ss (Fig. 15). However, the amount and distribution of white on the animal is brought about by several genes which modify the ss genes. For example, there is a pair of incompletely dominant genes, $Lw\ Lw,$ in which the animal is almost completely pigmented (Fig. 72); $Lw\ lw$ is intermediate, showing about one-half white and one-half pigmented (Fig. 73); and $lw\ lw$ in which the animal is almost completely white (Fig. 74). In this situation, it is apparent that the $Lw\ lw$ individuals, which are intermediate in pigmentation, will produce offspring of which about one-fourth are heavily pigmented, one-half are intermediate, and one-fourth are almost white.

Another modifier of ss is Pl = pigmented legs (Fig. 75), and pl = nonpigmented legs (Fig. 76). The Pl gene causes pigment to appear on the posterior portions of the legs, well below the knees and hocks (Fig. 75). An animal that is Pl and $lw\ lw,$ almost white, appears to have stockings because of the pigmented legs. It was pointed out earlier that Pl can modify S^H (white face), causing brockle face (Fig. 14).

A third modifier of white spotting is Dl = distal leg spots (Fig. 77), and

114

Fig. 72. White-spotting in cattle modified by *Lw Lw* (little white), resulting in almost complete pigmentation of the animal. *(Courtesy Oregon Dairy Breeders Association, Corvallis, Ore.)*

Fig. 73. Intermediate white-spotting effect resulting from the heterozygous, *Lw lw*, condition of the modifier of *ss*. *(Courtesy Oregon Dairy Breeders Association, Corvallis, Ore.)*

Fig. 74. A bull almost entirely white resulting from the modifier *lw lw*, in the pure state affecting *ss*. *(Courtesy Oregon Dairy Breeders Association, Corvallis, Ore.)*

Fig. 75. Ayrshire cow showing pigmented legs resulting from the modifier, *Pl*, acting on *ss*. Note pigment on posterior areas of legs even in a largely white animal. *(Courtesy Oregon State College.)*

116

Fig. 76. Ayrshire cow showing absence of pigmented legs. She is *pl pl, ss* in genotype. *(Courtesy Oregon State College.)*

Fig. 77. Holstein cow showing distal leg spots. This results from the gene *Dl* acting on white-spotting *ss. (Courtesy Oregon State College.)*

117

Fig. 78. Ayrshire calf showing absence of distal leg spots. The genotype of this calf is *ss dl dl*. *(Courtesy Oregon State College.)*

dl = no distal leg spots (Fig. 78). Animals that carry *Dl* will have pigmented spots just above the hoofs. The color of the spots will be the color of the animal, i.e., black, red, etc. Since this gene is considered undesirable in certain breeds, it has been given consideration in selection. However, it is not considered undesirable unless the pigmented area extends around the foot. If breeders considered the character very objectionable and would cull all animals showing any distal leg spot, it could be completely eliminated because a dominant gene is so easy to eliminate.

Some breeds are almost entirely pigmented, showing no more than a star on the forehead or a white switch in the tail. These animals carry a fourth modifier, in addition to *Lw Lw*. This gene, *Wr* = white restrictor, *wr* = nonrestricted, affects the distribution of white. Animals of the genotype *Wr Wr* or *Wr wr* will have the white restricted largely to the head, abdomen, and tail switch. In conjunction with *Lw Lw,* the gene *Wr* causes almost complete pigmentation, and only a star on the forehead or white in the tail switch will show. The gene *S* is completely dominant over *s* and will cause self-color when *SS* or *Ss* (Fig. 12). There is a dominant modifier *In* of *S* which causes white to appear in the inguinal (cod or udder) region (Fig. 79). This gene may be present in *ss* animals, but since they generally show white in this region as a result of the *ss* genotype, a white spot caused by the *In* gene cannot be detected

Fig. 79. Angus heifer showing inguinal white. The gene *In* modifies *S* solid color. *(Courtesy Oregon State College.)*

when it occurs in a white area. In the *S*, solid-colored animal, *In* is clearly detectable. The effects of *In* in heavily pigmented animals can be confused with the white caused by *ss*. Generally, if the white is anterior to the navel region, it is caused by *ss*. In the *in in* animal there is no white about the cod or udder of *S* animals (Fig. 80).

A sex-influenced modifier of blackish has already been described in cattle in which males that are homozygous or heterozygous for the darkening are dark, whereas females must be homozygous to be dark. Females that are heterozygous for darkening or homozygous for light will be light blackish. Three pairs of dilution genes which are not specific affect the intensity of color

Fig. 80. Angus heifer showing no inguinal white. The genotype is *in in S—*. *(Courtesy Oregon State College.)*

in cattle. One (*D*) is dominant and will dilute black, blackish, or red. This gene dilutes black to a slate color and dilutes red to a dull yellow or dun. Another dilution gene is recessive (*I* = intense and *i* = dilute). Red or blackish animals that are *ii* will show considerable dilution. This gene, when homozygous, *ii*, causes general dilution. Another dilution gene is found in Jerseys and apparently affects *Bs*. This dilution factor causes whitening about the muzzle, on the underline, and between the hind legs. This recessive modifier shows its greatest effect on *Bs* animals, although it may be observed in *bb* (Guernsey) and *B* animals. The genes, *W* = no whitening and *w* = whitening, are postulated, since whitening is a recessive modifying factor.

One very important modifier of the *S^H* gene is *Re,* red eye (Fig. 81). Animals of the genotype *re re* will show no pigment about the eyelid; these are called "white-eyed" by Hereford breeders (Fig. 82). These animals have eyes that are quite sensitive to sunlight, dust, and plant pollens, and consequently their eyes are under continual irritation much of the time on the western ranges. Another character, cancer eye, is inherited, but whether it expresses itself depends largely upon stimulation. The irritation that is caused by dust, sunlight, and plant pollens acting upon the white-eyed Herefords is apparently

Fig. 81. Hereford heifer showing pigment about the eye, "red eye." The gene *Re* modifies Hereford pattern S^H to give the red eye. *(Courtesy Oregon State College.)*

Fig. 82. Hereford bull showing no pigment about the eye, "white eye." The genotype is *re re* $S^H S^H$. *(Courtesy Oregon State College.)*

sufficient to stimulate cancer development in the eyes of those animals which inherit the susceptibility to it. The white-eyed Herefords that are not susceptible to cancer eye may show severe irritation from dust, etc., but will never develop cancer eye. The white-eyed animals that inherit susceptibility to cancer eye, on the other hand, will develop cancer eye when their eyes are subjected to much irritation. In areas where there is little dust, blowing pollen, or brilliant sunlight, incidence of cancer eye is markedly lower. "Red-eyed" animals very seldom show cancer eye, even though they inherit the susceptibility to it. The reason is that "red-eyed" Herefords show little or no irritation to the eyes from dust, sunlight, or plant pollens.

It is apparent that a breeder's selection program should favor the "red-eyed" Herefords over the "white-eyed" ones. This may be contrary to what some breeders may like from the appearance standpoint because "white-eyed" Herefords do make a more pleasing appearance. Breeders must consider utility rather than beauty factors in their meat production programs, however.

Modifying genes are found in horses, sheep, and swine, as well as cattle. In horses, the genes Dl = distal leg spots and dl = no distal leg spots also modify the white-spotting gene, S. However, before they can show, there must be a modifier that causes white spotting to appear on the legs, causing what is called *white socks* or *white foot* in the horse. This gene, Dl, causes spots above the hoof which may be mere flecks or may extend around the foot.

A dominant dilution gene, D, causes dilution of black, bay, or chestnut. Blacks are made into mouse or slate color, bays into duns, and chestnuts or sorrels into Palominos. When the dilution gene is in the homozygous state, DD, along with bb, chestnut or sorrel, the animal is a glass-eyed white. The pigmentation is so reduced in these bb animals by DD that there is little pigment even in the eyes. Since Palominos are heterozygotes of the genotype $bb\ Dd$, they will produce a ratio of 1 glass-eyed white:2 Palominos:1 chestnut (or sorrel) when mated. If a breeder wants to produce all Palominos ($bb\ Dd$), he should mate chestnut mares ($bb\ dd$) to a glass-eyed white stallion ($bb\ DD$).

One of the most interesting examples of modifying genes to be found is present in guinea pigs and has been thoroughly studied by Ibsen (1951). These two modifiers affect the distribution of long hair. For guinea pigs to have long hair, they must be of the genotype ll, since short hair, L, is dominant over long hair, l. One pair of modifiers, Po = long hairs posterio-dorsally only (Figs. 85 and 86) and po = long hairs likely over entire part of body (Figs. 83 and 84), modifies where the long hairs will be found. The other pair of genes affect the interspersion of long with short hairs (wherever Po or po permits long hairs to appear), In = all long hairs (wherever Po or po will permit), in =

Fig. 83. Guinea pig showing long hairs over all the body with no short hairs interspersed with the long hairs. It is of the genotype *ll, po po, In. (Courtesy Kansas State College.)*

Fig. 84. Guinea pig with long hair over entire body but with interspersion of short hairs with the long hairs. It is of the genotype *ll, po po, in in.* This animal is also rough *(R)* as shown by sworl on rump. *(Courtesy Kansas State College.)*

interspersion of long with short hairs (wherever *Po* or *po* will permit long hairs to appear). Animals that are *po po* will have long hairs over the entire body. If they are *in in*, the long hairs will be interspersed with short hairs (Fig. 84), but if they are *In In* or *In in*, there will be all long hairs over the body (Fig.

Fig. 85. Guinea pig showing long hairs posteriorly only. There is no interspersion of short hairs with the long hairs. It is of the genotype *ll, PO—, In—. (Courtesy Kansas State College.)*

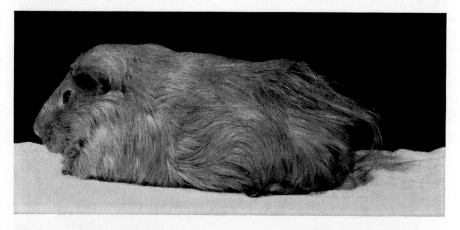

Fig. 86. Guinea pig showing long hairs posteriorly and short hairs interspersed with the long hairs. It is of the genotype *ll, PO—, in in. (Courtesy Kansas State College.)*

83). Animals that are *Po Po* or *Po po* will have long hairs only posterio-dorsally. With *in in* these long hairs will be interspersed with short hairs posterio-dorsally (Fig. 86). With *In In* or *In in*, all the posterio-dorsal hairs will be long (Fig. 85).

EXERCISES

1. Briefly but concisely discuss main genes, specific modifying and general modifying genes so that you clearly differentiate each from the other two.

2. Explain why Palomino horses do not breed true. How could they be produced most effectively?

3. Give the appearance of a Holstein cow which is of the genotype *In In*, for inguinal white.

4. In cattle:

S = solid color	*Lw Lw* = little white
s = white spotted	*Lw lw* = Intermediate
	lw lw = much white

Ss Lw lw × *Ss Lw lw*

(a) Give the appearance of the male and females.

(b) Work the cross phenotypically.

5. In guinea pigs:

L = short hair	*Po* = long hairs posteriorly, dorsally
l = long hair	*po* = long hairs over body

In = all hairs long
in = interspersion of long with short hairs

Ll po po In in ♂ × *ll Po po in in* ♀ ♀

(a) Give the appearance of the male and females.

(b) Work the cross phenotypically.

(c) Work the cross genotypically.

(d) Why do the genotypic and phenotypic ratios differ?

10

COLOR INHERITANCE IN FARM ANIMALS

Color is generally of little importance in livestock production as far as its association with rate of gain, feed efficiency, and milk production are concerned. However, color does have aesthetic value, and most breeds of livestock are based to a certain extent on color as "trademark." Color in sheep is of great economic importance because pigmented fibers do not lend themselves to dyes so well as white fibers do. Color is also important in adaptability of the animals to certain environments. Dark-colored animals do not sunburn so readily as white animals. On the other hand, dark-colored animals (pigs) may not be able to make the needed vitamin D in areas where sunshine is very limited, while white ones may be quite capable in this respect. Color and color patterns are for the most part simple in their inheritance, but several genes may alter or modify a basic color or pattern.

CATTLE

The best general summary on the inheritance of cattle colors and color patterns is that of Ibsen (1933). As early as 1919, Hooper presented data on Jersey cattle which showed that white spotting is recessive to solid (self) color. Lloyd-Jones and Evvard (1916) presented data which indicated that black is dominant to red. Their data on roaning showed that the roaning factor is incompletely dominant. Cattle that are pure for the roaning factor are white with pigment on the inner portion of the ears (Fig. 8), the heterozygotes are roan (Fig. 9), and those pure for nonroan are colored, with no interspersion of white hairs (Fig. 10). The roan factor can operate in red or black-colored animals.

There appears to be no chocolate or chestnut color in cattle. Black, blackish (black spotting), and red are the general basic colors. Black is completely dominant to red; therefore, the genes B = black and b = red have been proposed. Black is epistatic to blackish, which means that only in the *bb* animal can blackish show, although black animals may carry the gene for blackish. It appears that the genes *Bs* = blackish and *bs* = nonblackish are appropriate. One factor, brindling, affects blackish, the pattern being such that perpendicular stripes of blackish and red alternate (Fig. 87). This causes the brindling

Fig. 87. A Beefmaster bull showing brindling. To show brindle the animal must be *bb*, red, and carry blackish *Bs* as well as the brindle *Br* genes. *(Courtesy Lasater Ranch, Matheson, Colorado.)*

character. Brindling can show only when blackish is present and when this, in turn, can show. Black is epistatic to brindling because black covers up the expression of blackish and brindling acts only on blackish. The genes *Br* = brindle and *br* = nonbrindle are suggested. As pointed out, roan, the interspersion of white hairs with the colored hairs, can act with any color. Black roans or blues, red roans, blackish roans, and brindle roans are all possible. The genes *NN* = white, *Nn* = roan, and *nn* = nonroan have been suggested.

Ibsen (1933) postulated a modifier of roan. Animals that are *Nn* and should be roan would be red if they were *rm rm* because the roan modifier, *rm*, modifies roan to red. One does not need to examine many roan animals to see that a great deal of variation occurs. It appears that some modifiers of roan certainly exist. Some roan animals approach the red so closely that one might err in classifying them as red. Also, some roans are so nearly white that one might err in classifying them as white. The great variation which exists in roans makes it doubtful that one pair of genes acting as modifiers is sufficient to explain all these variations in roan.

One pair of sex-influenced genes modify the intensity of blackish. Males and females that are pure MM are dark, ML males are dark but ML females are light, LL males and females are light blackish.

There are five color-pattern genes in a multiple allelic series:

$$S^H = \text{Hereford pattern (Fig. 11)}$$
$$S^D = \text{Dutch belt (Fig. 16)}$$
$$S^C = \text{Color-sided (Fig. 17)}$$
$$S\ \ = \text{Solid (self) colored (Fig. 12)}$$
$$s\ \ = \text{white-spotted (Fig. 15)}$$

Since these genes have been discussed in a previous section, their allelic interactions will not be presented here.

One modifier of S is the dominant gene In which causes inguinal white (White and Ibsen, 1935). Cattle that are $in\ in$ show no inguinal (udder or cod) white markings. Several modifiers of ss affect the amount and the distribution of pigmented and white areas. One pair of genes which modify ss is incompletely dominant, with $Lw\ Lw$ animals showing little white, $Lw\ lw$ animals about equal in white and pigmented area, and $lw\ lw$ animals almost entirely white. It appears that Lw and lw may also modify the Hereford pattern S^H.

Another pair of genes, Pl = pigmented legs and pl = nonpigmented, affects the pigment on the posterior positions of the legs of both ss and S^H animals. Animals with the Hereford pattern, S^H, that have pigmented legs, Pl, will be brockle face, since it appears that the Pl gene not only causes pigmented legs but also causes brockle face. The pair of genes Dl = distal leg spots and dl = no distal leg spots affects the area just above the hoof. Animals that are $Dl\ Dl$ or $Dl\ dl$ have pigmented spots just above the hoof on one or more of the legs, while animals that are $dl\ dl$ show no pigmented area above the hoof. Whether Dl would show in Herefords is not known. Since it is a dominant gene, making it very easy to eliminate, and because it would be considered very objectionable in Hereford cattle, it may be that Herefords have been so bred that all are now $dl\ dl$.

Modifiers of the Hereford pattern, besides Lw, lw and Pl, pl, are those affecting red neck, line backs, and pigment around the eyes. Ibsen (1933) postulates that $Rn\ Rn$ individuals are red neck (Fig. 88) and $Rn\ rn$ individuals have a reduced amount of white on the withers and top of the back of the neck, while $rn\ rn$ individuals show the desired Hereford pattern. The gene Re (red eye, Fig. 81), which causes the animal to have pigment around the eyes,

Fig. 88. A Hereford bull showing red neck. *(Courtesy Oregon State College.)*

is completely dominant to *re,* the "white-eyed" condition (Fig. 82). Cattlemen are now aware that "red-eyed" Herefords are less susceptible to cancer eye than are "white-eyed" Herefords. At one time "red-eyed" Herefords were looked upon with disfavor, but today just the opposite is true.

It appears that red neck and line neck (white extends down the back) may be the results of complementary gene action. Red-neck Herefords have been reported to produce animals with the desired Hereford pattern. Also, desirably marked Herefords have been reported to produce calves with red necks. It is not known whether there is error in these reports or whether more than one pair of genes is involved to make this situation possible. The same applies to line backs. Line-back Herefords have been reported to produce calves with the desirable Hereford pattern. Also, desirably marked Herefords have been reported to produce calves with line backs. The only way in which this could occur is for more than one pair of genes to be involved with line backs, resulting from complementary action of the genes. All the modifiers of white spotting and Hereford pattern would be prevented from showing in the solid colored animals, even though such animals would possess and transmit these genes.

Ibsen (1933) postulated that the white Nellore cattle are due to recessive white. The genes he uses are Wn = not white and wn = Nellore white. Another kind of white cattle, the white English Park cattle, is considered by Ibsen to be dominant. He suggests that Wp = white Park and wp = not white.

The variation in intensity of pigmentation, particularly of the blackish but perhaps in the red and black also, is brought about by two separate pairs of dilution genes. The dominant dilution gene, D, would dilute blacks and reds to lighter shade, either in the homozygous DD or heterozygous Dd condition. Animals that are dd would show no dilution of either red or black. The other dilution gene is recessive, where I = intense and i = dilute. This pair of genes is found largely in those breeds of cattle carrying blackish, such as Jerseys.

Two other genes have been described by investigators. One causes whitening along the underline and between the rear legs up to the tail. This pair of genes apparently modifies blackish more than red or black, but some red animals show this whitening. It is assumed that W = no whitening and w = whitening, because the whitening factor appears to be simple recessive. White and Ibsen (1935) discussed a modifier of white spotting which restricts the white, causing an ss animal to be almost entirely pigmented, with only a spot of white on the forehead or in the switch of the tail. The gene symbol suggested was Wr, white restrictor, and this gene (wr = no restriction or reduction in white) reduces the white and restricts it to the head and tail switch. White and Ibsen suggested that the red neck and the white-restrictor gene may be one and the same. If this is true, the gene has a much greater effect in ss than in S^H animals.

Albinism has been reported in cattle by Cole, et al (1934). This is recessive to colored and reduces all pigmentation, including that in the eyes. Albino cattle are not completely devoid of pigment because they show a ghost pattern of the areas that would have been colored, if they had not been albinos, in contrast to the white-spotted areas. Because of the small amount of pigment in the eyes, albino cattle are very sensitive to bright light, and their vision is very poor, particularly on bright days.

Pigmented skin spots are due to a dominant gene, Ps, while the allele, ps, results in the absences of pigmented skin spots. Presumably, the Ps gene could account for the smutty noses of such animals as Herefords, in which this character is considered objectionable.

Genetic composition for color in various breeds of cattle

1. Aberdeen-Angus

BB or b	dd	II	in in or In	nn	SS or s	WW	Wn Wn	wp wp

This breed does not carry Bs because red Angus are not blackish; they likely are $bs\ bs$. They may carry brindling but are probably $pl\ pl$, since the white-spotted animals cropping out from the Angus do not show pigmented legs.

It is impossible to determine their genotypes relative to the other modifiers of white spotting because so few white-spotted Angus occur.

2. Holstein-Friesian

BB	dd	II	nn	ps ps	ss	Lw lw	pl pl	WW	Wn Wn	Wp Wp	Dl dl
or b				or Ps		Lw Lw					dl dl
						lw lw					

The inguinal white, red eye, roan modifier, red neck, and similar genes in the Holstein are not known because it is not possible to see expressions of these genes in this breed.

3. Jerseys

bb	br br	Bs Bs	ML	dd	ii	nn	SS	Lw Lw	ww	Wn Wn	wp wp	Dl dl
or B		or bs	MM	or D			Ss	or				dl dl
			LL				ss	Lw lw				

Such modifiers as inguinal white, red neck, red eye, and others are not easily seen in Jerseys; therefore, one cannot be certain of the genotype of Jerseys for these modifying genes.

4. Ayrshire

bb	br br	Bs Bs	ML	dd	II	nn ps ps	ss	lw lw	pl pl	WW	Wn Wn	wp wp	dl dl
or	or	MM				or Ps		Lw lw	Pl pl				
Br	Bs	LL						Lw Lw					

Since many Ayrshires are almost entirely white, they may carry brindling without this being noticed or considered in selection. A few Ayrshires have been observed that show brindling.

5. Hereford

bb	bs bs	Br br	dd	nn	ps ps	SH SH	rn rn	re re	Lw Lw	pl pl	WW	Wn Wn	wp wp
		or			or		or	or	Lw lw				
		br br			Ps ps		Rn	Re re	lw lw				

One cannot be certain about inguinal white in Hereford cattle.

6. Shorthorn

bb	bs bs	dd	Nn	II	Rm Rm	ps ps	ss	Lw Lw	Rn Rn	Pl Pl	WW	Wn Wn	wp wp
			nn		rm rm	Ps ps		Lw lw	rn rn	pl pl			
			NN					lw lw					

One cannot be sure about inguinal white, red eye, red neck, and such modifiers in Shorthorn cattle.

7. Guernsey

bb	bs bs	dd	ii	nn	ps ps	ss	Lw Lw	pl pl	WW	Wn Wn	wp wp	Dl dl
		Dd			Ps ps		Lw lw	Pl pl	ww			dl dl
							lw lw					

One cannot be certain about the genes carried by Guernseys for inguinal white, red neck, roan modifier, red eye, etc., because these genes are not expressed in this breed.

HORSES

There have been several attempts made by various investigators to explain color and color-marking inheritance in the horse. Since some differences of opinion exist, it appears certain that any proposed explanation of color inherit-

Fig. 89. A black *B* horse with white-spotting *S*. To show black it is also *ee*. It does not show distal leg spots. *(Courtesy Oregon State College.)*

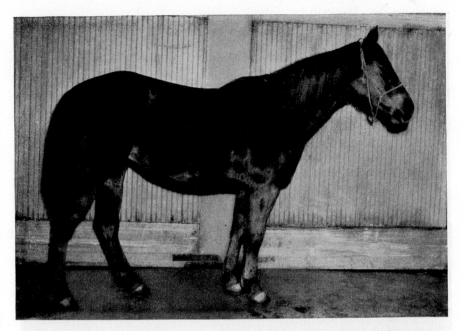

Fig. 90. Horse showing chestnut-colored body, mane, and tail. It is *bb* in genotype. *(Courtesy Oregon State College.)*

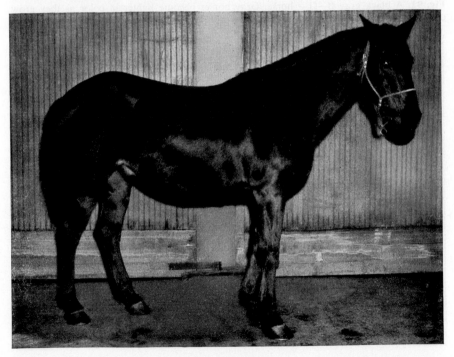

Fig. 91. A bay *B—E—* horse. The bays show black mane and tail. *(Courtesy Oregon State College.)*

133

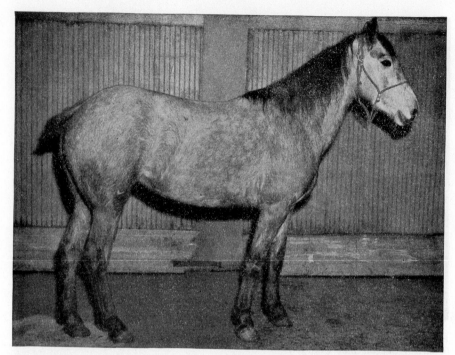

Fig. 92. A black gray B—G— horse. Gray horses become lighter in color as they grow older. *(Courtesy Oregon State College.)*

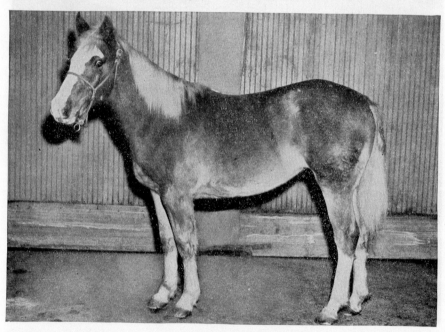

Fig. 93. A Palomino horse showing white-spotting *Dd bb S—*. *(Courtesy Oregon State College.)*

134

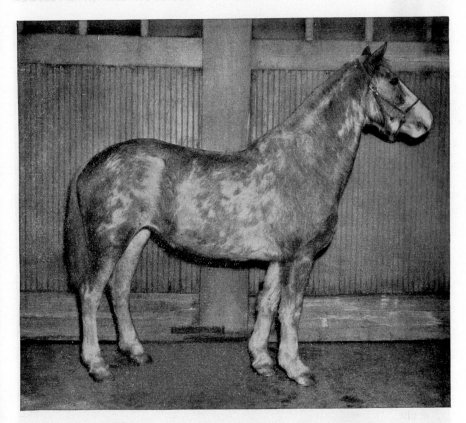

Fig. 94. A white-spotted *S—* chestnut roan *bb R—* horse. *(Courtesy Oregon State College.)*

ance in horses will find exceptions to it in the literature. It seems advisable to present what appears to be the situation in horse-color inheritance and to refer the reader to material that agrees and that disagrees with the material presented. In this way, the reader may find it possible to develop his own concept regarding color inheritance in horses.

One reason for some error in studies on color inheritance in horses has arisen from the use of stud registry records. It so happens that color has been involved in the recording of animals in some of the breeds; therefore, some bias exists in these data.

Black (Fig. 89) is dominant to chestnut or sorrel (Fig. 90). When sorrel or chestnut animals are mated they never produce black offspring. The genes B = black and b = chestnut are proposed for this pair of alleles. The black may be extended over the entire body or it may be restricted largely to the mane, legs, and tail. When the black is restricted, the red shows in those parts

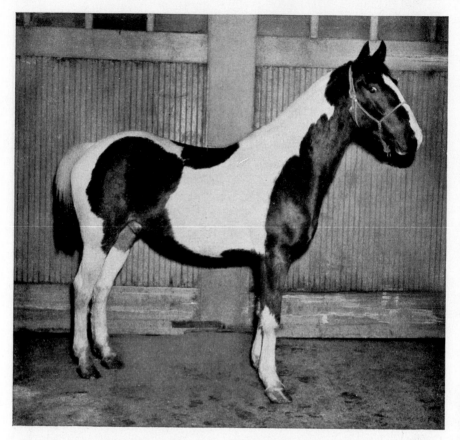

Fig. 95. Pronounced white-spotting in a horse. *(Courtesy Oregon State College.)*

of the body which are not black, and such an animal is known as a bay (Fig. 91). The genes E = restriction of black to mane, tail and legs (or a bay) and e = extension of black over the body are proposed. The action of E and e in the chestnut, bb, animal will be similar. Animals that are EE or Ee bb will have chestnut manes and tails and more reddish or lighter colored bodies, while animals that are ee bb will show the chestnut color over the body as well as the mane and tail. These genes determine the basic colors—black, bay and chestnut—but other genes modify the expression of these basic colors.

There are two kinds of interspersions of white hairs with the colored hairs, both of which are dominant. Gray (Fig. 92) is dominant to nongray. An animal that is GG or Gg will be gray, while one that is gg will show no gray. Gray animals are born with no interspersion of white hairs with the colored but usually show a few white hairs with the first shedding. Gray animals become more gray with age until a white condition is reached in aged animals.

Sometimes, with the loss of pigment in the hairs, there is an accumulation of pigment in the colon, called *melanomas,* or tumors containing the black pigment melanin. Gray is usually found associated with black because the two genes are common in one breed, the Percheron, and it may be also found with bay or chestnut where breed-crossing has been practiced. The other type of interspersion of white with the pigmented hairs, roan, differs from gray in that a roan is born a roan and does not show an increase in white with age. Animals that are *RR* or *Rr* are roan (Fig. 94), while animals that are *rr* are nonroan. Roan is usually associated with bay or sorrel because the breeds, which show roaning, such as Belgians, are also sorrel or bay. In some horses, roan is also found with black. Thus, the roan gene expresses itself with all three of the basic colors, i.e., black, bay, or chestnut.

It appears that chestnut and sorrel are the same color, but breeders of light horses (saddle horses) prefer the term *chestnut,* while heavy, draft-horse breeders refer to this color as *sorrel.* The two are used interchangeably here.

The dilution gene *D* is incompletely dominant over *d.* In the heterozygous condition, the dilution of blacks, *Dd,* produces slate or mouse color; the dilution of bay produces dun, a dull brick color; and the dilution of chestnut produces Palomino (Fig. 93). In the homozygous condition *DD,* the chestnut (*bb*) animal is a glass-eyed white. What effect *DD* has on black and bay animals is not well known because it has not been the practice to mate buckskins (dilute blacks) or duns (dilute bays). The mating of Palominos has been practiced as a means of producing more Palominos. This mating results in a ratio of 1 chestnut:2 Palominos:1 glass-eyed white. Actually, the most effective way of producing Palominos would be to mate a glass-eyed white stallion to chestnut mares. Such a mating would give all Palominos.

White spotting (Fig. 95) is dominant over solid color in horses. Animals that are *SS* or *Ss* are white-spotted, while *ss* animals are solid color. White-spotting occurs with all colors. If it affects only the face, it is called *blazed* face (Fig. 89). Should the white area extend over the eye, the white spotting removes the eye pigment, resulting in a glass-eyed white. One or both eyes may be affected by white spotting. If white spotting occurs over the body, it may give "pinto" or "calico" spotting effects (Fig. 95). White-spotting that covers the legs is described as "white stocking" (Fig. 89) and is looked upon by some horsemen with disfavor because of the greater tenderness of white legs and because dirt on a white area shows more than on colored areas. There are many modifiers of white-spotting, but these modifying genes have not been thoroughly studied. Where the white-spotting appears on the legs, some animals show small pigmented spots just above the hoof. These distal leg spots are evidently due to a dominant gene. The genes proposed for this modifier

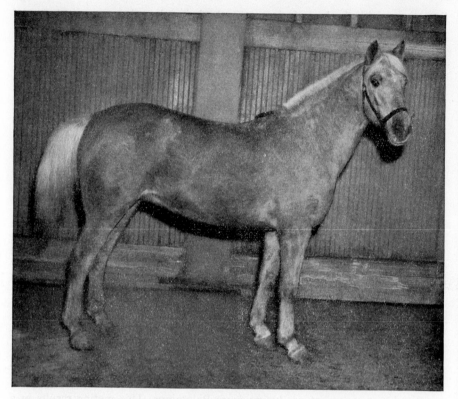

Fig. 96. A chestnut horse with flaxen mane and tail, *bb mm. (Courtesy Oregon State College.)*

are *Dl* = distal leg spots and *dl* = no spots above the hoof. The expression of the *Dl* gene is only in the *S* (spotted) animal, and only then when the legs are white.

White horses result from an epistatic white which is dominant. The white, *W,* is not found in the homozygous condition, which might suggest that *WW* is lethal, and only *Ww* exists as a result. This white covers up the expression of all colors.

There appears to be one pair of genes affecting the mane and tail of chestnut horses. Some show flaxen manes and tails (Fig. 96), while others show chestnut manes and tails (Fig. 90). The gene *M* which is completely dominant over *m,* causes chestnut manes and tails, and an animal that is *mm* will have flaxen mane and tail.

Numerous modifiers affect variations in shades of the basic colors, the graying and roaning, and the spotting, but these appear to be multiple factors, each with a small effect, for which the mode of inheritance has not been determined.

Fig. 97. A Berkshire sow. The Berkshires have black bodies with white on the snout, tail, and feet. *(Courtesy American Berkshire Association, Springfield, Illinois.)*

SWINE

There appear to be four basic colors in swine: black, brown or sepia, red, and white. The black of such pigs as the Hampshires (Fig. 98) apparently differs from the black of Poland Chinas and Berkshires (Fig. 97). It has been assumed that the Hampshires possess two genes for black, while the Poland Chinas are recessive for one pair of the two pairs of genes which contribute to the black of the Hampshire. The genes B' = black, b' = red, and b^t = black (with white or sandy points) and b = red are proposed. The Hampshire is assumed to be $B'B'$ b^tb^t, while the Poland China and Berkshire are $b'b'$ b^tb^t. The gene b^t is not completely dominant over b; therefore, crosses of Poland China with Duroc Jersey result in black-and-red-spotted pigs. It is not known whether sepia is an allele of the Poland China black or a separate color controlled by another pair of genes. This color is not common.

White is either completely or incompletely epistatic to all colors. The white of Chester White (Fig. 100), Yorkshire, and Landrace will prevent the red of Duroc Jersey or the black of Poland Chinas from showing. It only partially inhibits the black of the Hampshire. Ghost patterns often show when Hampshires are crossed with Chester Whites. The skin on the areas other than the belt may be dark, either with black roan showing in the hair or dirty white hairs on these areas, as contrasted with the clear white skin and hair on the

Fig. 98. Hampshire boar showing the typical black with white belt. This boar is an outstanding sire as shown by his record below. *(Courtesy Hampshire Swine Registry.)*

KING EDWARD 602301 PR 93 CMS (Edwards Bright Boy—Master Premium PR)
Owned by L. L. Stewart & Son, Frankfort, Ind. Certified by Dean Snyder, Good Hope, Ill. Bred by A. Ruben Edwards, Corso, Mo. Also served in herd of Carr Bros., McNabb, Ill.

Unanimous Hope 1417602 PR 1047 (Preference Model PR 63—Unanimous)

| (Dean Snyder, Good Hope, Ill.) | 11 | 666.1 | 196 | 210 | 29.25 | 1.33 | 4.43 |
| | | | 200 | 214 | 29.6 | 1.43 | 4.17 |

Miss Remarkable 1444220 PR 1105 (Remarkable PR 91—Dividend PR 66)

| (Dean Snyder) | 11 | 584.0 | 220 | 216 | 29.57 | 1.4 | 5.03 |
| | | | 220 | 216 | 29.5 | 1.5 | 4.06 |

Judy Anna 1432066 PR 1101 (Mid-West—Prairie Owen Rogers PR 25)

| (Dean Snyder) | 10 | 572.7 | 210 | 244 | 29.25 | 1.5 | 4.23 |
| | | | 205 | 239 | 30. | 1.47 | 3.79 |

Bi Queen 1418866 (Silver Bond PR 59—Star Bound)

| (Dean Snyder) | 8 | 388.8 | 230 | 250 | 31.5 | 1.47 | 5.21 |
| | | | 225 | 245 | 30.5 | 1.7 | 4.58 |

Glory Queen 1444230 PR 1221 (Remarkable PR 91—Dividend PR 66)

| (Dean Snyder) | 8 | 359.0 | 200 | 224 | 29.25 | 1.4 | 4.79 |
| | | | 185 | 209 | 29.0 | 1.1 | 4.47 |

Star Fashion 1444238 PR 1104 (Remarkable PR 91—Perfect Pattern)

| (Dean Snyder) | 9 | 472.3 | 225 | 249 | 29.5 | 1.3 | 4.91 |
| | | | 225 | 249 | 29.5 | 1.5 | 5.26 |

Miss Fashion 1519466 PR 1221 (New Special PR 81—Remarkable PR 91)

| (Dean Snyder) | 8 | 389.1 | 230 | 202 | 30.5 | 1.53 | 5.71 |
| | | | 230 | 202 | 30.0 | 1.53 | 4.78 |

Miss Sue 1444210 PR 1152 (Remarkable PR 91—Dividend PR 66)
86)

| (Dean Snyder) | 9 | 429.4 | 180 | 212 | 39.75 | 1.2 | 4.84 |
| | | | 190 | 222 | 29.0 | 1.23 | 4.69 |

Champ Barrow 57 Conf. Gr. Ch. over all breeds Ill. State Fair carcass contest (on foot and in carcass):

Wt., 215 lb.
Length, 31.1 in.
Backfat, 1.2%
Loin, 4.91%
Lean Cut, 56.79%

Sired by a certified meat sire. Bred and fitted and shown by Carr Bros., McNabb, Ill.

Fig. 99. Hampshire barrow showing a variation in the belt from that which is most desired. Although the belt is a trade mark in purebred Hampshire breeding, a commercial breeder would be more concerned with his carcass yield. *(Courtesy Hampshire Swine Registry.)*

Advance Queen 1346002 PR 1045 (Perfect Pattern—Star Bound)
  (Dean Snyder)

11	552.8	185	231	29.0	1.3	4.82
		190	236	29.0	1.3	4.49

Fair Lass 1475282 (Lum 3rd—Remodel)
  (Duane Carr, McNabb, Ill.)

8	349.8	190	260	29.2	1.33	3.64
		190	260	28.5	1.27	3.94

El Esquires Belle 1407260 PR 1213 (El Esquire 3rd—B. O. Masterpiece)
  (Carr Bros., McNabb, Ill.)

9	333.7	185	209	28.9	1.2	4.35
		195	219	29.6	1.47	3.86

Barbara 1810965 (Hoosier Colonel PR 219—Echo)
  (L. L. Stewart & Son, Frankfort, Ind.)

10	404.9	193	205	28.9	1.4	3.66
		197	209	29.4	1.5	3.68

Indiana Girl 1679590 (Greater Preference—Commander True Glory)
  (L. L. Stewart & Son, Frankfort, Ind.)

11	413.8	185	207	28.87	1.27	4.02
		185	207	28.5	1.58	3.88

Indiana Girl 1st 1823318 (Greater Preference—Commander True)
  (L. L. Stewart & Son, Frankfort, Ind.)

10	706.3	220	202	31.1	1.37	4.14
		220	202	31.2	1.47	4.47

Fig. 100. Chester White gilt. The dominant white is epistatic to red found in Duroc Jersey and black of Poland Chinas and Berkshires, and is incompletely epistatic to the black of Hampshires. *(Courtesy Chester White Record Association, Rochester, Indiana.)*

belt areas. This suggests that the dominant gene, W, is not completely epistatic to the black of Hampshires. It is completely dominant to w, not white.

The white belt is dominant to the nonbelted condition (Fig. 98). The genes B^e = belt and b^e = nonbelted are proposed. Belting will show in black, black and red, and red pigs, even though we normally think of black-belted pigs because of this coloration in Hampshires. The white spotting is distinct from the belt. White face of the Hereford hogs is apparently dominant over the solid-colored condition, although this has not been satisfactorily established. Both the white-spotting and the white-belt conditions are influenced by several modifiers (Fig. 99). It is not uncommon to see marked variations in the location and extent of the belt. A summary of color marking of purebred Hampshires in one herd revealed that 40 per cent of the pigs were not eligible for registration because of improper belting. This one color factor limited the selection pressure, which could be applied for all other traits, to 60 per cent of the pigs produced in this herd.

Red varies in shade from a deep cherry red to a sandy or very light dull red. It appears that several pairs of genes are involved in the control of shade of red. Some hog breeders prefer the dark reds and some prefer the yellows or sandy reds (Fig. 101).

White pigs or pigs with white belts are subject to sunburning. On the other

Fig. 101. A red (Duroc Jersey) hog. This hog is intermediate in shade but variations from sandy to cherry reds occur. *(Courtesy Oregon State College.)*

hand, white pigs are more capable than dark-colored pigs of making their own supply of vitamin D in areas of reduced sunlight. Color in swine may have adaptive value for different climatic conditions.

Several other factors have been described, such as agouti *A* and nonagouti *a,* roaning; dilution, and others, but they are either not common in hogs of the United States or the inheritance of them is not understood. These characters are not discussed here, and the reader is referred to the references covering them.

SHEEP

Color in sheep is very important because of the greater value of white wool over colored wool. The result has been that sheep are bred for white fleeces. The white, *W,* is dominant to colored, *w,* (black) and is epistatic to all color combinations. Most of the concern with sheep color is with black fibers in the black-faced sheep and with leg color in such white-faced sheep as Columbias and Targhees.

Terrill (1947) reports that leg color in Columbia and Targhee sheep occurs in about 15 per cent of the sheep. It has no relationship to production characteristics other than wool quality. Since matings of noncolored × noncolored give some lambs with colored legs, and matings of colored × colored give some noncolored, Terrill concludes that more than one pair of genes is involved. These genes apparently are complementary in their action. Heritability of leg color was estimated at 26 per cent in Columbias and 34 per cent in Targhees by intra-sire regressions of offspring on dams.

Black fibers in the fleece are objectionable in the black-faced breeds such as Hampshires and Suffolks. The exact mode of inheritance of black fibers is not known. The number of black fibers may vary from a few to a condition of gray in which the black and white fibers are almost equal.

In colored sheep, those characters that do not carry the epistatic white, badger face, and reversed badger face are inherited. Badger face is dominant to solid color and reverse badger face is dominant to solid color but recessive to badger face.

Dominant black in Welsh mountain sheep prevents the gene for badger face from showing. The dominant black is modified by a dominant gray in that white fibers are interspersed with the black and recessive bleaching reduces the black to brown. Also, a dominant spotting factor acts to produce a white spot on the head and tip of the tail in these black sheep. Also, the necklace, a white stripe around the neck of black sheep, has been reported as a dominant.

In our white breeds of sheep, such as the Rambouillet, a chalk-face condition, which is dominant, causes long hairs on the face at birth, but these are not expressed in adult life. In some white sheep, the Gromet Pattern, characterized by black marks over the eyes and black ears with gray margins, is inherited as a recessive.

Karakul sheep color has been reported to be due to the interaction of two pairs of genes. The genes postulated are B = black, b = absence of black; and R = red, r = absence of red. The genotypes $BB\ RR$, $Bb\ Rr$, or $Bb\ rr$ would be black. $BB\ Rr$ is chocolate, $bb\ Rr$ is red, and $bb\ rr$ is white.

RABBITS

In rabbits, B = black and b = chocolate, or cinnamon. Black is completely dominant over cinnamon. A pair of genes which modify black and cinnamon are A = agouti and a = nonagouti. Animals that are A will show a band of red or white in each hair near the tip. The aa animals are not agouti and therefore they show no band in the hairs. The Belgian hare is an example of an agouti in which the band in the black hairs is red. The Chinchilla (Fig. 102) is an example of an animal in which the band in the black hair is white. The agouti pattern can show in either black or cinnamon animals.

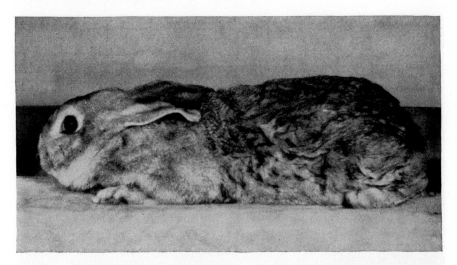

Fig. 102. A Chinchilla rabbit. It is $B-A-C^{ch}$ in genotype because the hair is black with white band near the terminal ends. *(Courtesy Oregon State College.)*

A multiple allelic series is found in the color locus. The red color, C, is dominant over each of the other alleles. Thus, the agouti that is $BB\ AA\ CC$ would have the red band showing in the black hairs. There have been mutations to c^{ch}, c^h, and c, in which the gene c^{ch} causes a white instead of a red band to show in the agouti. In animals that are black or cinnamon without the agouti, CC and $c^{ch}c^{ch}$ individuals show no difference because in each case the only color showing would be black or cinnamon. The c^{ch} gene is dominant over both c^h and c. The c^h gene causes the animal to be white, with the exception of the ears, nose, feet, and tail. This is the Himalayan character and it is dominant over c. Animals that are $B\ c^hc^h$ will have black ears, nose, feet, and tail, while $bb\ c^hc^h$ animals will have chocolate-colored ears, nose, feet, and tail. Animals that are cc are pink-eyed white (Fig. 103).

Another multiple allelic series affects the distribution of the black or cinnamon over the body. The gene E causes black and cinnamon to become steel-gray, with the black becoming a darker steel than the cinnamon. This gene is dominant over the other members of the allelic series. The gene e^g causes the pigment (black or cinnamon) to be distributed over the entire body (Fig. 104). It is dominant over e^j (partial expression), the gene which causes the black or cinnamon to appear only on certain areas. The other areas will be either red or white, depending upon the genes in the C locus. Since this gene is dominant to e, ee animals will show no black or cinnamon on the body, or the pigment will not be extended over the body. Animals that are $ee\ CC$ are

Fig. 103. A New Zealand white, *cc,* albino. These pink-eyed white rabbits may have any of the genes affecting color except those in the *C* series, but none will show. *(Courtesy Oregon State College.)*

Fig. 104. A black rabbit *B—aae⁰—. (Courtesy Oregon State College.)*

red (Fig. 105), and those that are *ee c^{ch}c^{ch}* are white. In both cases, the eyes are dark. The white animal, *ee c^{ch}c^{ch}*, differs from the albino white, *cc,* in that the former has dark eyes while the latter has pink eyes, a condition due to the absence of pigment in the eyes. A dilution factor, *D,* causes the black or

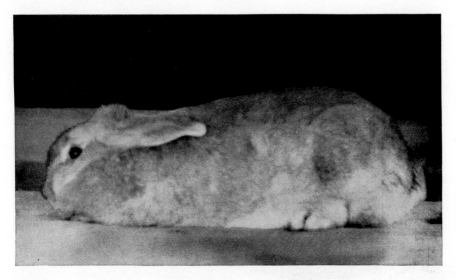

Fig. 105. A New Zealand red rabbit. It is *ee CC* in genotype because it is red with no black or cinnamon showing. *(Courtesy Oregon State College.)*

cinnamon to become less intense (Fig. 106). It is completely dominant over *d,* the absence of dilution.

White-spotting

There are three types of white-spotting, all of which are separate and distinct. The English white-spotting, *En,* is dominant to solid color, *en,* and causes irregular dark spots on a white background. Dutch belt, *du,* causes a white belt over or just behind the shoulders. The absence of Dutch belt, *Du,* is solid color and is completely dominant over the belting. Several genes modify the expression of the belt so that the pure breeding of desirably belted animals is difficult to obtain.

Vienna white causes blue-eyed white rabbits. The solid color, *V,* condition is dominant over Vienna white, *v.* These white rabbits differ from the *c^{ch}c^{h} ee,* dark-eyed whites, and the *cc,* albino, because the Vienna whites have blue eyes. This color is the result of reduction in the eye pigment which is not sufficient to cause pink eyes but which is great enough to prevent dark eyes from showing. The genes *en* and *Du* are linked, with only 1 per cent crossing-over occurring between them. Another linkage group is *C* and *B,* with 43 per cent crossing-over between them. It appears that these genes are in opposite ends of the chromosome.

There are some other less well-known characters affecting color in rabbits. The Martin (Fig. 107) is the result of interspersion of white hairs with black

Fig. 106. Lilac-colored rabbit. This is a dilute cinnamon. *(Courtesy Rockland Farms, New City, New York.)*

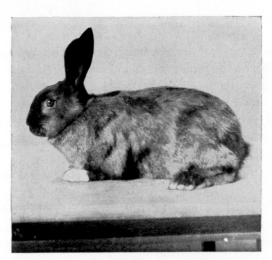

Fig. 107. A black silver Martin rabbit. *(Courtesy Oregon State College.)*

or cinnamon hairs, a pattern in which the guard hairs are white and the fur is colored. Many combinations are possible in the Martin, such as black, cinnamon, and blue (dilute black). The Champagne de Argente is the result of an interspersion of white with pigmented hairs, producing a "silvering" characteristic that apparently involves several genes. Selection for more white hairs has resulted in the development of this breed of rabbit.

EXPLANATION OF COLOR IN MAMMALS

Several workers have made studies on pigmentation, some by histological, some by chemical, and some by enzymatic methods. Bogart and Ibsen (1937) made a microscopic study of hairs of cattle and found two types of pigment, black and red. The shade of black or red depended upon the amount and distribution of black pigment, as well as the intensity of the red pigment. Black pigment in large clumps near the surface of the hair caused the hairs to appear dark. Diffused black granules did not darken the hair as much as clumps of black pigment, and the black pigment near the medulla of the hair had less darkening effect than the same amount of pigment near the hair surface.

Fox (1936) summarized the various pigments in animal coloration from a chemical standpoint. Baker and Andrews (1944) made a chemical study of pigments in guinea pig hair. They found a difference between red and black pigment but obtained evidence for red oxidizing to black. No difference between black and chocolate pigments could be detected chemically. The conclusion was that the difference between black and chocolate may be due to differences in physical structure.

Wright (1917) developed a theory for explaining pigmentation in mammals. It was assumed that a colorless chromogen is present in the cytoplasm upon which enzymes from the nucleus act to bring about coloration. Thus, enzyme I, acting alone, would produce red when in full force or yellow if in reduced amount. In combination with enzyme I, enzyme II would produce the dark pigments of black and chocolate. Enzyme II would have no effect without the presence of enzyme I.

The chromogen and enzymes involved in mammalian color formation, as postulated by Wright, is shown in Fig. 108. Theoretically black would be the result of enzymes I and II acting fully on the chromogen (Fig. 109). Dilute black would be due to full action of enzyme II but reduce action of enzyme I. Chocolate (chestnut in horses, cinnamon in rabbits) would be produced by full action of enzyme I but by reduced effect of enzyme II (Fig. 110). If both enzyme I and II were reduced, the result would be a dilute chocolate. Red would be produced by the action of enzyme I, in the absence of enzyme II, on the chromogen (Fig. 111). A light red would result from reduced enzyme I. White could result from a lack of enzyme I, either in the absence or presence of enzyme II. By using varying amounts of chromogen, enzyme

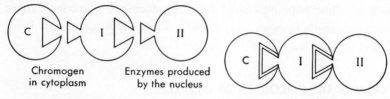

Chromogen   Enzymes produced
in cytoplasm   by the nucleus

Fig. 108. Chromogen and enzymes postulated for the production of pigmentation in mammals.

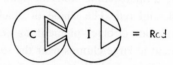

= Black

Fig. 109. The chromogen and enzyme reaction which results in the formation of black pigmentation in mammals.

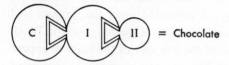

= Chocolate

Fig. 110. The chromogen and enzyme reaction system which results in the formation of chocolate pigmentation in mammals.

= Red

Fig. 111. The chromogen and enzyme system which results in the formation of red color in mammals.

I and enzyme II, and by assuming that some of the inhibitory genes prevent enzymatic action even though the enzymes and the chromogen are present in sufficient quantities, a large variety of colors could be formed. Also, it would be possible to have whites of several different kinds, although it would be necessary to consider spotting factors as genes which localized the production of the enzymes.

No attempt is made to explain all colors by use of Wright's theory, and there may well be some colors which it cannot explain. Nevertheless, it has one basic concept which is sound; i.e., that color is the result of gene-controlled enzymatic activity. The work of the Russels (1939) tends to support his theory. These investigators found the presence of enzymes in tissue slices to be in accordance with the phenotype of the animals tested for their oxidative activity on dopa, 3, 4-dihydroxyphenylalanine.

EXERCISES

1. By use of enzymes and chromogen, develop an explanation of the following colors:

               (a) Chestnut in horse
               (b) Blackish in cattle
               (c) White in hogs
               (d) Albino rabbits

2. Give two reasons why more is known regarding the inheritance of color in farm animals than about inheritance of such traits as growth and milk production.

3. For information on the effects of genes on color in rabbits, you are referred to the test.

Bb Aa cc ♂ × *bb aa Cc^h* ♀ ♀.

(a) give the appearance of the male and the females.

(b) work the cross phenotypically.

4. Tell how you produce Palomino horses in order to obtain nothing but Palomino foals.

5. A bay stallion is mated to a bay mare. You have no knowledge of the genotype of these animals but you do know color inheritance in horses. What are the possibilities of the color of the expected foal? Which color is the foal most likely to be? Why? Could this foal be a Palomino? Explain.

6. A Jersey cow was bred to a Hereford bull and produced a white faced, brindle calf. From which of the parents did the calf receive the brindle gene? Explain why it has to be this parent and can not be the other parent.

11

SYSTEMS OF BREEDING IN LIVESTOCK PRODUCTION

There are two major livestock breeding programs: (1) purebred, in which the object should be the improvement of the genetic worth of the herd or flock, and (2) commercial production, in which the object is to exploit the genetic material so that the greatest possible production can be achieved. The breeding programs in the two, purebred and commercial livestock production, are so different that they must be presented separately.

PUREBRED BREEDING

Two systems of breeding are used in purebred breeding: (1) continuous outbreeding, and (2) some form of inbreeding.

Outbreeding

By *continuous outbreeding* is meant the yearly mating of the females in the herd or flock to males that are unrelated to them. This system has been used a great deal because the possibility of undesirable genetic outcrops is less than from inbreeding. Also, when unrelated animals are mated, there is greater chance of heterozygosity in the offspring, and hence there is more chance for heterosis or hybrid vigor within the purebred herd. A disadvantage, however, even though the animals are well chosen, is that the herd will lack *prepotency* despite the fact that it will show highest performance and will make the best appearance. Prepotency is the ability of an animal to stamp its characteristic onto its offspring, and this ability to breed true results from the fact that the animal is more homozygous, particularly for the dominant genes.

Likewise, even when the sires are well chosen and the herd or flock exhibits high performance and appearance, the low-transmitting ability of a continu-

152

ously outbred herd produces males that are highly heterozygous. When these males are used in commercial herds, they will sire offspring that vary greatly, some of which may be quite undesirable.

This system of breeding provides the purebred breeder with the opportunity for presenting nice-appearing animals for sale to commercial producers. As stated before, purebred animals developed by the continuous outbreeding method, however, may give quite unsatisfactory results when used in the commercial herds. This explains why commercial producers are becoming more interested in how males from a certain herd or line of breeding perform when used in their herds than they are in the level of performance or appearance of the animals in the purebred herd from which breeding stock is secured. It will be probably essential for a purebred breeder to go outside his own herd for breeding males until he has built up his herd to a satisfactory level of performance. On the other hand a very high level of performance may make it difficult to find a superior herd whose breeding stock can bring improvement to the existing herd. In this case it is better to consider breeding within the herd. Certainly, if the herd or flock is of sufficient size to require the use of two or three sires, this method of mating males and females within the same herd will be satisfactory.

Inbreeding

The system of breeding in which related animals are mated is known as *inbreeding*. Whenever a breeder closes his herd to outside breeding sources, he is practicing inbreeding. Close inbreeding is generally considered to be brother × sister, sire × daughter, and son × dam. Some also consider half-sib * matings as close. Such matings as cousins are considered as mild inbreeding.

Sometimes the emphasis in the breeding program is placed on a certain outstanding animal in order to transmit to the herd as much as possible of its inheritance. Obviously, such concentration will require some inbreeding, although the objective may be to hold inbreeding to a minimum and still obtain this preferential breeding. This system of breeding is called *linebreeding* and is one phase of inbreeding.

Linebreeding has much to commend it, particularly if linebreeding is the result of selection in which breeding of certain individuals has been concentrated because of their outstanding merit. Commercial breeders who purchase breeding stock from someone who is practicing an intelligent linebreeding program have a much greater chance that these animals will do well than if

---

* Sibs are brothers and sisters, half-sibs are half-brothers and half-sisters in which either the sire or the dam is common.

animals were purchased from someone who practices outbreeding. Thus, the commercial breeder takes advantage of the selection which has been practiced in the linebreeding program. By using linebred males that are unrelated to one's own herd, it is possible to take advantage of the greater heterozygosity which results.

Whether or not a system of inbreeding (a closed herd) will be successful depends upon three factors.

1. Merit of the Animals with which the Program Starts

When one considers the merit of the foundation animals, it is of importance to note that reference is not made only to phenotypic merit, but also to genotypic merit. Animals that are relatively free from undesirable and deleterious recessive genes (such as lethals), those that are high in fertility, and those that have good vigor are the ones which will most likely hold up well when the herd is closed to outside breeding.

Wright and Eaton (1929), using guinea pigs, started over 30 lines in which no intentional selection was practiced and in which full-sibs were mated. Some of the lines failed to survive this inbreeding. Thus, only those lines which had superior genetic material present in the foundation stock could stand up under the inbreeding program.

2. Amount of Selection Practiced

If the selection which is practiced favors vigor, livability, etc., rather than some fancy points, this will go a long way toward success in developing a good herd under a closed breeding program. Certainly, the more selection of this type, the more likely is the closed herd to be a success. Helen Dean King (1918 and 1919) inbred rats by full-sib matings for over 60 generations and maintained a high level of production. However, her selection was rigidly controlled and based upon those factors which contributed to the survival of the lines. As will be mentioned later, her selection probably maintained heterozygosity for certain traits, since this colony of rats is not so homozygous as one would expect from the calculation of homozygosity which should have been produced by this much inbreeding.

There may be a possibility that selection during the period in which the herd is closed will tend to favor the heterozygous state for those traits in which there is overdominance. If the heterozygote is superior to either homozygote for a particular trait, it is obvious that, through selection, animals heterozygous for that trait will be kept for breeding. This should not be harmful to a closed herd of a purebred breeder practicing linebreeding unless there are many such traits, in which case no progress would be made. It might be undesirable in the development of inbred lines for converging, as has been done in hybrid corn production. Even so, as Winters postulates, the livestock breeder must be concerned with the performance level of his inbred lines because these lines may be impossible to maintain if no consideration to performance is given in their production and maintenance.

3. Rate of Inbreeding

Inbreeding tends to increase homozygosity. It will increase the homozygosity for desirable and undesirable genes alike. If inbreeding is practiced intensely, homozygosity for the undesirable genes may occur at such a high rate that considerable financial shock will be experienced by the livestock breeder. In addition, very rapid inbreeding may create homozygosity so quickly that there are no possibilities for selection, which are necessary for increasing the genetic worth of the herd. Thus, a purebred breeder, to be successful with a closed herd, should have good foundation material; he should have a rigorous selection program for production characteristics, and he should keep inbreeding sufficiently low to allow selection for the desired traits.

Operators of a one-sire herd will find it quite difficult to keep from doing intense inbreeding. Perhaps the solution to their program is to secure breeding stock from a larger breeder who is practicing linebreeding. This will be practicable as long as the genetic merit of the animals is superior to that of the one-sire herd.

If one should have a closed herd in which, in spite of selection, vigor should decline to the extent that new blood must be found, it is better to choose stock of some other breeder who is using a closed-herd breeding program, rather than that of one who practices outbreeding. In this way, one will take advantage of the fact that many undesirable and deleterious genes have been eliminated and will not be brought into the herd through this outcross. After such an outcross has been made, one can again close his herd to outside breeding.

When, and if, it becomes necessary to introduce new breeding into the herd, it may be desirable to try the cross in a gradual manner on only a few animals from another closed herd to see how the combination will perform, rather than making a complete herd outcross. If performance is not satisfactory with this outcross, another may be used.

Recently, the principle of using inbreeding as a tool in selection has been developed. By this method several small lines are intensely inbred to locate those lines which are relatively free of deleterious genes and which as a consequence can withstand intense inbreeding. These superior lines can then be converged to form a herd which can be closed and which should have relatively few undesirable outcrops. However, it is evident that such a principle can be effectively employed only by a large breeder.

A breeder must calculate the inbreeding coefficient in order to know how rapidly homozygosity is developing. Also, for use in selection, he needs to know how much an animal is inbred so that he may keep the best animals within each level of inbreeding. Otherwise, he may have a tendency to keep the less inbred animals at the expense of the more highly inbred ones.

Two general methods are used for calculating the coefficient of inbreeding, but both are based on the fact that the inbreeding of an individual is one-half the relationship of the two parents. One method, the relationship chart, is more useful where a closed herd is maintained, since it can be kept current and little calculation is necessary to bring it up to date each year. The other method is more useful to calculate the inbreeding of an individual only. The formula proposed by Wright (1923) for calculating inbreeding by the second method is

$$Fx = \Sigma[(\tfrac{1}{2})^{n + n_1 + 1} (1 + F_A)]$$

where Fx is the coefficient of inbreeding of an animal under consideration, n is the number of generations from the sire back to a common ancestor, n_1 is the number of generations from the dam back to the common ancestor, and F_A is the inbreeding coefficient of the common ancestor.

A common ancestor that is not inbred will have zero for F_A. Then $1 + 0 = 1$, which will appear in the parentheses on the right. This, times the part of the formula on the left, $(\tfrac{1}{2})^{n + n_1 + 1}$, will not in that case alter the value obtained for $(\tfrac{1}{2})^{n + n_1 + 1}$ because the product of any number times one is equal to the number itself. Therefore, in cases where there is no inbreeding of the common ancestor, this part of the formula is ignored.

It will be more easily understood how the inbreeding calculation is made if we use an example.

$$X \begin{cases} A & \begin{cases} C \\ D \end{cases} \\ B & \begin{cases} C \\ D \end{cases} \end{cases}$$

The common ancestors are C and D. Since this pedigree does not show the ancestors of C and D, we shall assume that they are not inbred. This pedigree can be graphically displayed to show the common ancestors more clearly.

X — A (Sire), B (Dam) — C D = common ancestors

To calculate the inbreeding of X, one must remember that the contribution to the inbreeding of X through C, plus the contribution to the inbreeding of X through D as the common ancestors, must be summed to give the inbreeding of X. The number of generations from the sire, A, back to the common ancestor, C, is one. The number of generations from the dam, B, back to the common ancestor, C, is one. Then, the contribution of C to the inbreeding of X is

$$(\tfrac{1}{2})^{1+1+1} \text{ or } (\tfrac{1}{2})^3$$

The number of generations from the sire, A, back to the common ancestor, D, is one. The number of generations from the dam, B, back to the common ancestor, D, is one. Then the contribution of D to the inbreeding of X is

$$(\tfrac{1}{2})^{1+1+1} \text{ or } (\tfrac{1}{2})^3$$

To sum these two, add $(\tfrac{1}{2})^3 + (\tfrac{1}{2})^3$, which is $\tfrac{1}{8} + \tfrac{1}{8} = \tfrac{1}{4}$, or 0.25. Thus X has the coefficient of inbreeding of 0.25, which would be expressed on a percentage basis by saying that X is 25 per cent inbred. This can be interpreted to mean that 25 per cent of the genes that were in the heterozygous state were made homozygous by this one generation of full-sib mating.

Let us now, since we have learned how to use this method, consider a pedigree in which more than one generation of inbreeding has been practiced.

$$
X \begin{cases}
A \begin{cases}
C \begin{cases} E \\ F \end{cases} \\
D \begin{cases} E \\ F \end{cases}
\end{cases} \\
B \begin{cases}
C \begin{cases} E \\ F \end{cases} \\
D \begin{cases} E \\ F \end{cases}
\end{cases}
\end{cases}
$$

In this case, there have been two generations of full-sib matings. We shall assume that E and F are not inbred or related. The pedigree arrangement shows that C, D, E, and F are common ancestors, and that C will have the same parents, regardless of where he is, and that D will have the same parents, regardless of where in the pedigree she appears. Thus, it is not possible to go through C on the sire's side of the pedigree and through C on the dam's side of the pedigree to establish that E and F are common ancestors. Only through C on the sire's side of the pedigree and D on the dam's side of the pedigree can we determine that E and F are the common ancestors. Likewise, with D on the sire's side and C on the dam's side of the pedigree tracing back to E and F, the common ancestors are again established. This may be more clearly understood if we diagram it.

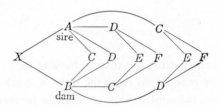

By using the inbreeding formula, we find the following:

$$C = (\tfrac{1}{2})^3 \qquad\qquad F = (\tfrac{1}{2})^5$$
$$D = (\tfrac{1}{2})^3 \qquad\qquad E = (\tfrac{1}{2})^5$$
$$E = (\tfrac{1}{2})^5 \qquad\qquad F = (\tfrac{1}{2})^5$$

By summing these values we have:

$$(\tfrac{1}{2})^3 + (\tfrac{1}{2})^3 + (\tfrac{1}{2})^5 + (\tfrac{1}{2})^5 + (\tfrac{1}{2})^5 + (\tfrac{1}{2})^5$$

which is 0.375. Hence the inbreeding coefficient of X in this case is 0.375. A simple arrow pedigree diagram can be used to show the paths.

$$
\begin{array}{c}
A \leftarrow C \leftarrow E \\
X \diagup \diagdown \diagup \diagdown \\
B \leftarrow D \leftarrow F
\end{array}
$$

$$
\begin{array}{ll}
A - C - B + 1 & = (\tfrac{1}{2})^3 \\
A - D - B + 1 & = (\tfrac{1}{2})^3 \\
A - C - E - D - B + 1 & = (\tfrac{1}{2})^5 \\
A - D - E - C - B + 1 & = (\tfrac{1}{2})^5 \\
A - C - F - D - B + 1 & = (\tfrac{1}{2})^5 \\
A - D - F - C - B + 1 & = (\tfrac{1}{2})^5
\end{array}
$$

and

$$(\tfrac{1}{2})^3 + (\tfrac{1}{2})^3 + (\tfrac{1}{2})^5 + (\tfrac{1}{2})^5 + (\tfrac{1}{2})^5 + (\tfrac{1}{2})^5 = 0.3750$$

So far we have not used the $1 + F_A$ part of the equation. Let us take an example in which sire $\times$ daughter matings have been made and in which the sire is inbred.

$$X \begin{cases} A \begin{cases} C \begin{cases} E \\ F \end{cases} \\ B \begin{cases} E \\ F \end{cases} \end{cases} \\ D \begin{cases} A \begin{cases} C \\ B \end{cases} \\ T \begin{cases} A \\ O \end{cases} \end{cases} \end{cases}$$

It can be seen that A is the common ancestor. It can also be seen that A is inbred because E and F are common ancestors of A. Let us calculate the inbreeding coefficient of A so that what A, as a common ancestor of X, contributes to the inbreeding of X can be increased by 1 + the coefficient of inbreeding of A. Then E contributes $(\frac{1}{2})^3$ and F contributes $(\frac{1}{2})^3$. By summation we have $(\frac{1}{2})^3 + (\frac{1}{2})^3 = 0.25$, which is the inbreeding coefficient of A. We can substitute 0.25 for F_A in the $1 + F_A$ part of the equation, which gives us $(1 + 0.25)$, or 1.25.

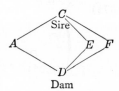

Let us now calculate what A would contribute to the inbreeding of X if A were not inbred itself.

It can be seen that A is the sire and the common ancestor. In the path through B to A, we have $(\frac{1}{2})^{0+1+1}$, or $(\frac{1}{2})^2$; and through the path B through T to A, $(\frac{1}{2})^{0+2+1}$, or $(\frac{1}{2})^3$. By summation we have $(\frac{1}{2})^2 + (\frac{1}{2})^3 = \frac{3}{8}$, or 0.375. We must remember that 0.375 is to be multiplied by 1.25 to give the actual inbreeding of X. An inbred common ancestor should contribute greater homozygosity to future generations than a common ancestor that is not inbred. Actually the coefficient of inbreeding is an estimate of homozygosity. Its accuracy for any particular animal may depend upon several factors.

$$
\begin{array}{r}
0.375 \\
1.25 \\
\hline
1875 \\
750 \\
375 \\
\hline
0.46875
\end{array}
$$

The coefficient of inbreeding of X is 0.46875, and we would normally round this off to 47 per cent.

Let us take the pedigree in which there has been three generations of full-sib matings.

We notice that C and D are not only common ancestors but that each is also inbred. Let us use the relationship method of calculating the inbreeding of X in this case, and assume that G and H are not related and are not inbred. We can now put 0 between G and H, showing that they are not related, and since they are not, E and F will have 0 for inbreeding coefficients. We may show this in parentheses just under the animal E and F, which are related because they have the same parents. If we relate the parents of E and F in all possible ways, we have

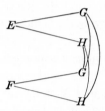

$$
\begin{aligned}
G \text{ with } G^* &= 1.0 \\
G \text{ with } H &= 0.0 \\
H \text{ with } G &= 0.0 \\
H \text{ with } H &= 1.0 \\
\hline
\text{Total} \quad &2.0
\end{aligned}
$$

and 2 divided by 4, the number of paths, equals 0.50, which is entered between E and F as the relationship between them. We see that C and D each have an inbreeding coefficient of 0.25 ($0.5 \div 2 = 0.25$), and we enter this in parentheses below the animals C and D.

We must now calculate how much relationship there is between C and D.

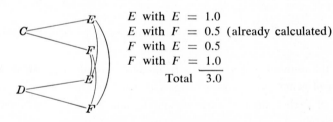

$$
\begin{aligned}
E \text{ with } E &= 1.0 \\
E \text{ with } F &= 0.5 \text{ (already calculated)} \\
F \text{ with } E &= 0.5 \\
F \text{ with } F &= 1.0 \\
\hline
\text{Total} \quad &3.0
\end{aligned}
$$

and 3 divided by 4 equals 0.75, which is the relationship between C and D. We enter this between C and D. Since C and D are 0.75 related, then A and B are each inbred 0.375 ($0.75 \div 2 = 0.375$). We enter this in parentheses under A and B, although it will not be used in calculating the inbreeding of X.

Our next step is to calculate the relationship between A and B. Here we have an additional factor to consider and that is that C and D are both 0.25 inbred. The relationship of C to itself will be 1 plus its inbreeding, or 1.25. The same is true for D.

---

* An animal is related to itself times 1 plus its inbreeding coefficient. In the case of G, since there is no inbreeding, it is related to itself times 1.

$$
\begin{aligned}
C \ \text{with}\ C &= 1.25 \\
C \ \text{with}\ D &= 0.75 \ \text{(as calculated)} \\
D \ \text{with}\ C &= 0.75 \ \text{(as calculated)} \\
D \ \text{with}\ D &= 1.25 \\
\hline
\text{Total} &\ \ 4.00
\end{aligned}
$$

and 4 divided by 4 equals 1.00. Then A and B are 1.00 related. This is entered between A and B, and means that A and B are as closely related as a non-inbred individual is to itself. In other words, A and B would be as likely to produce gametes carrying the same genes as would a non-inbred individual at various times.

We can now determine the inbreeding of X by dividing 1.0 by 2 (½ the relationship of the parents = the inbreeding of the offspring); this gives us 0.50. We enter this under X as the inbreeding of X.

In a closed herd one will find it advantageous to develop a numerator relationship chart. Suppose we use the herd in which X, inbred 50 per cent as shown in the example, was produced. This numerator chart (Emik and Terrill, 1949) can be kept current at all times simply by listing the animals on the side and top of each generation and calculating the relationship. One formula for calculating the relationship between any two animals, x and y, is as follows:

$$
R_{xy} = \frac{\Sigma[(\tfrac{1}{2})^{n+n_1+1}(1 + F_a)]}{\sqrt{1 + F_x}\ \ \ \sqrt{1 + F_y}}
$$

where n is the number of generations from x to a common ancestor, and n_1 is the number of generations from y to the common ancestor. The term F_a is the inbreeding of each common ancestor; and F_x and F_y are the inbreeding of x and y (Table 6).

Table 6. NUMERATOR RELATIONSHIP FOR USE IN DETERMINING INBREEDING IN A CLOSED BREEDING HERD OR FLOCK

Animal No.	Sire	Dam	Inbreeding	Animal Number							
				H	G	F	E	D	C	B	A
H	—	—	0	1.0000							
G	—	—	0	0	1.0000						
F	G	H	0	0.5000	0.5000	1.0000					
E	G	H	0	0.5000	0.50000	0.5000	1.0000				
D	E	F	0.2500	0.5000	0.5000	0.7500	0.7500	1.2500			
C	E	F	0.2500	0.5000	0.5000	0.7500	0.7500	0.7500	1.2500		
B	C	D	0.3750	0.5000	0.5000	0.7500	0.7500	1.0000	1.0000	1.3750	
A	C	D	0.3750	0.5000	0.5000	0.7500	0.7500	1.0000	1.0000	1.0000	1.3750

Since *A* and *B* are 1.000 related, it follows that the offspring, *x,* produced by them will have an inbreeding coefficient of 0.500, or an inbreeding of 50 per cent.

BREEDING COMMERCIAL LIVESTOCK

There are two general systems of breeding useful in commercial livestock production: grading-up and crossbreeding.

Grading-Up

By grading-up is meant the generation-after-generation use of purebred males of the same breed on the grade females of the herd. In this system the males used are unrelated to the grade females because the level of performance is probably not sufficiently high to warrant inbreeding. This system of breeding was studied by the U.S. Department of Agriculture, the University of Missouri, and the Weekly Kansas City Star at the Sni-A-Bar Farms, using Shorthorn cattle. It was found that the greatest improvement was made in the first generation, in which purebred sires were used on rather nondescript cows. However, performance and type more nearly approached that of the purebred Shorthorns with succeeding generations. After the third generation, in which purebred Shorthorn males were used on selected grade cows, the characteristics of the calves approached rather closely those of a Shorthorn herd. After six generations of using purebred Shorthorn bulls on selected grade cows, the grade herd of Shorthorns could not be distinguished from a purebred herd (Fig. 112). In fact, it became necessary to search for outstanding purebred Shorthorn bulls in order to find one good enough to bring about any further improvement. As far as the genetics is concerned, one can see that the six generations in which purebred Shorthorn bulls were used would substitute most of or all the genes from the Shorthorn bulls for the genes existing in the original nondescript cows with which this study was started.

The grading-up system of commercial production is useful in such animals as dairy and beef cattle because the cost of top-level breeding stock is high and reproductive rate is low. A herd of outstanding performance can be developed by this method in 20 to 25 years without having to put out a large sum of money in order to get started. However, this system of breeding has nothing to offer in the production of poultry or hogs and not too much to offer in sheep production. A breeder can start out with animals of high merit in swine or poultry without a great expense, and the cost of these breeding animals is distributed over a large number of offspring, since reproductive rate is high for both swine and poultry.

One thing that should be considered in a grading-up program is that the production level of the males must be high. In other words, animals of low genetic merit cannot be accepted for use in a grading-up program. However, deviations in fancy points can be tolerated; e.g., color, which might be discriminated against in a purebred herd. For example, "red necks" or "line backs" in Herefords might not be looked upon with favor in a purebred Hereford herd, but the use of such bulls in a grading-up program in commercial cattle breeding would in no way injure the program. Incidentally, this should be given consideration by purebred breeders. It would be worth while to give more thought to what is needed in commercial herds than to give strong consideration to these fancy points. On the other hand, faulty conformation, low rate of gain, low fertility, low milk production, or inefficient feed conversion into gains would all be very deleterious in a sound grading-up program.

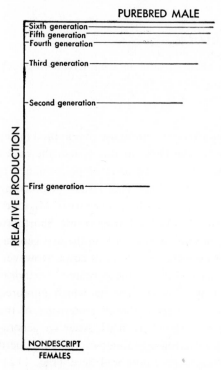

Fig. 112. Relative levels of production obtained through use of grading-up with good purebred males over six generations.

Crossbreeding

Crossbreeding may vary according to the "width" of the cross. An example of a very wide cross would be that of two species or genera. A narrower cross would be that of two breeds or of two strains or lines within a breed. Crossing generally results in an increased state of heterozygosity with rather uniform phenotype in the F_1 population. Heterosis, or hybrid vigor, in which the crossbred population shows more vigor than either of the parental stocks used in making the cross, may be associated with crossbreeding.

Wide Crosses

Very wide crosses are known in farm animals. A generic example is the jack $\times$ the mare in the production of a mule, or the reciprocal cross in the production of the hinny. Such a crossbred shows remarkable hybrid vigor as a work animal because of its ability to withstand extreme hardships and heavy work loads. When horses and mules were used in road construction, it was always necessary to make special provisions for horses which were unnecessary to make for mules. In many cases where mules were used, a corral was provided in which grain, hay, and water were supplied in abundance. The mules were worked all day and then unharnessed at night and run together in this corral. It was left up to the mule to eat hay and grain and to drink water as he chose. There were no cases of founder or other digestive disturbances although these would always occur in horses so treated. These mules were worked hard in all kinds of weather and in mud or dust and seemed to thrive under such treatment.

Mules are generally sterile, although a few cases of fertile mules have been reported. The explanation for this sterility in mules lies in the fact that the chromosome number differs in the jack from that present in the mare. The mule, in undergoing spermatogenesis or oogenesis, has some chromosomes with which there are no homologues for synapsis. These extra chromosomes are unpaired, and this results in germ cell production in which unbalanced chromosomal situations exist. These unbalances in the chromosomes result in nonviable germ cells and consequent infertility. It is only when a balanced chromosomal arrangement, similar either to that produced in germ cells by the mare or by the jack, occurs that viable germ cells are produced. These germ cells could be fertilizable and would explain the fertile mules which have been reported. Although fertility in the mule is very low, more fertile matings with mules would be known if they were regularly bred, but farmers generally recognize their low fertility and therefore very few mules have been bred.

Buffaloes have been crossed with domestic cattle with the result that hybrids called "cattalo" are produced. Due to the shape of the crossbred animal, which is transmitted by the buffalo, the cross is more satisfactory when buffalo females are mated to domestic cattle bulls. When the cross is made this way, calving difficulties are lessened. The hybrid male resulting from crossing buffalo with domestic cattle is sterile, but the females are fertile.

A fertile, wide cross is found when Brahman *(Bos indicus)* cattle are crossed onto our English breeds *(Bos domesticus* or *Bos typicus)*. This cross has been made for the production of new breeds, the Santa Gertrudis and the Beefmaster, and is used extensively in the south in order to obtain cattle possessing heat and tick resistance. Warwick, in a summary of studies in which Brahman cattle were crossed with the English breeds, shows not only the importance of the heat and tick resistance but also the advantage resulting from hybrid vigor.

Breed Crosses

Crossbreeding of well-established breeds has generally given hybrid vigor and is used largely by chicken and swine breeders for obtaining increased meat production. Today over 90 per cent of the hogs sold for slaughter in the hog belt are crossbreds. There are several reasons why crossbreeding is so common with chickens and pigs. Reproduction is at such a high rate that it is not difficult to maintain the breeds of purebred animals and to produce the commercial animals largely by crossbreeding. In cattle, maintaining the breeds requires a sizeable portion of the females produced, so that it is more difficult for a commercial breeder to get into a crossbreeding program. In hogs, it has been shown by Dickerson and Grimes (1947) that a high level of sow productivity (fertility and suckling ability) is associated with slow gains and efficient conversion of feed into meat. Where such a genetic relationship exists, it is clear that the crossing of breeds would be most advantageous. The concept of keeping crossbred females and using purebred males of different breeds, or alternating the use of males of two breeds on them, has made it possible to use heterosis in obtaining greater female productivity. This concept also paves the way for the greater use of crossbreeding in such animals as beef cattle and sheep, since females are selected from the crossbred population and are bred to purebred males.

Winters, et al (1935 and 1936) presented data on a swine crossbreeding study conducted for six years in which they used three systems of crossbreeding:

1. Use of purebred sows × purebred boars of another breed.
2. Three-breed cross, in which crossbred sows were mated to a purebred boar of a third breed.
3. Criss-crossing, in which each generation of crossbred sows were kept mated back to boars of alternate breeds.

Obviously, if straight-bred females (or purebred females) are bred to males of another breed, a crossbreeding program with a species in which reproduction is low would be limited. The only hybrid vigor exploited is in the offspring itself, and also there is a sizeable need for replacement females. These would have to be procured from some other breeder, or a separate herd of this breed would have to be maintained on the farm in addition to the one used for crossbreeding. This first system of crossbreeding definitely has limitations which do not exist in other systems. Even so, the results of the Minnesota station showed clearly that crossbred pigs were superior to the purebreds in growth rate and feed efficiency.

The mating of crossbred sows to a boar of a third breed makes it possible to use the hybrid vigor of the crossbred sows to obtain greater sow productivity. It also provides pigs that show hybrid vigor. This program can be carried on for many years.

Duroc Jersey × Poland China ————————————→ crossbred pigs
Crossbred sows (D.J. × P.C.) × Hampshire boar ————————→ crossbred pigs
Crossbred sows (D.J. × P.C. × Hamp.) × Chester White boar ——→ crossbred pigs

This could be continued until boars of all recognized breeds were used, keeping crossbred gilts each time for the production of the pigs. The criss-crossing requires only two breeds. One may illustrate this with the Duroc Jersey and Poland China breeds:

Poland China × Duroc Jersey   ————————————→ crossbred pigs
Crossbred sows (D.J. × P.C.) × Duroc Jersey boar ————→ crossbred pigs
Crossbred sows (D.J. × P.C. × D.J.) × Poland China boar ——→ crossbred pigs

This can be continued indefinitely by always keeping crossbred sows and mating them to a boar of a breed opposite to that of their sire. This criss-cross system of crossbreeding also uses the hybrid vigor of the sows to obtain greater sow productivity, and the pigs show hybrid vigor in growth and feed efficiency.

Lush, et al (1939), at the Iowa station, obtained similar results with crossbreeding swine. The Iowa and Minnesota studies may be summarized:

1. Crossbred sows were superior to the purebred sows for producing market hogs.
2. Crossbred pigs grew more rapidly and required less feed per unit of gain than purebred pigs.
3. Less death loss occurred in crossbred pigs.

It must be emphasized that with any of these systems of crossbreeding, purebred boars are used to sire the pigs. If one used a crossbred boar as well as crossbred sows, the genetic variation would be extreme. These variations would occur not only in color and other similar superficial characteristics, but also in type, rate of gain, feed efficiency, etc. This lack of uniformity would be undesirable; consequently, the use of purebred males in any crossbreeding program is preferred.

Purebred males used in crossbreeding need to be selected just as rigidly for such production factors as fertility, suckling ability, rate of gain, feed efficiency, and carcass merit as they would if they were to be used in purebred herds. However, superficial characteristics, such as coat color, may be ignored completely in crossbreeding with no deleterious results. For example, a Hampshire boar that has no belt, though unsatisfactory for use in a purebred Hampshire herd, would be quite satisfactory for crossbreeding.

Erroneous ideas may develop in the minds of livestock producers relative to the use of crossbreeding. Since crossbred pigs, for instance, have more vigor and greater livability, one might assume that in crossbreeding these animals the necessity for proper sanitation, feeding, and management is less. Nothing could be farther from the truth, for it is just as essential to use the best possible production and management practices in crossbreeding as it is in raising animals that are purebred.

In the event that one is using females of one breed and crossing to males of another breed, the way the cross is made may determine to a large extent the value of crossing. An example will illustrate how crossing the same breeds might give desirable results in one case and undesirable results in another. Good fat lambs may be produced by crossing the Dorset Horn ewe to a Southdown ram. The Dorset Horn is a fairly large sheep, highly fertile, and a remarkable milk producer. She will have one or two large lambs at birth and an ample milk flow for them. The Southdown is the model in mutton type but is small. The mutton type, as well as the smaller size, will be imposed, in part, upon the lambs. With this good type and with the smaller size, along with a big food supply, the lambs will show high finish at smaller sizes as well as good type, a combination that makes an ideal market lamb.

Suppose that the Southdown ewe was crossed with a Dorset Horn ram. Being sired by a Dorset Horn ram, the crossbred lamb will tend to grow more than a pure Southdown lamb. The Southdown ewe, however, gives only enough milk for a smaller lamb. Since the first part of the body to grow is the skeleton, the second is the muscle, and the last is fat deposition, lambs of this cross will be inferior to either Dorset Horn or Southdown lambs because the milk supply would be adequate only for skeleton and part of the muscle growth. This crossbred lamb will be long-necked, leggy, shallow-bodied, and lacking in finish.

This brings us to a fundamental concept for exploiting the desirable traits of two breeds in crossbreeding. Always inject the characteristics of female productivity into the cross by using females of the breed strong in these characteristics. Always introduce such factors as type and ease of fattening by using a male of a breed strong in these characteristics. In this way, both types of characteristic are combined into the offspring. If the cross were made in the other direction, the results would be very disappointing.

Roberts and Carroll (1942) have shown that for each characteristic such as number of pigs farrowed, number weaned, weight-for-age, etc., the crossbred pigs may not significantly exceed the best of the two parents. Their analysis of data may be subject to criticism because the analysis used tended to make each experiment small and this could have prevented a significant difference from showing. In considering the use of hybrid vigor, the over-all result in the production of meat animals must be considered. This can be illustrated by considering breeds A and B, where A is high in fertility and milking ability and B is high in gains and feed efficiency (Table 7).

Table 7. COMPARISON OF CROSSBRED WITH PUREBRED PIGS FOR
SHOWING OVER-ALL MERIT OF CROSSBREDS

	Breed A	Breed B	Crossbreds
Number of pigs	11	7	11
Wean weight	32 lb.	28 lb.	32
180-day weight	190 lb.	225 lb.	225
Gain per 100 lb. of feed	22 lb.	30 lb.	30

In this hypothetical case the crossbreds have purposely been prevented from exceeding the best of the two parents in any characteristic. However, 2,475 lb. of pork per litter of crossbreds is to be compared with 1,575 lb. for breed B and 2,090 lb. for breed A. This final result, with the feeds we have available, is the one which means more meat on the consumer's table.

Results from crossing sheep at the Oregon station have shown the advantages of crossbred ewes for fat lamb production and the marked differences in performance of the lambs as a result of breed of ram used on the crossbred ewes. In general, the rams of medium-wool mutton breeds sired lambs possessing better conformation and the ability to make greater gains and to score higher than rams of the long-wool mutton breeds. Rams of the smaller type and better conformation breeds, such as Southdown and Cheviots, sired smaller lambs possessing better conformation and finish than rams of the larger breeds, such as Hampshires and Suffolks. Which kind of ram to use would depend upon how discriminating is the market. If the lambs that are fatter and of better conformation will bring a sufficient price increase per pound to more than offset the smaller weight, one could afford to use Southdown or Cheviot rams. On a less discriminating market, the Hampshire- and Suffolk-sired lambs would be more profitable because of the additional weight.

The main point to bring out is that breeds differ in their combining ability and breeds of sires differ in their ability to sire desirable offspring when used on crossbred females. One should study the breeds, the type of conditions under which they are expected to produce, and the demands of the market in his area in planning his crossbreeding program.

Experimental results at the Montana station, the Ohio station, the California station, and the U.S. Range Livestock Station, Miles City, Montana, have all shown advantages from crossing the English breeds of beef cattle. Reduced mortality of calves and greater rate and economy of gain were generally reported. However, only limited studies have been made in which crossbred cows have been used to raise calves. Knapp, et al (1949), had some results in which Shorthorn × Hereford cows were crossed with Angus and with Hereford bulls. These crossbred cows showed a greater advantage in weaning weight of calves over purebred calves than the advantage of crossbred calves over the purebreds when the dams of the crossbreds were purebreds. This limited study indicates that crossbred cows might show greater cow productivity as a result of hybrid vigor. The results, however, are confused by the effect of a third breed.

Line and Strain Crosses

The best examples of hybrid vigor from single * and double * crossing are found in the production of hybrid corn. A much greater production of corn in the Midwest is the result of the use of hybrid corn. In fact, most of the corn that is grown is now hybrid corn, and farmers are of the opinion that they cannot afford not to grow hybrid corn.

Single- and double-cross farm animals have not been studied to any great extent because most of the work has been in the development of inbred lines. Considerable work has been done with poultry, and double-cross chicks within and between breeds are now commercially available. These birds show reduced mortality, increased growth rate, and greater egg production. The results with hybrid chickens is comparable to that of hybrid corn. It is much easier to use hybrid vigor in chickens than in pigs because baby chicks of any combination can be produced and sent to any place in the United States. It does not necessitate the production of line-cross hens and line-cross cocks which would be used on the farm to produce hybrid chicks. This would be necessary in swine or beef production and will limit the use of double-crossed hybrid hogs or cattle.

Considerable work has been done on the use of inbred or line-cross boars on outbred sows. The Wisconsin station has numerous comparisons of inbred and line-cross boars with outbred boars used in the same herd. The general results indicate about a 10 per cent advantage of the inbred or line-cross boars over the outbred boars in swine production. At present, the hybrid corn concerns are handling line-cross and line-cross-bred boars which are put out for farmers to use on their outbred sows for commercial pig production.

One reason for using line-cross rather than inbred boars in farm herds is the fact that the better appearing line-cross boars are generally more acceptable to the farmer than the inbred, less attractive boars. The heterosis from using line-cross boars should be sufficient to justify the use of such boars, but probably it is not equal to heterosis resulting when inbred boars are used. Certainly, the vigor, fertility, appearance, etc., are in favor of the line-cross boars.

---

* By single cross is meant the combining of two inbred lines. Double-crossing is the combining of two different line-crossed populations so that four lines are represented.

EXERCISES

1. Under what conditions and with which species would you use grading up as a breeding program?

2. What is accomplished genetically by (a) inbreeding, (b) crossbreeding?

3. Upon what factors does success with an inbreeding program depend?

4. When would you use crossbreeding, and how would you exploit fully the advantages of heterosis?

5. Explain why inbreeding is often accompanied by reduced vigor and why crossbreeding generally results in heterosis.

6. What is line breeding? How does it differ from inbreeding?

7. Calculate the percentage of inbreeding and explain what your answer means genetically.

(a)
$$
X \begin{cases} A \begin{cases} C \begin{cases} E \\ F \end{cases} \\ D \begin{cases} E \\ F \end{cases} \end{cases} \\ B \begin{cases} A \begin{cases} C \\ D \end{cases} \\ T \begin{cases} A \\ Y \end{cases} \end{cases} \end{cases}
$$

(b)
$$
X \begin{cases} A \begin{cases} C \begin{cases} E \begin{cases} G \\ H \end{cases} \\ F \begin{cases} G \\ H \end{cases} \end{cases} \\ D \begin{cases} E \begin{cases} G \\ H \end{cases} \\ F \begin{cases} G \\ H \end{cases} \end{cases} \end{cases} \\ B \begin{cases} C \begin{cases} E \begin{cases} G \\ H \end{cases} \\ F \begin{cases} G \\ H \end{cases} \end{cases} \\ D \begin{cases} E \begin{cases} G \\ H \end{cases} \\ F \begin{cases} G \\ H \end{cases} \end{cases} \end{cases} \end{cases}
$$

(e)
$$
X \begin{cases} M \begin{cases} A \begin{cases} B \begin{cases} D \\ E \end{cases} \\ C \begin{cases} D \\ E \end{cases} \end{cases} \\ N \begin{cases} P \\ S \end{cases} \\ O \begin{cases} N \\ T \end{cases} \end{cases} \end{cases}
$$

(c)
$$
X \begin{cases} A \begin{cases} C \begin{cases} F \begin{cases} J \\ K \end{cases} \\ G \begin{cases} J \\ T \end{cases} \end{cases} \\ D \begin{cases} F \begin{cases} J \\ K \end{cases} \\ H \begin{cases} J \\ S \end{cases} \end{cases} \end{cases} \\ B \begin{cases} C \begin{cases} F \begin{cases} J \\ K \end{cases} \\ G \begin{cases} J \\ T \end{cases} \end{cases} \\ E \begin{cases} F \begin{cases} J \\ K \end{cases} \\ I \begin{cases} J \\ Y \end{cases} \end{cases} \end{cases} \end{cases}
$$

(d)
$$
X \begin{cases} A \begin{cases} C \begin{cases} E \\ F \end{cases} \\ D \begin{cases} E \\ F \end{cases} \end{cases} \\ B \begin{cases} M \begin{cases} O \\ P \end{cases} \\ N \begin{cases} O \\ P \end{cases} \end{cases} \end{cases}
$$

(f)
$$
X \begin{cases} A \begin{cases} C \begin{cases} G \\ H \end{cases} \\ D \begin{cases} T \\ J \end{cases} \end{cases} \\ B \begin{cases} E \begin{cases} G \\ K \end{cases} \\ F \begin{cases} L \\ M \end{cases} \end{cases} \end{cases}
$$

With *G* and *M* inbred 0.25.

8. What effect would a selective advantage for the heterozygote have on the homozygosity which would be produced by inbreeding?

12

FACTORS THAT INFLUENCE RATE OF PROGRESS MADE BY SELECTION

Farm animals have been under domestication for a long time, and breeding animals have been selected by some method, but many persons are disappointed in the progress that has been made in the improvement of farm animals. It is obvious that there has been improvement made in at least some characteristics, such as type and conformation, but even the improvement made for these characteristics has been disappointing to many breeders. Certainly, there are some outstanding animals, but even in good herds many quite undesirable animals are produced. Since selection may not mean the same to everyone, it seems desirable to clarify its definition.

One way to think of selection is that one keeps what he wants and discards what he does not want. Another approach is to think of selection as keeping the best and eliminating the worst animals in the herd. This may be far from the true situation if one considers what is best from the standpoint of the animal. What we want may actually be undesirable as far as survival of the species is concerned. Even if we recognize this and think of keeping what we want and eliminating what we do not want, selection may still be only partly understood. Suppose that we want rapid rate of gain in the herd and we select the two most rapidly gaining bulls, one (*A*) gaining 3.7 lb. per day and the other (*B*) gaining 2.8 lb. per day. In our breeding program, we breed only 7 cows to produce 7 calves by bull *A* and 35 cows to produce 35 calves by bull *B*. Actually then, we have selected with five times the pressure for bull *B* with 2.8 lb. of gain as for bull *A* with 3.7 lb. of gain. Now, if we should keep only 1 calf from the 7 produced by bull *A* and should keep 20 of the 35 produced by bull *B*, we have actually selected with 20 times the pressure for the lower gain of 2.8 lb. per day than for the higher gains. Selection, then, is *differential reproduction*. The more offspring that are produced and used for breeding by the desirable individuals in contrast to the less desirable individuals, the greater is our selection for the desired.

It seems appropriate to discuss some of the factors which influence progress made by selection so that we may see some of the causes contributing to inefficiency of selection. Perhaps more progress could be made if we knew some of the factors that hinder progress, so that they may be corrected. Perhaps we may learn that progress must be slow because of the nature of the conditions existing with farm animals.

NUMBER OF GENES AFFECTING A CHARACTER

If the character desired were controlled by only one pair of genes, it would be very simple to obtain the desired even in the homozygous state. A recessive that is desired should be homozygous for it to express itself and, with the genotype known, could be used for breeding. A population possessing this desired recessive could soon be developed, and all those showing the dominant could be eliminated, while a desired dominant could be increased in a population very rapidly. It would eventually be necessary to progeny-test to locate the homozygous ones which could be mated for the continuation of the desired character in a pure condition in the herd. However, once this desired character, which is due to one pair of genes, has been obtained in the pure state, no further progress by selection can be made. The only variations in the character would be those resulting from environmental differences. Consequently, with only one or a very few pairs of genes, progress is rapid at first but discontinues after a short time.

Most of the characters of economic importance with which we deal in livestock improvement are under the control of many genes. Where there are many genes controlling a character, achievements by selection in each generation will be small, but progress can be made for a longer period of time.

An experiment was started in 1896 at the Illinois station in the selection of corn for (1) high protein, (2) low protein, (3) high oil, and (4) low oil content. The corn was produced as lines within each of these four groups, since no outside genetic material was introduced. Self-fertilization was prevented by detasseling part of the corn and using ears from these stalks only, so that they would have to be cross-fertilized. Two rows of kernels were used from each ear for chemical analyses and selections were based upon results obtained. Ear-row plantings were made. There was some inbreeding because the lines were closed. The selection was phenotypic, since no progeny test was made.

After 28 years of selection for high-protein and high-oil content, there was no indication of reaching genetic or physiological limits. Variation still occurred and progress from selection was effective (Winter, 1929). A physiological limit was reached with the low-oil line because germless seeds were produced when the oil content reached a certain low level.

A genetic limit was reached in eight generations of selecting for low protein content. The results, when compared with the original corn from which the experiment started, showed that in 28 years the protein content of the high-protein line had increased 50 per cent while the protein content of the low-protein line had decreased only 23.4 per cent. Greater changes were made in oil content by selection. The high-oil line had increased 109.8 per cent and the low-oil line had decreased 67.9 per cent. The genes for high protein appear to be mostly dominant, with those for low protein mostly recessive, because it was possible to reach a homozygous state for low-protein content in only a few generations. On the other hand, the high-protein line did not become homozygous even after 28 years of selection, which would indicate that the genes for high-protein content were dominant.

The interpretation of the results of oil content are different from those with protein content. Neither the high-oil nor the low-oil line became homozygous. The limit imposed on the low-oil line was physiological rather than genetic. It would appear that there were both dominant and recessive genes affecting high- and low-oil content. Consequently, neither line has become homozygous.

One point that has become clear from this experiment is that where many genes are involved, progress from selection is slow but can be made over a long period of time. Our farm animals generally have a long interval between generations. The interval between generations may be as low as a year for swine and poultry, but sheep generally require two years, and cattle and horses four years. With characters that are determined by many genes, and with a long interval between generations, progress will be slow.

NUMBER OF CHARACTERS

If selection is made for only one characteristic in which there are large genetic variations, progress will be relatively rapid. Even where there is only moderate control of the genetic variations, considerable progress can be made when there is only one characteristic for which selection is applied. For example, Warren and Bogart (1952) were able to separate two lines of rats with three generations of selection for early and late sexual development.

However, the addition of a second characteristic, unless it is closely associated with the first, will reduce the effectiveness of the selection for the first characteristic. If one assumes that the segregation of genes affecting one of the characteristics is independent of the segregation of genes for the second characteristic, it is easy to see that the chances of finding an animal which is highly desirable for both characteristics are much less than the chances of finding an animal which is highly desirable for one of the characteristics.

Now, suppose that a breeder considers all the possible characters, both productive and aesthetic, which he might like to see in his herd or flock. There might be some 20 or 30 such traits. Obviously, if he attempts to select for all, progress made in any one will be so small that he might not be able to see any progress in his lifetime. Therefore he will be forced to select only for those characteristics which are of greatest importance if he expects to make measurable progress. It would appear that a sound approach would be to consider which characteristics will contribute most to profits, and which will provide the greatest amount of animal product of good quality to the consuming public. Certainly, the unimportant superficial and aesthetic characteristics should give way to the more important economic characteristics, since undue emphasis on the development of the unimportant traits may lead breeders to overlook the important ones, thus permitting them to deteriorate. The over-all effect of a situation like this would not be advantageous. In Chap. 13 characteristics will be listed which are important to consider in the selection of each class of farm animals.

GOAL OF THE BREEDER

If a breeder has in mind today just one selection objective, but ten years later adopts an entirely different objective, progress toward improvement will be very little or maybe none at all. A clear-cut example of this is found in swine type. At one time breeders wanted pigs that would lay on excessive amounts of fat even at small sizes. The result was that selection for this kind of hog gave us the "hot-bloods" or "cob-rollers." Pigs were so short-legged and deep-bodied that they could roll a corn cob with their bellies. The unfortunate thing about this kind of hog was that fertility and suckling ability deteriorated because the sow concentrated on storing food in her own body rather than providing nourishment for her offspring. With this type of hog, a breeder raised singles and twins, or with luck, triplets. Certainly this was far from sound.

As a result of this development, breeders swung to the other extreme and soon were striving for the very large, long-bodied hog. Some animals were produced that weighed well over a 1,000 lb. and were so high that a short man could not stand behind one of the animals and look down its back. These animals were very long-bodied and high-arched in the back. They were fertile and good mothers in general, but they had to be developed to rather large sizes before they made desirable carcasses. These traits caused a swing back to the smaller, thicker hog, but the recent, great surplus of lard, which has sold for considerably less than live hogs, has stimulated farmers to grow a leaner type of hog which does not approach the extreme of the big type that once existed.

The point to be stressed in this example is that when the emphasis was shifted from the "cob-rollers" to the big type of hog, all the progress that had been made in establishing the "hot bloods" had to go by the wayside. In fact, the progress that had been made served only to impede progress that was desired in the opposite direction. From a practical standpoint, the shifting of type resulted in most breeders producing what few people wanted. Also, breeders were paying good prices for what they did not have during the period when swine type was being shifted.

The solution for the breeder is to take as his goal something which is basically sound and then to stay with it. He may see times when fads and fancies will bring more immediate money than his sound objective, but sooner or later the demand will be for what he has to offer. When that day comes, he will make a real contribution to the livestock industry. He can never go far wrong by adopting as a goal the economical and rapid production of a product of good quality.

RATE OF REPRODUCTION

In a class of animals such as beef cattle in which only one calf is produced from a cow each year, one cannot expect to make the progress through selection which is possible in animals like chickens, where more than 100 offspring can be raised from a female during a year. In the case of cattle, nearly 40 per cent of the female offspring are needed for replacements in order to stabilize the herd size. This means that very little selection among the heifers can be practiced, while considerable selection of bulls is possible because only about 5 per cent of the bulls will be needed for replacements. It can be seen that selection of females in chickens can be greater than males in cattle. Thus, one can expect more progress to be made in poultry improvement than in beef cattle improvement in a given time. Poultry have a much higher reproductive rate, and the interval between generations is much less than for beef cattle.

Reproductive rate is important within a species. If one producer is raising a 95 per cent calf crop, whereas another raises only a 60 per cent calf crop, the former can practice one and one-half times as much selection as the latter. Fertility is important in itself but it is also important because it affects the selection to be practiced for other traits. Whether a low number of offspring raised is due to genetic causes or to improper management practices, the result is that it will interfere with the possibility of selecting for other traits. It is very important, then, that the livestock breeder care for his animals properly so that young in large numbers can be raised.

An example of how lack of care may influence selection was found in swine. A young man had ten sows that were due to farrow. He had put each sow in a separate farrowing pen. One very cold and disagreeable night he decided not to stay with the sows. Four of the ten sows farrowed that night and lost all of the 43 pigs farrowed. The other six sows farrowed later and raised 39 pigs. Thus, in one careless night the selection possibilities for that crop of pigs were reduced approximately one-half. It is not the intention to convey the idea that super special environments for the pregnant females or for the developing young should be provided in order to raise them. Certainly they should be able to produce under what would be considered an adequate situation, but good care at time of delivery is always important.

DISEASE

Certain diseases are epidemic in nature and may cause the death of an entire herd or flock. Instances of entire swine herds lost from cholera were common before the days of routine vaccination. Certain diseases, such as Bang's abortion, lower fertility and cause death of the developing young during pregnancy. There are other diseases which may cause animals to be unthrifty. Chronic erysipelas, for example, may not kill swine, but the affected animals become unthrifty and quite unproductive. Acute erysipelas, on the other hand, may cause great death loss. The chronic diseases are more insidious because they do not cause death and as a result do not alarm the breeder to the same extent as death losses. However, more difficulties in an improvement program may result from these insidious diseases because they may cause a breeder to discard valuable genetic material.

Diseases have three major, harmful influences upon a livestock improvement program: (1) They may reduce the fertility, which cuts down on the number of animals from which selections may be made. (2) They may cause the death of valuable breeding animals. (3) They may mask the effects of desirable genes so that it becomes impossible to recognize the more desirable animals from a production standpoint.

The most logical approach to handling the problem of disease is to employ a strict sanitation program. One great hazard is that of introducing a disease when animals are brought into the herd from other farms. A breeder should have facilities for isolating such animals so that they may prove that they are healthy before being placed with the herd or flock. It is also desirable to have a separate isolation quarter in which to put sick animals that may develop in the herd or flock. Sanitation in general should be practiced. Pasture rotation, in which certain areas have no animals on them and can be cleansed of diseases and parasites, helps a great deal. Animals should be vaccinated against those diseases which can be controlled by such methods.

LINKAGE RELATIONS

There are examples in which the desirable of one trait is linked with the undesirable of another. Dickerson and Grimes (1947) showed evidence in swine that high sow productivity (fertility and suckling ability) is associated with low rate and economy of gains. The reciprocal in which high rate and economy of gains is associated with low sow productivity also exists. This type of relationship could be due to genetic linkage or to physiological limitations. If the explanation lies in linkage of genes for high sow productivity with genes for low rate and economy of gains, there may be sufficient crossing-over so that selection for both these groups may eventually result in pigs that are highly fertile, good milkers, rapid gainers, and efficient feed utilizers.

It is possible that an active thyroid gland brings about a higher level of fertility and milking ability but also causes greater general activity which would result in much of the feed eaten being used for activity, and hence, in slow gains and inefficient feed utilization. If a physiological limitation of this nature is involved, we cannot ever expect selection to give us pigs which are highly desirable in all the traits.

Whether there is linkage or physiological association of the desirable genes of one trait with the undesirable of the other, either brings about a marked lowering in the progress which can be made by selection. A commercial breeder could advantageously use crossbreeding to increase his production whenever such associations exist. A purebred breeder may continue to select for the desirable genes of both, hoping eventually to have crossing-over so that animals which are pure for all the desirable traits can be obtained. Selection should be effective for the genes that are not so linked and should maintain a high state of heterozygosity for those which are linked adversely.

So far the discussion has centered on the linkage or association of desirable genes of one trait with the undesirable genes of the other trait because it is this situation which reduces progress made by selection. Instances are known in which there is an association of the desirable of two traits. An example is found in rate of gain and efficiency of feed utilization in swine and in beef cattle. These associations make it possible to achieve a great deal from selection. In fact, it is possible to secure considerable improvement in feed efficiency through selection for rapid gains. Dickerson and Grimes (1947) showed that in swine one might make more progress for efficient utilization of feed by selecting for fast gains than by selection for the more efficient animals. This association may be due either to linkage of genes or to the manifold effect of genes.

From a practical standpoint, it is a great help to obtain improvement in both rate and efficiency of gains by selecting for more rapid gains. It is not a difficult task to weigh animals. They may be run together and fed in groups without interfering with gains made. However, it requires special facilities and a great deal of labor to individually feed each animal so that efficiency of feed use can be determined. Even though a breeder may not obtain as much progress in feed efficiency by selecting for rate of gain, he may be willing to accept the reduced progress because of lack of facilities and labor to obtain records needed to determine efficiency of feed use.

OVERDOMINANCE

It has been shown previously that some alleles interact in such a way that the heterozygote is superior to either of the two homozygotes. This type of condition is known as *overdominance*. In the event of overdominance, selection would be expected to maintain the heterozygous state because such heterozygotes have a selective advantage.

Overdominance will not interfere with initial progress made by selection, but it will prevent the development of homozygosity by selection. A point will be reached where no further progress can be made, and selection will have to be continued to maintain level of performance; otherwise, segregation would destroy favorable combinations.

PHENOTYPE VERSUS GENOTYPE

Much selection practice is based on the phenotype rather than the genotype of the animals. Sometimes the phenotype is not very closely associated with the genotype. Environmental influences may affect such production characteristics as gains and milk production as much as, or more than, the inheritance does. Where environmental influences are great, little progress can be made from phenotypic selection because most of the variations will not be inherited. We speak of the variations that are attributable to additive genetic effects as *heritability*. Other variations are caused by dominance, epistasis, gene-environment interaction, and the environment.

A good way to comprehend heritability is to think of it as that portion of variations obtained from those one reaches for in selection. Let us take an example. Suppose a herd of beef cattle have an average rate of gain of 2 lb. per head per day. There is considerable variation in rate of gain, ranging from 1 lb. to 3 lb. each day. If we select a group of animals, which averages 2.5 lb. a day, from this herd as our breeding stock we have reached for a ½ lb. a day increase in rate of gain. When this group, averaging 2.5 lb. a day, produces offspring, the offspring would be expected to average 2.5 lb. a day if all the variations in gains were from genetic effects. If the gains of these offspring averaged only 2 lb. a day, this would show that all the variations in rate of gain were the result of environmental influences. Perhaps offspring averaging 2.35 lb. a day were produced, and although we had reached for an increase of a ½ lb. (2.5 − 2.0 = 0.5) increase in gain when we selected these animals, by breeding test it was found that we actually got 0.35 lb. increase in gain (2.35 − 2.0 = 0.35). If the increase we obtained in the offspring is divided by the increase we reached for in their parents (0.35 ÷ 0.50 = 0.70), we get 0.70. If this is multiplied by 100, we get 70 per cent. It is apparent that we got 70 per cent of what we reached for in our selection. We can say, then, that rate of gain is 70 per cent heritable.

There are other methods of computing heritability, but the main point at present is to understand that characters which are low in heritability (0 to 20 per cent) will not be improved very rapidly by phenotypic selection. Characteristics that are high in heritability (50 to 100 per cent) can be improved quite rapidly by selection. What is needed is a method for determining the genotype of individuals so that genotypic selection can be made. Some methods for this purpose are available, but they have certain limitations, which will be given later.

INBREEDING

It has been shown that inbreeding has the general effect of producing homozygosity. The more the animals become homozygous, the less effective selection can be. In pure lines of plants where self-fertilization is the method of reproduction, selection is relatively ineffective. If an organism were completely homozygous, selection would have no effect whatever. The reason is that there could be no genetic variation. All the variation would be environmental and selection of environmental variations would be completely ineffective.

Inbreeding has another detrimental effect on progress made by selection, in addition to the fact that more homozygosity lessens the effectiveness of selection. An animal may become homozygous for one or more undesirable recessive genes which are epistatic to many of or all the desirable genes. Such a situation would result in an animal that is quite undesirable and would naturally be culled. However, it is possible that such an animal may possess many more desirable genes than the best performing animal in the herd, but that these are indeterminable, and therefore cause the discard of much good genetic material through selection.

It is unfortunate that inbreeding may be necessary in a selection program for our farm animals. It may not be possible for a breeder to go to another herd or flock for breeding stock because no records may have been kept in other herds or flocks which will permit wise selections. Also, he may find that he has his herd or flock at a level which is higher than the level of other herds or flocks from which breeding stock might be obtained. The only way in which inbreeding can be kept low, so that little homozygosity is being produced, is to operate a selection program with a large herd or flock in which several males can be used.

FOUNDATION ANIMALS

Selection will not create new genes nor cause genes to mutate. If the foundation animals with which a breeder starts are homozygous for certain undesirable traits or for some undesirable epistatic genes, no amount of selection can bring about improvement for these traits. For that reason, line crosses, strain crosses, or breed crosses make excellent foundation stock with which to establish a herd.

The frequency of desirable or undesirable genes within the foundation herd is important. Desirable recessive genes in low frequency will be very difficult to obtain rapidly in greater frequency. Desirable dominant genes in low frequency will increase much more rapidly by selection. Undesirable dominant genes in low frequency may be eliminated rapidly with relative ease by culling. Undesirable recessive genes in low frequency are not rapidly eliminated by culling.

LEVEL OF PERFORMANCE

It was shown previously that if one starts with a herd that is not at a high level of performance, rapid progress can be made by use of good males. The same applies in a selection program within a herd or flock. Marked progress is made in the initial phases of the improvement program, but eventually progress may slow down rather markedly. There are two reasons for this: (1) The possibility of locating breeding animals much superior to the average is great at the beginning of improvement but lessens as one approaches a high performance level. (2) Homozygosity, at least for the desirable recessives, is soon reached, and this homozygosity prevents further change in the frequency of those genes.

A breeder would not be alarmed if he were not able to get the closed herd or flock on a high level of performance before improvement slowed down. Sometimes the selection is not very effective in a closed herd because one or a few undesirable recessive, epistatic genes prevent the other genes from full expression.

SIZE OF HERD OR FLOCK

Let us take an unlikely condition in which one has a herd of one male and one female. Any kind of unproductive condition such as sterility would end the herd. It would be less likely for this kind of condition to prevent selection if one had a herd of one male and ten females, but in this case another type of limitation is imposed upon selection in that the possibility for genetic segregation is very restricted.

In a one-sire herd or flock, an error in selection of the male will affect the entire herd. In a large herd in which several males are used, it is unlikely that errors would be made in the selection of all the males. Also, in a large herd or flock great genetic diversity would occur. Thus, possibilities for genetic improvement through selection are markedly higher in larger herds. This does not mean that small operators have a hopeless situation. If breeding stock is obtained from a breeder who practices rigid selection on a sound basis, great improvement can be made in small herds.

EXERCISES

1. What effect does overdominance have on progress made by selection? Explain fully.

2. List 4 factors not included in the first question that might affect progress made in selection and explain how each factor will influence progress.

3. From a practical farmer's standpoint which of the factors influencing progress of selection will be most important? Why?

13

IMPORTANT CHARACTERS OF FARM ANIMALS FOR SELECTION

Since the inclusion of many characteristics in a selection program results in little progress in any one of them, the suggestion is made that only the most important characteristics should be given consideration. The important things to consider in a selection program may vary with areas of production and with the objectives of the farm enterprises. For example, survival may be one of the important characteristics under a rigorous environment, whereas maximum rate of production may become more important where adequate feed conditions prevail. If a breeder is in an area of grassland farming, the production of feeder animals may be his objective. However, the way his animals do in the feedlot will determine the number of customers who return to purchase feeder animals.

The discussion of traits to consider in a selection program must be general. Since it differs from one class of animals to the next, beef cattle, sheep, hogs, and rabbits will be considered separately. The reader is referred to such works as Jull (1952), Lerner (1950), and Warren (1953) on poultry, and Gilmore (1952) on dairy cattle breeding, since these publications give excellent coverage of the important traits to be considered in these animals.

BEEF CATTLE

The objective in beef cattle production is to produce meat, but the greatest over-all efficiency may be reached where the maximum use of roughage is made. An improvement program should be aimed at a high rate and economy of production of a desirable meat product. Six major characteristics contribute to this aim.

Fertility

The word *fertility* is used in a broad sense to mean an animal's ability to produce normal, healthy young that are capable of surviving. Fertility is only

183

moderately heritable, but the level of fertility in the herd affects the possibilities for selection of other traits. The economic importance of fertility is illustrated in the following example:

A breeder ran bulls with his cows all year as a general practice. During a three-year period, one cow produced three calves while a second cow produced only two calves. It is apparent that the calves from the latter cow must sell for 1.5 times the offspring by the first cow in order for the two cows to be equally profitable. This would be quite unlikely. Unfortunately, a breeder may fail to recognize the importance of this difference in fertility and may keep a son from the cow that is of lower fertility because it is a slightly better calf otherwise.

Early calves are generally very important. The results at the Oregon station show that earlier calves gain more rapidly while nursing their dams than do later ones. Also, a calf crop which is uniform in age is important. If the breeding season is limited to not more than 90 days, a great deal can be done to have a calf crop fairly uniform in age. Also, this will contribute to increased fertility of the herd because those cows that fail to settle in the 90-day breeding season can be promptly marketed for beef.

Upon initiation of a program of culling for low fertility, one may seem to market some good cows, but generally any nice-looking cows which are among those culled will prove to have been "boarders."

It is more practical to sell the nonpregnant cow in the fall rather than to keep her till spring only to learn that she is not pregnant. One can determine whether a cow is pregnant by rectal palpation at 60 to 90 days after the last service. However, the accuracy of pregnancy diagnosis depends upon the skill and experience of the operator. It may pay to obtain the service of a trained person who can palpate the cow herd in the fall because at present there are no chemical or biological analyses of blood or urine which are satisfactory pregnancy tests for cattle. If this examination shows any cows to be nonpregnant, they can then be sent directly to slaughter.

Some owners prefer to breed for a longer season so that a larger calf crop can be produced, after which all the late-calving cows and their calves are marketed. This method is satisfactory if the breeder adheres to a rigid culling program.

All the discussion on fertility is based on the assumption that conditions will permit a cow to raise a calf every year. One may find it necessary to make adjustments if the conditions are so severe that a cow cannot raise a calf each year without depleting her to such an extent that she may not survive. Range improvement and supplemental feeds should be considered if this situation exists. Control of diseases, such as Bang's abortion, is necessary for putting into effect a rigid selection program directed toward greater fertility. Culling the nonpregnant cows in the fall may also help to control certain diseases, such as Leptospirosis, by removing diseased animals which might otherwise serve to spread the disease.

In summary, a breeder wants his cows to come back into heat soon enough after calving so that an early calf can be produced. The cow should settle readily and carry the calf through to normal development. Late-calving and open cows should be culled. It has been indicated in many herds that late- or early-calving patterns are inherent characteristics. Late-calving cows will usually establish a late-calving pattern even after skipping a year, which should have permitted them to calve early if a period of rest were needed to restore depleted reserves.

Suckling Ability

The *weight* of a calf at weaning is a combination of date of birth, milk production of its dam, and its genetic capacity for growth. If the weights of all the calves are adjusted to a common-age basis, as has been suggested by various workers, the effect of age of the calf at weaning can be eliminated. Most of the variation in weaning weight corrected for age will reflect differences in milking ability of the cows. A simple method for comparing the growth of calves during the suckling period is to subtract birth weight from weaning weight and divide this difference by the age of the calf at weaning (in days). This gives the daily gain during the suckling period.

$$\frac{\text{Weaning weight of calf} - \text{birth weight of calf}}{\text{Age of calf at weaning in days}} = \frac{\text{daily gain during}}{\text{suckling period}}$$

A calf that weighs 430 lb. at weaning at 200 days of age, and which weighed 70 lb. at birth, would have gained

$$\frac{430 - 70}{200} = \frac{360}{200} = 1.80 \text{ lb. per day}$$

Since gains of calves during the suckling period are largely due to milk production of the dams, one would consider culling the cow and her calves when low-gaining calves are produced. However, suckling gains will vary from year to year because the feed supply of the cows will greatly influence their milk production. A breeder should not cull all calves because of low gains made during a severe year, nor should he keep all calves because of good gains due to lush pasture conditions during a more favorable year. It is best to compare cows given similar opportunities within a given year.

Gains during the suckling period will vary with sex and with age of dam. Two-year-old cows cannot be expected to produce the milk flow that they will with more maturity. One may want to adjust the gains of calves for differences in age of dams so that calves from young cows will not be discriminated against, or one may want to keep the best-gaining calves from cows of each age group. This means that young cows would be compared with other young cows in making the selections. Bull calves will gain more rapidly than heifer calves. This becomes more evident when conditions are such that all calves can make good gains. Under severe range conditions the sex difference may become less marked. Since bull calves gain more rapidly, one should either adjust all gains to a basis of one of the sexes or compare bull calves only with other bull calves. Similarly, heifer calves should be compared only with other heifer calves. The simplest method is to add the difference between the means of the two sexes within the herd to the weaning weight of the heifers.

In order to appraise the milking ability of a beef cow, it is essential that only the dam of the calf provide the milk for the calf. When nurse cows are used to raise beef calves, the selection pressure is completely removed as far as milking ability of the cow is concerned. If nurse cows are extensively relied upon, a herd could be developed in which cows lack the ability to provide sufficient milk for their own calves.

A bull selected from such a herd for use in a commercial herd will tend to transmit low milk-production to his daughters. The rancher cannot provide a string of dairy cows for raising his beef calves. When he gets a cow herd that gives insufficient milk for the calves, low weaning weight of calves is the result. When he brings in little "dogies" and undernourished calves weaning at 250 to 300 lb., it means dollars that will never be received, and this means that the rancher will not go back to that breeder for any more bulls.

The use of nurse cows cannot be condemned too severely, for there has never been a practice which has done more harm to the commercial beef cattle industry. How intelligent purebred breeders can adopt such a system of production is beyond comprehension. One unfortunate result of purebred bulls siring heifers which cannot give milk enough to raise a good calf is that many commercial producers are saving grade bulls from the commercial herd and feel that they are producing more pounds of beef as a result. This is not as it should be. Our purebred herds and flocks should be improved to the point that commercial producers can afford to use only purebred males. If this is to be realized, then purebred breeders must set their goals in line with the requirements of a commercial producer. It should be pointed out that a close working relationship between the purebred and commercial breeders contributes to the success of both. In general, each group of breeders is dependent upon the other.

Post-weaning gains

If calves are fed *ad libitum* from weaning until the next grazing season, those which gain the most rapidly are the ones which generally have the inheritance for rapid gains. This characteristic is measured by gains per day during the feeding period. If one subtracts the weaning weight from the weight at the end of the feeding period and divides this difference by the age of the calf at the end of the feeding period, minus the age at weaning, the value obtained is the gain per day.

$$\frac{\text{Weight at end of feeding period} - \text{weaning weight}}{\text{Age at end of feeding period} - \text{weaning age}} = \frac{\text{gain per day during}}{\text{the feeding period}}$$

The calf that weighed 430 lb. at weaning when 200 days of age, and weighed 790 lb. at 360 days of age when the feeding period ended, would have gained

$$\frac{790 - 430}{360 - 200} = \frac{360}{160} = 2.25 \text{ lb.}$$

per day during the feeding period.

Rate of gain under standard feed conditions is largely due to an animal's genetic constitution; therefore, progress can be made by selecting for more rapidly gaining calves. This is important to the producer because more rapidly gaining calves will weigh more and bring in a greater return at the same ages than the slower gaining calves. If one were feeding to a given weight, fast-gaining calves could be marketed sooner than the slower gaining ones.

It may be possible that a producer finds it more desirable to rough the calves through the first winter on pasture and hay and depend upon the lush pasture season during the summer for putting on the rapid gains. Under this system of production, one would want to calculate the gains made on pasture as well as those made during the winter.

$$\frac{\text{Weight at end of summer grazing} - \text{weight at beginning}}{\text{Age at end of summer grazing} - \text{age at beginning}} = \frac{\text{gain per day on}}{\text{summer grazing}}$$

If a 600-lb. calf at 360 days of age reached 990 lb. at the end of the grazing season, at which time it was 510 days of age, its gain would be

$$\frac{990 - 600}{510 - 360} = \frac{390}{150} = 2.6 \text{ lb.}$$

per day during the grazing season.

Feed Efficiency

The ability of a beef animal to convert feed, primarily roughage, into gains is important because about 80 per cent of the cost of producing beef cattle is the cost of feed. Since the ability of an animal to convert feed into gains is also under genetic control, selection for greater feed efficiency will result in herd improvement for this important characteristic.

If one feeds the animals during the first winter, it would be possible to construct a manger set-up so that feed could be weighed to each calf individually (Fig. 113). If the pounds of feed eaten by a calf during the feeding period are

Fig. 113. Stall arrangement for individual feeding of beef cattle. The animal is tied for 3 to 4 hours twice daily while eating. Water is available in drinking fountains between each two calves. Calves are turned loose at all other times and run in groups of six. *(Courtesy Oregon State College.)*

divided by the gains made during this same period, the amount of feed required per unit of gain is obtained. This can be expressed as gain per unit of feed or feed per unit of gain. Suppose a calf ate 1,320 lb. of feed and gained 300 lb. The feed per 100-lb. gain is 1320/300 × 100 = 400 lb.

Three methods of feeding calves have been used to obtain data on efficiency of converting feed into gains. The first is to feed from one date to another date. This method has the convenience of putting all calves on test at one time and of ending the test on all calves at one time. Its disadvantage is that calves will vary in age and weight at the beginning and at the end of the test period. This may not be so important in gains, since the calves may gain about the same rate during all these weight ranges. Larger calves may have a small advantage in rate of gain over smaller ones. The primary objection to this method is found in feed efficiency. Slower-gaining calves will be given a decided advantage, and faster-gaining calves will be given a decided disadvantage in feed efficiency. Since the more rapidly gaining calves when fed over a constant time will become larger than the slower gaining calves, the comparison will be made of calves of different sizes. Feed efficiency decreases as weight increases (Fig. 114), and therefore, this comparison would make a

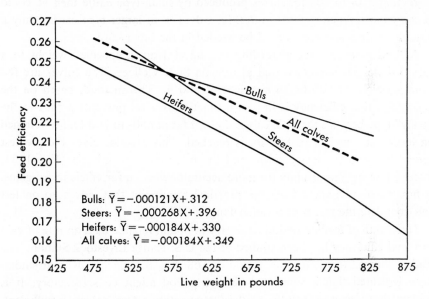

Fig. 114. The relation of feed efficiency to live weight in beef cattle. Efficiency decreases as weight of animal increases. *(Courtesy Oregon State College.)*

more rapidly gaining calf appear less efficient under a constant-time program of feeding than it actually would be. Moreover, this method has a tendency to blot out real differences between calves because a faster gaining calf, due to the greater size he reaches, becomes less efficient. The slower gaining calf, because of his smaller size, is more efficient.

A second method is to feed each calf to a given grade, starting all calves at the same time. This method has the advantage of one factor being constant (grade) but it has some disadvantages because it takes a well-trained person to determine when a calf reaches a certain grade. It means that calves are taken off the test at various times, but this is a disadvantage only from a management standpoint. The greatest fault of this method is that it places a premium on the calf that fattens at the smallest weight. A calf of the smaller type will fatten at lighter weights than the larger type of calf, and therefore the smaller type of calf will finish the feed test at a lighter weight than the larger type of calf. Calves are more efficient at lighter weights than they are at heavier weights, so that by taking out the smaller type of calves at the lighter weights, a decided advantage in feed efficiency is given to them. If this method is used in a selection program, it will have a tendency to give a selective advantage to cattle of small type. However, many of the costs of production of beef cattle are fixed costs. A rancher's returns would be materially less from marketing 650- to 700-lb. calves produced by small-type cattle than he could obtain from marketing 800- to 900-lb. calves from larger-type cattle. Only a little more time and feed would be needed in the latter case.

A third method, that of feeding the calves from a specified weight to a specified weight, has been used at Oregon State College. The calves are fed from a weight of 500 lb. to a weight of 800 lb. This method, based on the knowledge that efficiency is in part a function of size, prevents a shift to the "pony" type because the little calves that get fat at 650- to 700-lb. are retained on test until a weight of 800 lb. is reached. This practice gives the greatest spread between the less efficient and the more efficient animals (Fig. 115), thereby offering opportunity for more accurate selection for efficiency of gains. It has the disadvantage from the practical standpoint that calves go on test and complete the test over a rather long period.

The length of feeding period necessary to obtain reliable data on rate of gain and feed efficiency has been studied at the U.S. Range Livestock Station. The studies showed that a feeding period of 168 days is sufficient. Recent studies have indicated that a somewhat shorter period might be satisfactory. It is evident that a gain of 300 lb., as the Oregon station tests calves, is sufficient. Calves vary in body weight from day to day due to differences in fill. A feed-test period of sufficient length or with sufficient gain to minimize errors due to fill is important.

One factor that may help to cut down error is to feed regularly and to weigh at the same time of day. It can be seen that a period of 28 days may give apparent tremendous gains. Suppose a calf had just urinated and defecated but had not drunk any water just before the initial weight was taken. If this same calf had just filled with water when the next weight was taken, a difference of 25 lb. could have been obtained. Over a short period, for example a 28-day period, this would be about a pound a day.

The period of adjustment necessary after weaning before the feed test begins depends on how much the cattle have been handled. At the Oregon station where calves are weighed each week, one finds that a two-week period of adjustment at weaning is sufficient. Calves coming off the range might need a month to six weeks to become adjusted to handling and to get used to dry feed.

Live Animal Merit

Since we cannot make carcasses out of animals and then use those which have the most desirable carcasses for breeding, it is necessary to estimate carcass merit from the live animal. This is done by placing a score on the animal according to estimated carcass value.

Since carcass appraisal is the real objective of scoring animals, it is evident that a score has its greatest value if the scoring is done at the time in the animal's life when it would normally be marketed for beef. Many people score animals at other times but scores on small animals have little relation to what the carcass will be like when the animal becomes larger and is slaughtered. Scores on adult animals appear rather illogical because a score at time of slaughter on the offspring of these adult animals would be of more value in appraising the adult animals.

The score of an animal is influenced by its fatness. The kind of animal that has been scored immediately before viewing another kind of animal may also influence the score. It is very difficult to keep from overscoring an average animal if it is viewed immediately after scoring an inferior animal. It is also difficult not to score an average animal too low if it is viewed immediately after scoring a superior one. If the estimator judges the areas of valuable meat cuts and lets these play an important part in appraising the worth of a meat animal, the score will have considerable merit. If the scoring is done at the time in the animal's life when it normally would be made into a carcass, the appearance of the animal after that may be ignored. Good producing adults cannot always maintain a beautiful appearance and should not be discriminated against.

Freedom from Inherited Defects

Defects that will interfere with the well being of the animal should be eliminated, but genetic abnormalities of this type cannot be eliminated from a herd simply by getting rid of the affected animal. Since the sire and dam of such an animal must carry the inheritance for such conditions, some of the sibs and half-sibs of the affected animal are likely also to have the gene for this abnormality and should also be eliminated. These genetic abnormalities include such defects as blindness, dwarfism, jaw distortions which interfere with eating,

Fig. 115. Feed required to make 300-lb. gain on a good-doing (left) and a poor-doing (right) bull. Note that appearance does not indicate which animal is more efficient. *(Courtesy Oregon State College.)*

udder or teat deformities which interfere with milk production, and crippled conditions. Abnormalities that do not interfere with the well being of the animal, such as wry tail and asymmetric heads, may not be desired but should not be culled with the same intensity as the more serious defects.

It will be noted that no mention has been made of color markings, horn shape, etc. These factors have been given a great deal of consideration by purebred breeders of certain breeds, but they are not related to meat production, with the exception of certain colors which permit the animals to adapt themselves better to certain conditions. In general, emphasis should be given to characteristics concerned with rate and economy of production and to quality of product being raised.

SHEEP

There are two systems of sheep production. In one the object is to market fat lambs off the ewes that are running on pasture. This is the farm-flock type of system, in which fertility and suckling ability of the ewes, and growth rate, fattening ability, and mutton conformation of the lambs are very important. Wool is secondary with farm-flock sheep because only about 15 per cent of the income is from wool, with the other 85 per cent of the income being derived from the sale of fat lambs. In the range-flock system wool is of greater importance because 35 per cent of the income is derived from the sale of wool and 65 per cent from the sale of feeder lambs.

One purebred Hampshire breeder has set as his goal the production of 200 lb. of lamb per ewe each year. He has several ewes in his flock that have done this well or better over a three- or four-year production period. For a ewe to produce 200 lb. of lamb per year, she must produce twins and supply them with plenty of milk. The lambs must have the inherited capacity to grow rapidly and must be born early so that the desired weight can be reached before the grass dries up in July.

Farm flock sheep will be discussed first.

Fertility

A ewe should lamb every year. The lamb crop should be early and uniform in age, and there should be a large percentage of twins. No farm flock is completely successful when the lamb crop is less than 150 per cent.

Late lambing is a tendency which is quite undesirable because, before the lamb can be marketed, the grass will dry up and internal parasites will increasingly become a problem. This will result in a small, out-of-condition lamb which will sell at a disadvantage for slaughter purposes. If the lamb is fed after weaning to increase its condition, the seasonal price decline in fat lambs (which generally occurs) will be enough to offset the increase in selling price resulting from better condition. The object then is to get all lambs early enough so that they can become fat while nursing ewes that are on the early lush pastures. Uniformity in lambing date is helpful in shortening the lambing season because constant attention day and night is necessary only for a short period of time. In one flock lacking this uniformity, there were lambs weighing 90 lb. at the same time that other lambs were coming. This meant an extended lambing season during which constant attention had to be given. It also meant that fat lambs in small lots were ready for market over a long period.

The most effective method for assuring a short lambing season is to limit the breeding season to a 40-day period. All ewes that have not been bred during this period are then sent to market for slaughter. If this breeding season is early, it will also eliminate late-lambing ewes. When this method is used as a selection basis, at first there will be a high number of ewes leaving the flock, but soon a flock of uniformly early-lambing ewes will be established, after which only a few ewes will need to be culled each year because of weakness in this respect.

Milking Ability of Ewes and Growing Capacity of Lambs

Ewes must give an abundant supply of milk for lambs to make fast gains. The lambs must also have the ability to grow fast and to get fat. Since it is quite difficult to separate the influence due to the mothers' milk supply from the lamb's ability to do well, it is best to consider weight-for-age and condition score as measures of both the ewe's milking ability and the lamb's growing and fattening capacity.

A good practice is to weigh and go over the lambs about every week or ten days, locating the lambs that are large enough and fat enough to make good market lambs. They may be scored at this time and the weights recorded, and they may be marketed or retained for replacements. February lambs that have not reached a marketable weight or finish by July 1 may as well be weaned. The ewes that produce such lambs, as well as the lambs, should be sent to market because neither the lambs nor their dams have a place in a breeding flock. Lambs that are heavy and fat in May, and their dams, should be the first ones selected to stay in the breeding flock. If a ewe is doing a good job, her February lambs should weigh 80 to 90 lb. and grade choice or prime by June 1.

Twin lambs will not gain so rapidly or be so fat as singles on the average. The results at the Oregon station indicated a 15- to 20-lb. advantage of single over twin lambs at weaning time. A correction factor for weight and condition score should be developed so that twins will not be discriminated against when weight and condition are considered in a selection program. This must be done in each flock, since a correction factor developed from one flock may not be applicable to a different flock. A simple method is to determine the average gain of singles and twins, and add to the gains of the twins a factor equal to the difference in gains of the two kinds of lambs. Suppose the singles average 0.7 lb. gain per day and twins average 0.6 lb. per day. If twins that were quite good had each gained 0.75 lb. per day, one would add 0.1 lb., making their adjusted gain 0.85 lb. per day. These twins would be compared with singles in making selections. A similar correction could be made in scoring for condition, using the average score for twins and singles and adjusting the twins to a basis of singles. Calculation of gain per day can be determined in the same manner described in the section on beef cattle.

Conformation

Mutton conformation is important in determining the carcass value of the fat lamb. Lambs should be blocky, straight over the top with great width of back, loin, and rump, have a long, level rump, and be full and plump in the leg. Use of a score card for evaluating conformation may help a great deal.

Wool

Although wool is of minor importance in farm-flock (mutton) sheep, the amount and quality of the wool produced should be considered. The quantity of wool is best measured by weight of clean fleece, and its quality may be graded in the fleece or on the sheep. It is generally better to consider the amount of growth and quality of the wool on the lamb in deciding which rams and ewes shall be retained and which shall go to market. Weight and grade of the fleece should not count more than one-fifth that of weight, grade, and conformation of the fat lambs.

Freedom from Inherited Defects

Blindness, undershot and overshot jaws, dwarfism, cryptorchidism, hernia, and such abnormalities are serious. Not only the lambs that are so affected should be culled, but also the sire and dam. Also, one must consider that some of the sibs and half-sibs to such affected lambs may inherit the abnormality. Judgment must be exercised in doing the culling. Slight undershot or overshot conditions should be selected against but are not sufficiently detrimental to justify culling an entire line of breeding which is superior in other respects.

Wool blindness interferes with a sheep's ability to graze and to avoid hazards. An effort should be made to develop an open-faced flock. The studies at the U.S. Sheep Breeding Laboratory have shown that wool-blind ewes, on the average, wean lambs which are 11 lb. lighter than those produced by open-faced ewes. The studies at this station show clearly that the open-faced condition can be developed through selection.

Black-faced sheep may be prone to "bare-bellies" or black fibers in the wool. The former reduces wool production, while the latter reduces the value of the wool. Some consideration should be given these undesirable traits. However, one must keep in mind that large fat lambs are much more important than the wool, and that culling a high-producing ewe because of some black fibers in her wool may not be justified.

Range sheep selection is practically the same as that for farm flocks. The major differences are that wool production, wool quality, and ability to withstand adverse conditions are more important in range sheep. Methods are now available for rapidly estimating the weight and grade of clean fleece. These characteristics, along with length of fiber, are among the most important factors in determining the value of wool produced. When selection for production traits is practiced successfully under range conditions, the results indicate that the producer has automatically selected as well for the flock's ability to withstand adverse conditions.

SWINE

Sow productivity and rate and efficiency of gains are the most important characteristics in hog production. Price differential for superior conformation has generally been small. At present there is a tendency toward a demand for more lean and less fat. Since this appears to be biologically as well as economically sound, a producer may well consider raising the leaner type of hog.

Fertility, mothering ability, rate of gain, feed efficiency, carcass merit and freedom from defects are the important characteristics to consider in swine selection.

Fertility

The ability of a sow to come into heat as soon as a litter is weaned and to settle at the first service is not sufficient in itself. She must farrow a large litter of strong pigs. Good sows should farrow at least ten strong pigs. It has been shown by work at the Missouri station that very small pigs at birth have little chance of surviving and that those that live are usually runts. About 85 per cent of the pigs under 2 lb. in birth weight died before weaning.

It goes without saying that a sow will not raise more pigs than she farrows unless other pigs from another litter are transferred to her for nursing. A sow must farrow a large litter of strong pigs because improvement in all other traits is dependent upon the number from which selections can be made. A good practice is to retain more sows and gilts than are to be kept. Gilts, and sows without other strong points, that do not settle on the first service should go to market. If all settle at first service, one may keep the best ones or those which came into heat first and sell the excess sows and gilts to other breeders or for slaughter.

Mothering Ability

A sow must produce a heavy flow of milk for the pigs because they are entirely dependent upon her for their food for the first three weeks of their lives. She must be a good mother in other respects, being careful not to trample the pigs or to lie on them and willing to claim the pigs at birth. An outstanding gilt may be given another chance if she does not raise a litter, but generally this nonproductiveness is inexcusable and should be cause for sending the animal to slaughter.

If there are generally low weaning weights, if there are many runt pigs, or if several pigs in the litter are lost, the sow should be considered for culling and all her pigs should be marketed for slaughter. Replacement pigs should be kept only from litters in which uniformly large pigs are produced.

Inverted nipples will not function, and mastitis interferes with milk production. No pigs should be saved from sows that are affected with inverted nipples (Fig. 68) or mastitis (Fig. 69). Inverted nipples are inherited and the tendency to develop mastitis appears also to be inherited. It is wise to examine the nipples on both the gilt and boar pigs which are under consideration for replacements. Inverted nipples will usually show at this time and can be used as a criterion in selection. The number and placement of teats is also important. A sow should have 12 well-spaced teats in order to "set a proper table" for a hungry litter of pigs (Fig. 116).

Good pigs should weigh at least 35 lb. each at a weaning age of eight weeks, and the size of the pigs at weaning should be uniform. A replacement pig that weighs 40 lb. at weaning and which is out of a very uniform litter may be a better prospect than one that weighs 50 lb. at weaning and which is out of a litter where some runts are produced. The Missouri station has shown that feed costs of maintaining the sow and producing the litter up to weaning plays a big part in cost of production of pigs. Feed costs per 100 lb. of pork produced from good producing sows in which 10 growthy pigs were raised was 341 lb., as contrasted with 571 lb. of feed per 100 lb. of live hog marketed from inferior sows raising only four pigs per litter, (Table 8).* Pigs are generally weaned at eight weeks of age (56 days), and no correction for size at weaning is necessary because all can be compared for size at the same age. Corrections may need to be made for differences between years or seasons or even for differences between farrowing dates within a season if farrowing extends over a period of two or three months.

* From Weaver and Bogart, Missouri Agri. Exp. Sta. Bul. 461.

UNANIMOUS HOPE 1417602 PR 1047
Dam of World's First Certified Litter
1954 All-American Aged Sow

An 8-star PR Sow: These eight litters averaged 12.37 pigs farrowed and 9.37 pigs raised to a 56-day litter weight of 480.84 lb.

Fig. 116. Hampshire sow showing an outstanding udder. Compare the udder on this sow with udders shown in Figs. 68 and 69. Sows with a record such as this contribute to herd improvement. *(Courtesy Hampshire Swine Registry.)*

Table 8. THE AMOUNT OF PORK MARKETED AND THE FEED COST OF PRODUCTION FOR SOWS OF INFERIOR, MEDIUM, AND GOOD PRODUCTIVITY.

Kind of Sow	No. Pigs	Weight at Weaning, lb.	Weight 6 Months of Age, lb.	Up to Weaning,* lb.	Feed Consumed Fattening Period,† lb.	Total	Feed per 100 lb. of hog marketed, lb.
Good		Litter 320	2,595	1,950	6,911	8,861	341
Producer	10	Per pig 32	259	195	691	886	
Medium		Litter 186	1,314	1,830	4,061	5,891	448
Producer	7	Per pig 27	188	261	580	841	
Inferior		Litter 116	666	1,710	2,090	3,800	571
Producer	4	Per pig 29	167	428	523	951	

* Feed of sow from breeding and sow and litter to time pigs weaned. All animals fed on clean pasture. No allowance has been made for pasture or for gain or loss in weight of sows.
† Pigs self-fed on legume pasture.

Growth Rate

Rapidly growing pigs require less feed per unit of gain, investments are involved for a shorter period of time, and the same facilities can be used for spring and fall pigs if the pigs reach a marketable size of 200 to 210 lb. at five to six months of age. Since pigs are marketed or taken from self-feeders and put into the breeding herd when they reach a given weight (generally 200 to 210 lb.), a breeder may want to adjust the weights of pigs to a common age so that they may be compared directly when selections are being made. There are two ways of doing this: (1) by calculating the gain per day for each pig or (2) by calculating the weight of each pig at a given age. Calculation of gain per day can be done roughly by dividing the weight by the age in days. One method of calculating the weight of all pigs to a 154-day basis is by use of the following equation:

$$\text{154-day weight} = \frac{\text{actual weight} \times 94}{\text{actual age} - 60}$$

It is important to consider uniformity in growth rate as well as to select the larger pigs from the litter. A pig weighing 225 lb. at six months out of a litter in which all are large is a better prospect than a 240-lb. pig out of a litter in which some pigs may weigh only 150 lb. at six months of age.

Feed Efficiency

Pigs are not generally fed individually, but each litter is fed separately. Replacement pigs are selected from the litters having the best record for converting feed into gains. One should keep in mind that feed constitutes one of the major costs in swine production. Therefore, efficiency of conversion of feed into gains is extremely important. Feed efficiency and rate of gain are closely correlated. If one cannot obtain a record of feed efficiency, selection for increased rate of gain will bring about improvement in feed efficiency in a swine herd.

If all pigs are fed to a constant weight of 200 lb., feed efficiency in one litter is comparable with that in another. One must take care not to compare the efficiency of one litter carried to a weight of 240 lb. with another fed to a weight of only 180 lb. because efficiency goes down as the pigs become heavier. This change may be greater than the difference between litters and could cause a producer to keep the less efficient pigs.

Conformation

It has already been stated that spread in price of hogs has not been large. This means that farmers have not realized the economic advantage from better conformation in hogs which is allowed in sheep and beef cattle. Nevertheless, one should keep an ideal lean-type hog in mind and should use a scoring system to appraise the live hogs. This score can be used in selecting breeding animals. Also, some pigs in the litter can be slaughtered and the carcasses from them appraised. This appraisal can be used in selecting or discarding litter mates of the ones which were slaughtered. Since more lean and less fat is desired in swine carcasses, one may wish to measure the backfat thickness and select against excessive fatness. The lean meter may be used for this backfat measurement in the live hog. One may measure backfat thickness directly by inserting a small metal ruler through an incision until it reaches the lean region.

Freedom from Inherited Defects

Such abnormalities as "goose-stepping," cryptorchidism, hernia, hemophilia, and atresia ani are all very objectionable. The sire and dam of such affected pigs should be culled. In addition, some of the sibs and half-sibs to affected animals are likely to inherit the weakness. Therefore, it may be wise to discard an entire strain or family in which such weaknesses are prevalent.

RABBITS

Rabbits are generally marketed as fryers directly from the doe because little bunnies that are weaned and put onto feed make small gains for about two weeks after weaning. A good doe should raise eight young, each weighing 4.5 lb. at eight weeks of age. The bunnies should be fat and of a good meat type. This means that a good doe during a year should produce at least 108 lb. of marketable fryers. Important characteristics in rabbits are fertility, growth and fattening of the young, conformation, and freedom from inherited defects. The second characteristic is the result of good milking ability of the doe and growth capacity of the young.

Fertility

A good doe should settle at the first service and should deliver a large litter of strong bunnies. A litter of eight is considered desirable, but some exceptional does will produce and raise more than eight good bunnies. Certainly, fewer than six in the litter, or failure to settle, are causes for culling a doe. Unless a doe settles when bred the first time after a litter is weaned, she may not be able to produce the three litters per year which is necessary for profitable rabbit production. Rabbits either become pregnant or pseudo-pregnant (a false pregnancy in which the doe undergoes changes without bearing young) when bred; therefore a doe that does not become pregnant requires about 17 days before she can be bred again, a period during which she must be fed although she produces nothing in return.

Rabbits do not have a definite heat period but come into a stage during which they can be mated. They do not ovulate without mating. In case a rabbit does not accept the male, she may be force-mated in order to get her bred.

Size and Condition of Bunnies at Eight Weeks of Age

The young should grow rapidly and become fat. They should reach a weight of 4 to 5 lb. at eight weeks of age and be fat enough to make excellent fryers. Does, as well as the young from a litter, should be culled when they produce undersized and out-of-condition bunnies. Runts, if marked, should be also considered when culling the doe and litter. Generally, if the young have sufficient milk to reach 4 to 5 lb. at eight weeks of age, they will be fat enough to make excellent fryers.

Conformation

A desirable butcher rabbit should be well developed over the back, loin, hips, and in the leg. One can develop a score for appraising conformation which can be used in selecting breeding stock.

Freedom from Inherited Defects

Such abnormal conditions as "buck" and crooked teeth, blindness, crooked legs, hernia, and "flop" ears are very serious because they interfere with the well-being of the rabbits. The sire and dam of affected young as well as the entire litter should be culled. Also, half-sibs to the affected animals may inherit the weakness and should be considered for culling.

EXERCISES

1. Discuss the most important characteristics for which one should select breeding (a) cattle, (b) hogs, (c) sheep, (d) rabbits.

2. How do you measure each important characteristic for which you want to select?

3. Why do you consider the traits you listed in answering Exercise 1 as being the most important?

4. Since one can provide nurse cows for raising beef calves, why is it important to select for suckling ability of beef cattle?

14

USEFUL AIDS IN SELECTION

In the past, selection in farm animals has been based largely upon appearance, but this practice may not be effective when selecting for certain traits. It seems appropriate to discuss the bases or tools used in selection and to point out the advantages of each as well as the weaknesses of each.

APPEARANCE

Eye appraisals of animals can be used as a means of estimating the kind of carcass an animal will make. It can also reveal any physical defect, abnormality or illness. It is not possible to determine level of fertility, rate of gain, and efficiency by looking at an animal.

Since appearance is most useful in estimating the carcass merit of an animal, this appraisal should be made at the time in life when the animal normally would be made into a carcass. Appearance of adult animals or very young animals may not be a good guide to the carcass merit of the animal. It appears, then, that this tool should be used only for what it is worth and at the time when it has value. One should not assume that he can select only on the basis of the appearance of the animal and thereby obtain a fast-gaining, economical producer. Then why concern ourselves with the appearance of adult animals which have offspring on the farm? The kind of young they have produced is much more important than how the adult animals look.

An example of how one may be fooled by appearance is found in swine. If a judge sees a group of sows which have recently weaned large litters of well-fed pigs, he would likely criticize these sows for being "slab-sided," "cat-hammed," and "fish-backed," because they would be suckled down to a condition which permits all weaknesses in conformation to show. A group of fat, unproductive sows viewed by the same judge would be commended for their width down the backs, plump hams, etc. (Fig. 117). The fat they carry, since they have not

203

Fig. 117. Berkshire sows. The normal color for Berkshires and Poland China hogs is black, with six white points: the snout, tail, and four feet. The sow on the left raised 53 pigs in three years with an average weaning weight of 42 lb. each. The sow on the right, during this same period of three years, produced 28 pigs which averaged 31 lb. each. *(Courtesy Oregon State College.)*

been at work, is sufficient to cover up many weaknesses of conformation. This is why a breeder will do better to judge the offspring at slaughter time and then decide which sows to keep. In fact, the progeny test is the most accurate method for determining breeding merit, and in swine it is possible to progeny-test both the male and the female.

As stated earlier, the appearance is useful in noting any defect or abnormality which shows. It is well to make the most of this value of appearance and really give the animal a good viewing to see if it has any such defects. Pay attention to the eyes, the jaws, the testes, the udder and teats, and watch for hernia. If we assume that we can estimate carcass merit from the appearance of the animal, how much improvement can we expect to make by using this information?

The heritability of live-animal scores has been found to vary with the different classes of farm animals. In beef cattle it is moderately low, due to many years of selection on a visual basis, but of sufficient magnitude to enable one to make considerable progress for improving conformation of a herd. However, the heritability of score in sheep and swine is less than that of cattle, and although improvement is possible, it will be slow.

PEDIGREE

The pedigree shows the relationship of the animal to those in his line, some of which may be well-known animals of the breed. This is, in addition to the inbreeding, a function of the relationship between sire and dam. For some of our farm animals, a pedigree is merely a list of names because no production records of their forebears have been kept and no animal of proven production in the line still exists. In the instances where no records of production or other valuable information on the line are available, the only thing the pedigree shows is the amount of inbreeding. Two animals of equal merit, of which one shows inbreeding while the other does not, might differ considerably genetically. If two animals possess equal apparent merit, one would always select the more highly inbred animal because its chances of being more homozygous, and consequently of breeding true, are much higher.

Let us assume that we have pedigrees on which records of production are entered (dairy cattle pedigrees are good examples). There are several factors that must be considered in properly appraising the production data on a pedigree. In the first place, one must always recognize that a pedigree is manmade and is worth no more than the integrity of those who made it. Therefore, we should consider the pedigrees developed by our many reliable breeders in order to analyze the components of an acceptable form of this tool in selection. Honesty of the breeder is certainly a factor to be considered very seriously when one goes to an outside herd for breeding stock.

The pedigree may show some animals with extremely high merit. Keep in mind that those of low merit are just as important because it is just as likely that low production will come from a low producer in the pedigree as it is likely that high production will come from a high producer in the pedigree. A blank in the record can be accepted only as evidence of such low production that the pedigree appeared more desirable without it, unless it is known that there was a legitimate excuse for lack of data. Another factor to consider is interval in the pedigree in which the outstanding animal appears. If it is an outstanding sire or dam, it has great value, but if it is an animal six generations removed, it may mean little or nothing. The only way one can judge as important an outstanding animal six generations removed is when line breeding to him was practiced. If this animal appears several times in the pedigree, his importance increases.

In summary, to have value in selection, a pedigree must have records; it must be accurate; it must show the low as well as the high producers; and it must include immediate ancestors of merit rather than good producers which are distantly related (Fig. 118). When a pedigree reflects these conditions, the user will be in a position to evaluate its true worth.

The pedigree is a valuable guide for those characteristics of lowest to average heritability because it indicates what the breeding merit of an animal should be. Therefore it will be useful in choosing between animals before they have established their own records. For characteristics that are highly heritable, the record of the individual itself is most important. A combination of the pedigree and the individual's production record is useful and highly desirable. It is to

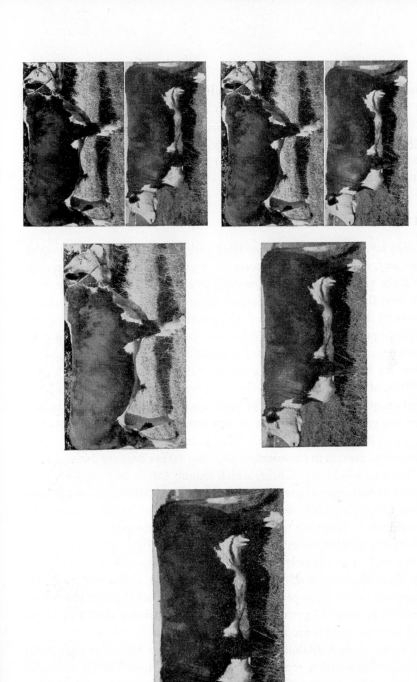

Fig. 118. The relative importance of parents, grandparents, and great-grandparents in the inheritance contributed by them. In this photographic representation, the size of the animal is considered to be the product of length times width times depth. Consequently, for an animal to be really one-half the size of another, each dimension in this animal should be 0.793 times that of the other animal. (*Courtesy Oregon State College.*)

be hoped that swine, sheep, and beef cattle breeders will eventually keep records and develop correction factors to standardize the conditions under which the records are established so that pedigrees of these animals can carry production records similar to those of dairy cattle. When this time arrives, we shall be in a position to make much greater use of the pedigree in selection of beef cattle, sheep, and swine.

PRODUCTION RECORDS

If fertility level, gains during the suckling period, rate of gain in the feed lot, feed efficiency, and conformation scores are highly heritable, then the records of these traits are all one needs for making intelligent selections. If the heritability is low, then most of the variations observed in the records are due to environmental differences. Selection for characteristics of low heritability will give very slow progress in improvement. Let us take some examples to illustrate how much progress would be expected with different levels of heritability.

Suppose we have a herd of beef cattle in which it takes 700 lb. of feed to make 100 lb. of gain. If we were to select for breeding from that herd a group of animals requiring only 500 lb. of feed, and if all the variations in feed efficiency are genetic, these animals should produce offspring which also require only 500 lb. of feed to make 100 lb. of gain. But suppose that 90 per cent of the variations are due to environment and only 10 per cent are due to genetic factors. Then we would get offspring which require 680 lb. of feed per 100 lb. of gain from these selected parents which required only 500 lb. of feed per 100 lb. of gain. Of course, this is some improvement over the 700-lb. requirement, but it would take a long time to make a big change in the herd.

It is fortunate that the heritabilities of many characteristics in beef cattle are reasonably high. For example, gains in the feedlot are 60 to 80 per cent heritable, feed efficiency is 45 to 60 per cent heritable, and gains during the suckling period are 30 to 40 per cent heritable. This is not the case with swine, where fertility is about 15 per cent, gains and feed efficiency are 20 to 25 per cent, and weaning weights are quite low in heritability.

In the cases where heritabilities approach or surpass 50 per cent, progress through use of production records can be made as rapidly as by any other method. Even where heritabilities are low, production records as well as all other tools available should be used in the selection of breeding animals because, if desirable and undesirable genes are closely linked or there is a case of overdominance, selection by production records will tend to maintain heterozygosity. This is perhaps the best thing that could be done because homozygosity in such cases would not be desirable.

PROGENY-TESTING—EVALUATING AN ANIMAL ON THE BASIS OF THE PERFORMANCE OF ITS OFFSPRING

The best idea of an animal's genotype is obtained from the records made by its offspring. Also, traits that can be measured in only one sex, such as milk production, are evaluated most effectively by progeny tests. This statement may lead the reader to think that the progeny test is the only good method to be used. However, there are several practical difficulties in carrying out a progeny test which are not found in other methods. In the first place, progress is slowed down materially by the increase in intervals between generations (called *generation interval*). It takes several years to produce offspring and to obtain records of them as a means of testing the breeding value of an animal. A second difficulty in such animals as beef cattle and sheep is that only the male can be adequately progeny-tested. Certainly, some offspring from a cow or a ewe are obtained but not enough to prove her breeding value and still have any reproductive life remain. A third practical difficulty lies in the fact that several rather than only a few males must be tested in order to find one that is truly outstanding.

For traits of lower heritability progeny-testing is a most valuable method, however. With traits for which heritability is only 10 per cent, selection based on production records of the individual, plus progeny-testing an adequate number of males, will result in progress that is much greater than selection on the basis of production records alone.

In cases where heritability approaches 50 per cent only double the progress would be made by progeny-testing the males as from selection by production records alone. The generation interval would be cut in half, so that progress from progeny-testing and that from selecting on production records alone would be equal.

In cases where heritability exceeds 50 per cent, the reduction in generation interval will more than offset the gain made by progeny-testing, and it would be more feasible in such cases to use production records alone. Furthermore, breeders should not fail to take advantage of the fact that some cows and/or bulls consistently produce superior offspring, and these animals as well as their offspring should find a place in the herd. Certainly a cow that produces a good calf each year should be kept in the herd as long as she produces a calf. A bull that sires outstanding calves every year should be used as long as he is serviceable. The same would apply in all classes of livestock. Although this is really a kind of progeny test, it differs from the method of progeny-testing in that superior breeding animals are identified in the regular breeding program rather than by special testing to locate them.

FAMILY SELECTION

It is obvious, from what has been said regarding the value of outstanding animals in a herd and the use of litter averages as a guide to selection, that one can take advantage of performance of families or strains within a herd. If one particular strain or line of breeding in a herd is showing unusual performance, this strain should be expanded by keeping a larger portion of the offspring from this strain than from the other less desirable ones. Family selection, like progeny-testing, is most useful where heritability of the trait is low. It is based on the assumption that a desirable animal from a superior strain is more likely to transmit this desirability than a desirable animal from a strain lacking superiority. The same principle can be applied by keeping more offspring from an unusually good female or male and by taking advantage of any outstanding family or strain for replacement animals to go into the herd or flock. Of course this outstanding family or strain must be judged by level of performance rather than by popularity with breeders, which may be based on the fact that someone paid an enormous sum for some outstanding show animal. The winnings at a show are not enough to prove an animal's breeding value. If he can sire offspring of which all perform at a high level, then he is one to which a breeder may look for breeding material.

LINE SELECTION

Most breeders would not want to take advantage of this tool of line selection, but it is one that has merit, for it is capable of developing outstanding breeding stock. If foundation breeding animals are obtained from a large number of herds and immediately inbred at as rapid a rate as possible, the breeder can locate those strains or lines of breeding which have deleterious recessives and which have recessive epistatic factors. These lines will soon perform at a very low level or have a large outcrop of abnormalities and can then be eliminated. Only those lines which hold up well with inbreeding should be used so that these better performing lines can be converged by reciprocal crossing to make a herd with a rather wide base. If the herd is large, it can be bred as a closed herd after line-converging without rapidly increasing the inbreeding rate. Thus, on a herd in which five or more sires are used on 100 or more females, only very mild inbreeding would be practiced if the herd were closed to outside breeding.

By use of this initial line-selection procedure, considerable genotypic selection can be made, and the result will be that a breeder should have relatively little difficulty after the herd is established by converging the better lines with any of the deleterious outcrops. This tool can be used only by a large operator and must be accepted as an expensive one in the initial stages. Regardless, it may prove to be the best method for effecting livestock improvement.

BRINGING A DESIRABLE TRAIT INTO A HERD OR FLOCK

The conventional method for bringing a desirable trait into a herd or flock is slow. The first step is to cross the breed or strain possessing this desirable trait (which may be quite undesirable in every other respect) with the good herd or flock that does not possess this trait. After the cross is made, the hybrids are continually intermated, and selection is practiced for all production factors of the good herd or flock, plus selection for the desired trait. This is a very crude method because a breeder has to retain all the good characters of his original herd as well as try to hold on to the new desirable trait.

A much simpler and more effective method after the first cross is made is to continuously back-cross to individuals in the herd or breed that was generally good, holding on to the desired trait by selection. The desirable genes of the generally good herd or breed are retained by continuously back-crossing to it. This system has been used by plant breeders for breeding disease resistance into a variety of plants and is a very effective tool.

EXERCISES

1. Suppose you have a herd of beef cattle that is ideal except for a susceptibility to a bothersome disease. Another breed of cattle is completely resistant to this disease, but it is undesirable in general. How could you develop this resistance to the disease in your cattle and still keep the good traits they now possess?

2. Of what usefulness is appearance in selecting farm animals? When is eye appraisal used for selecting farm animals?

3. Discuss the usefulness and shortcomings of a pedigree as a tool in selection.

4. Suppose rate of gain is 80 per cent heritable. Would you progeny-test for selecting this trait? Why?

5. For what type of traits are production records sufficient as a basis for intelligent selection?

15

RECORDS NECESSARY FOR SELECTION: HOW TO KEEP THEM

Records are essential for proper selection because the data needed are too numerous to remember. The more information available on animals, the greater are chances of making proper choices in selection. However, simple records provide the basic information needed and are not difficult to keep.

Some people prefer to keep records on cards which can be filed by animal numbers or by ages. Upon disposal or death of an animal, one can remove the card from the file of breeding animals and place it in the file of disposed animals. Cards are useful because one can remove cards and take them to the place where animals are being studied. They are more easily lost than sheets in a post binder notebook. Also, cards that are small enough to handle easily, not larger than 5 x 8 inches, may provide a space too small for entry of the records.

Two of the most important things to consider in the keeping of simple records which will be useful in livestock selection are: (1) a system of identification so that each animal can be properly and permanently identified, and (2) a suitable scale for weighing the animals. Since the required records differ from one class of animals to the next, they will be discussed for each class of livestock.

BEEF CATTLE

In the improvement of beef cattle through breeding there are six primary characteristics for which one should select: (1) fertility, (2) suckling ability, (3) rate of gain, (4) feed efficiency, (5) grade, and (6) freedom from defects (lethals and abnormalities). It follows, then, that a record system should be so devised that information may be entered and kept with the least effort. One of the main reasons why some breeders shy away from record-keeping is that many of the record forms are very complex. The type of record to be shown here is one of the simplest and easiest and provides all the essential information. A person who wants to keep more elaborate records can modify this form accordingly. The record form developed at Oregon State College can be kept either as a card or record sheet. Each breeding female has one sheet or card. Provision is made in the record form for recording the growth rate of the cow. The production of calves by the cow includes a record of birth weight, weaning weight and score, yearling weight and score, and eighteen-month weight and score. From these weights and dates one can calculate the gain per day during the suckling period and during the post-weaning periods. The reason for records of gains beyond the yearling age is to obtain a record of how the heifers and bulls will do on summer grazing. On the back of the cow record form, space is provided for breeding and health records.

Identification

Cattle must be identified. It is desirable to tattoo the calf in the ear at birth. If one can use a herd-number system that becomes a part of the animal's name in the pedigree, it is best. An example of a numbering system is that used by Oregon State College in which calves born in 1951 are assigned A, those in 1952, B, etc. Each calf is numbered 1, 2, 3, etc. The 1951 calf crop is numbered A1, A2, etc., while the 1952 calves are B1, B2, etc. In naming the calves for registry, they are OSC Miss A1 or OSC Sir A2. In addition to the tattoo, each calf carries an ear tag (Fig. 119) in each ear which bears the same number as the tattoo. Cattle that are not in heavy brush may carry a neck chain with the number on a round plastic tag (Fig. 120). These tags come in various colors, so that a different color can be used for each family, strain, or line of breeding. On the ranges that are rough and covered with brush, a brand may be used for identification. Some ranchers use a letter for the year designation, followed by a number for the animal. Others use the first two numbers to designate the year. For example, the fourth calf born in 1958 would be branded with 584.

Weight Determination

The birth weight of the calf may be obtained in the pasture by using a rod that goes from the saddle to the rider's shoulder and on which a spring-dial scale hangs. The calf can be suspended in a cloth swing which is hung on to the scale. The scale can be balanced by allowing for the weight of the cloth swing so that readings are direct.

Calves can be weighed on a 1-ton pit scale installed in the barn. Some prefer to use a portable scale which can be taken to the pasture for weighing. Brug-

BEEF COW RECORD

Breed _____ Reg. No. _____ Tattoo: Right _____ Left _____ Disposal _____ Herd Number _____

Sire: _____
{ Grandsire
  Granddam

Dam
{ Grandsire
  Granddam

Remarks: _____

WEIGHT AND SCORE OF THIS COW

Date	Age	Weight	Gain per Day	Score
	Birth		✕	
	Weaning			
	12 months			
	18 months			
	At weaning 1st calf		✕	

CALF PRODUCTION RECORD OF THIS COW

Year	Herd No.	Sex	Sire's No.	Birth Date	Birth Wt.	Weaning Record Date	Weaning Record Wt.	Weaning Record Score	Weaning Record Gain/Day	Wt. of Cow	Yearling Record Date	Yearling Record Wt.	Yearling Record Score	Yearling Record Gain/Day	Feed per 100 lb. Gain	18 Month Record Date	18 Month Record Wt.	18 Month Record Score	18 Month Record Gain/Day	Abnormality and Disposal Record

Prepared by Department of Animal Husbandry
OSC - Corvallis, Oregon   3-52 ACW

(Back side of Beef Cow Record sheet)

Cow No. _____

	Weight Record						Breeding Record								
						1st Service		2nd Service		3rd Service		4th Service		Remarks
Date	Age	Weight	Date	Age	Weight	Date	Bull No.	Date	Bull No.	Date	Bull No.	Date	Bull No.	

Health Record

Date	Condition	Treatment	Remarks

This cow record sheet provides a lifetime record for each individual cow in the herd. When a heifer is put into the herd as a replacement, a sheet can be started for her. The record sheets enable you to keep a record of grades and gains of each calf the cow produces, from birth to 48 months.

215

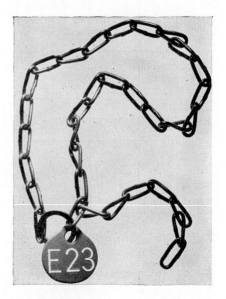

Fig. 119. Eartag used for identifying cattle at the Oregon station. The letter designates the year. Cattle are also tattooed in case of loss of eartag. *(Courtesy Oregon State College.)*

Fig. 120. Neck-chain tag for identifying cattle at the Oregon station. This is particularly desirable for easy reading. These plastic tags come in various colors. Each line has a different color. *(Courtesy Oregon State College.)*

man and Martin (1954) have described a portable scale for beef cattle and other state colleges have developed similar portable scales.

The breeder must either obtain birth weight and weaning weight from which gain per day during the suckling period can be calculated, or he must adjust weaning weight of all the calves to a common-age basis. This can be done by regressing weight on age, which will give general gain per day for the calves, and the records of each calf can then be adjusted for age. The calf that is older than the common age will have its weight reduced, and the calf which is younger than the common age will have its weight increased. Since birth weight is a good indication of general growth potential of the calf, and the calf must be identified at birth anyway, it is just as well to show birth weights on the record. The gain per day during the suckling period measures the combination of the milking ability of the cow and the growth capacity of the calf. The milk production of the dam is by far a greater influence than the calf's gaining ability.

The yearling weight and weaning weight make it possible to calculate gain per day during the post-weaning growth period of the calf. This measures the calf's gaining ability. It may be that the breeder will want to feed the calves individually and obtain feed efficiency. This is certainly to be recommended. In case it is not possible to obtain a record of feed eaten by each calf, some progress in increased feed efficiency may be made by selecting the faster-gaining calves.

Scoring

The score for calves is most important at the time the yearling or 18-month weight is taken. Scores on calves at weaning time are much less important, but they may be used in conjunction with weaning weight to appraise how well the dam has cared for the calf.

A score card which is quite simple has been developed by the extension workers at Oregon State College. This score card may be revised to meet the requirements of the one using it. For example, some might prefer to separate "scale and balance" into two items because an animal is often large enough but lacks balance. Another animal may be well balanced but be lacking in size. The two might be scored the same but for entirely different reasons. If these two items were separate, the score would be more descriptive. Another example of a change that might be desirable is to use a score for body as a whole instead of scoring for feet and legs. This change would classify crooked legs in with the other abnormalities and this condition could be used to eliminate an animal.

Feed Efficiency

To obtain feed efficiency, a manger may be constructed with a hopper so that feed may be in the manger at all times. Calves are either penned or tied separately for periods of eating but are run together for exercise. While they are not tied or penned for eating, they are shut away from the feed so that no calf will eat another calf's feed. If this method is used, a card tacked to the hopper can be used for recording the date and amount of feed put into the hopper each time the supply is replenished. Feed can be weighed each day by use of dairy scales. Where the feed is put into a hopper for self-feeding, a platform scale is best.

Calves may be tied while eating and the feed weighed to the calf twice daily. Any feed not eaten should be removed from the manger and placed in a sack in front of the manger. Once each week the feed not eaten can be weighed and this amount deducted from what was weighed out to the calf to determine food consumption for the week. If this is done, a monthly feed sheet is necessary

BEEF CATTLE GRADING GUIDE
Oregon State College
Extension Service

Points	Value	Your Score
Scale and balance	10–3	
Thickness of flesh	10–3	
Smoothness of body	10–3	
Head	5–1.5	
Chest	10–3	
Rear flank	5–1.5	
Back	10–3	
Loin	10–3	
Rump	10–3	
Round	10–3	
Feet and legs	10–3	
Total Score		

1 +	98–100
1	95–97
1 –	92–94
2 +	89–91
2	86–88
2 –	83–85
3 +	80–82
3	77–79
3 –	74–76
4 +	71–73
4	68–70
4 –	67

Grade Designation	Breeding Cattle Description
1	The top of the grade represents outstanding animals in strong competition. The middle and lower end of the grade represents excellent breeding animals from standpoint of type, conformation, quality, and character, capable of making a good showing in strong competition.
2	Cows in grade 2 are good enough to retain for breeding test in purebred herds. This is a practical top for commercial cattle. The top of grade 2 represents the best of range bulls; the lower end of herd bulls. Cattle in this grade are well down the line or out of the money in competition.
3	Cows usually should be culled from purebred herds; good commercial cattle; bulls rarely capable of making much improvement except on very plain cattle.
4	Plain, upstanding, thin-fleshed, slow maturing cattle lacking in quality and character and having serious defects of conformation. Should be culled from commercial herds.

This is the Oregon State College grading guide for beef cattle. Purebred breeders will want to produce and sell bulls that grade 2, or better. Bulls of this grade can go into average range herds and make improvement in the herds.

for each calf so that the amount given in the morning and in the afternoon can be recorded. Sheets like this can be used on a clipboard which can hang on the feed cart.

Abnormalities

A place is provided in the cow record sheet for recording abnormalities and disposal. The cow that produces abnormal calves may be considered for culling. Also, a cow that consistently produces calves which go to slaughter, because they do not have sufficient merit for retention in the herd or for sale as a breeding animal, may also be considered for culling. It is always desirable to record where each calf goes, i.e., into the herd, sold to Mr. Jones, sold for slaughter, etc.

SHEEP

For proper handling of sheep a dodge chute is highly desirable. An example is shown in Fig. 121.

Fig. 121. Cutting chute for separating sheep. (*Courtesy Oregon State College.*)

Identification

Lambs should be identified at birth by a flock ear tag (Fig. 122). A highly desirable system is one that uses a letter of the alphabet for the year and a number to identify each lamb born that year. In 1951, for example, one would have A1 to An, where A1 is the first animal numbered and An is the last one numbered that year; in 1952 one would have B1 to Bn, etc. When the lambs are registered, one ear tag bears the registration number, while another bears the flock number. If one tag is lost, it can be replaced because the remaining tag is sufficient to identify the sheep.

Fig. 122. Eartag used for identifying sheep at the Oregon station. The registration number is placed in one ear and the individual number in the other ear of purebred sheep. In grades, each ear has the individual number. The letter is year identification. *(Courtesy Oregon State College.)*

Weight Measurement

Lambs can be weighed at birth by suspending each lamb in a cloth swing which is hung on a dairy scale, or if this is not practical, a platform scale can be used with a small container to hold the lamb. Weights of the lambs at weaning and the ewes can be taken by a portable scale similar to the one developed at Oregon State College. Its advantages are that sheep need not be moved very far nor kept off grass very long to accomplish the chore of weighing. Snow fence can be used with steel posts to form a holding pen and chute for use in conjunction with the portable scale. The dial scale is most desirable for fast weighing (Fig. 123).

Record-keeping

Some people prefer a simpler record-keeping system. A card form has been developed for sheep by Oregon State College for this purpose. It is used primarily for mutton sheep because details of wool quality are not included in this form. It is also based on the assumption that the flock will be pasture-bred instead of hand-mated. This card has much to commend it because of the simplicity of record-keeping. Cards can be taken to the corral for sheep-selecting and sorted in any manner desired.

Fig. 123. Portable scale for weighing sheep is lowered to ground with ramps in place for sheep to enter (top). Hitched ready for moving to another place (bottom). *(Courtesy Oregon State College.)*

Department of Animal Husbandry   OREGON STATE COLLEGE

Record of Ewe No._____
Reg. No._____

Inbreeding coef._____

Pedigree   Breed ___Hampshire___

Birth Date ___1/29/49___	
Twin or Single ___twin___	
Birth Weight ___9.3 (lb.)___	SIRE
Weaning Weight ___92 (lb.)___	
Age at Weaning ___100 (days)___	
Yearling Weight ___163 (lb.)___	DAM
Date Taken ___8/1/50___	

REMARKS

Abnormalities, wrinkles, wool blindness, inverted eyelids, etc.

Date and Reason of disposal

	Body Weights & Scores				Breeding Record			Fleece Data & Shearing Records				Length			
Year	Breeding Season Weights		Weight at Weaning Time	Scores at Weaning Time		Date of First Estrus	Gestation Length	Services per Conception	Date Shorn	Grease Wt. of Fleece	Days-Growth	Grade	Shoulder	Thigh	Character Score	Remarks: (medullation, black fibers, etc.
	Start	End		% Conf	% Cond											
**	**		**	**		**	**	***	**	**	**	**	**	**	**	** * * * * * * * * * *
1950	163	165	160	93	90	9/15	143	1	4/20	9.1	445	3/8	—	—	—	** * * * *
1951	175	180	165	92	83	9/13	147	1	4/20	8.0	365	3/8	—	—	—	Few black fibers
1952	176	182	170	94	84	9/19	143	2	4/21	7.8	366	3/8	—	—	—	„ „
1953	180	186	172	92	88	9/13	149	1	4/19	8.0	363	3/8	—	—	—	„ „
Total						**			**	**	**					
Avg.						**			**	**	**					

PRODUCTION RECORD

Year	Birth Date	Sire No. & Breed	Lanb No.	Sex	Birth Weight	Weaning Weight	Gain	Age at Weaning	Gain/day	Weaning scores Conf. %	Weaning scores Cond. %	Disposal	Remarks (Abnormalities, etc.)
1951	2/10	Hamp. 19 of 48	A 6	F	9.1	88	79	100	.79	89	90	Replacement	
			A 7	M	10.6	96	85	100	.85	90	93	Sold to R. Jones, Rock Point.	
1952	2/7	Hamp. A 42	B 11	M	9.0	91	82	110	.75	90	89	Sold to M. Smith, Junction.	
			B 12	M	9.5	93	83	110	.75	93	94	"	
1953	2/14	"	C 31	F	11.9	92	80	99	.81	95	98	Replacement	
1954	2/9	Hamp. B 78	D 14	F	9.7	90	80	100	.80	94	92	"	
			D 15	F	9.8	89	79	100	.79	94	89	"	
Total	**	*****	*****	***	**	**						*****	*****
Ave	**	*****	*****	***	**	**						*****	*****

Rde B 12-52

EWE

Sire _____   *Birth Date* _____   *No.* _____

Dam _____   *Twin* ☐   *Birth Weight* _____   *Reg. No.* _____

Single ☐   *Weaning Weight* _____

Shearing Date									
Fleece Weight									

Year	Date	Sex	Flock Number	Birth Weight	Sire	Ram* Days	Weight	Date	Confor- mation Score	Condi- tion Score	Remarks (Disposal of lambs, etc.)

* Number of days from time ram turned in until lamb dropped.

REMARKS: Pertaining to ewe, such as spinning count of fleece, staple length, black, kempy, or medullated fibers, milking quality, raised singly, etc.

A.H. 5–53–3M   Dept. of Animal Husbandry, Oregon State College, Corvallis, Oregon

Scoring

For scoring sheep on conformation, the sheep score card shown here may be used. This card is for mutton sheep. If fine wool sheep were being bred, more emphasis would be given to wool.

The score for condition is usually a grade such as prime, choice, good, commercial, utility, and cull. Scores or unit scores are expressed in percentage for appraising condition. Lambs generally grow rapidly and become fat while the grass is green and tender and before parasites become a serious problem. It is generally best to go over the lambs and wean and score the lambs that pass a weight of 80 lb. and grade prime or choice. The growth rate of the lambs can be calculated as gain per day, or they can be adjusted to a common-age basis. If they stay with the flock until a certain date, at which time the later lambs should have reached a size for weaning, the early fat lambs will lose condition. This lays a definite penalty on them which should not exist. A good commercial producer would certainly "top out" and market lambs as they become large and fat enough. In this way, he would be paid extra for the early lambs.

SHEEP SCORE CARD

Date _____

Animal Numbers

Points	Value								
Size-for-age	10–3								
Constitution (spring of rib, width and depth of chest)	10–3								
Smoothness of body and natural fleshing	10–3								
Head	5–1.5								
Back and loin	10–3								
Rump	10–3								
Leg of mutton	10–3								
Feet and legs	10–3								
Balance	10–3								
Fleece	15–5								
Totals									

Total Score:
90 to 100, A
75 to 89, B
60 to 74, C
45 to 59, D

SWINE

Identification

Each pig must be identified at birth in order to keep a record for it. Pigs do not lend themselves to tattoo or to ear tags as well as sheep and beef cattle. However, pigs can be identified at birth by notching the ears. Several systems have been worked out for making notches equal certain numbers. A system devised by the Missouri station for numbering in a small herd was used successfully with one exception in which the numbers became duplicated in younger and older animals.

In the Missouri station system numbers through 6 were made directly. Number 7 was made from 4 and 3, 8 was made from 5 and 3, and 9 was made from 5 and 4. Similarly, 10 through 60 were made directly. The larger numbers were made by combinations (Fig. 124). It is possible to go to 200 with this system, and although this would take care of one pig crop, the next pig crop in a moderately sized herd would start again with 1, 2, etc. Thus, the replacement

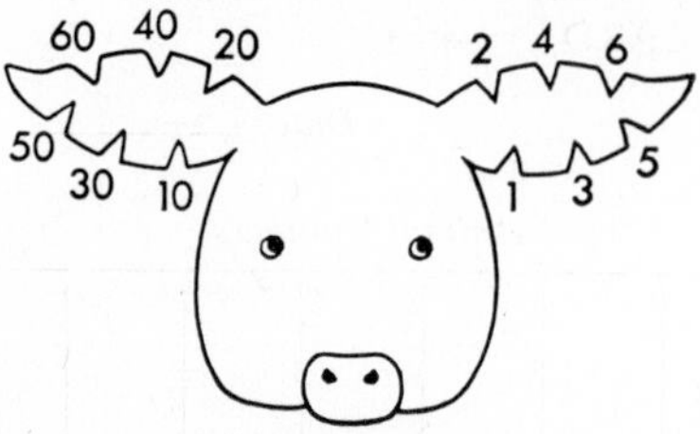

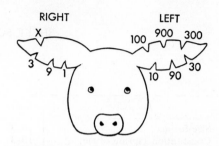

Fig. 124. Ear-notching system for identifying hogs used by the Missouri station.
By use of several notches pigs can be
numbered up to 200.

Fig. 125. Ear notching system for numbering hogs used by the Minnesota station. Double notches in each place allow
numbering several hundred hogs. The
upper right ear is used for litter or year
identification, whichever is most useful.

animals of the two crops of pigs might have duplicate numbers. Some have
used holes in the ear or a combination of holes in both ears to identify pig
crops.

The University of Minnesota uses a system with numbers from 0 to 990
which permits identification of litters. The numeral 1 is marked directly. The
2 consists of two notches in the number 1 position, 3 is marked directly, 4 is 3
and 1, etc. The numbers 1 to 10 are pig numbers within a litter and are in the
right ear. The numbers 10 through 990 are litter numbers. When more than 10
pigs are born in a litter, X in the upper right ear represents 10, and then the
numbers 1 to 9 can be repeated. Thus, number 13 would be X and 3. With this
system, very few duplications will occur, but there may be some. Certainly
there would be little likelihood of having animals near the same age with
duplicate numbers except in very large herds (Fig. 125).

Weight Measurement

Little pigs can be weighed on a small platform scale or on a dairy scale by
first balancing the scale with the container in which the pig is placed for weighing. Larger hogs may be weighed on installed (pit) scales or with a portable
scale. Some operators use a platform scale onto which a crate for retaining the
pig is bolted. A dial scale permits more rapid weighing. In all cases, a crate
for retaining the pig is essential. This may be bolted to the platform and the
scale balanced with this weight, or it may be located outside the platform. In
the latter arrangement, however, the pig may press against the platform and
alter its weight, whereas there is not a chance for error when the crate is bolted
to the scale platform.

Scoring

A modification of USDA Form A.H. 484 is excellent for recording information on the litter.

SWINE RECORD SHEET

Litter No. _____   *Sire of Litter* _____   *Sow No.* _____
Date Litter Born _____   *Sow's Sire* _____
                                                         Sire's Dam _____

Inbreeding Sow _____ *Litter* _____
Date Litter Weaned _____   *Vaccinated* _____

Pig No.	Sex	Birth Wt.	Wean Wt.	Wean Score	154-day Wt.	154-day score	Gain/day after weaning	Feed per 100-lb. gain	Disposal	Abnormalities and Defects

One may not find it possible to weigh pigs at 56 days of age. The weight can be adjusted to 56 days of age (Stewart, 1945; Whatley and Quaife, 1937; and Bywaters and Willham, 1935). The Minnesota method for adjusting weaning weights to 56 days of age is

$$56\text{-day weight} = \frac{\text{actual weight} \times 41}{\text{age} - 15}$$

A pig weighing 50 lb. at 60 days of age is equal to

$$\frac{50 \times 41}{60 - 15} = \frac{2,050}{45} = 46 \text{ lb.}$$

If it is impossible to weigh all pigs at 154 days of age, then their weights can be adjusted to 154 days. Several methods have been devised for this adjustment. The one used by the University of Minnesota is

$$\text{Weight at 154 days of age} = \frac{\text{actual weight} \times 94}{\text{age} - 60}$$

A pig that weighs 200 lb. at 160 days of age is equal to

$$\frac{200 \times 94}{160 - 60} = \frac{18,800}{100} = 188 \text{ lb.}$$

at 154 days of age.

Corrections can also be made for adjusting pig number and weaning weights to a mature-equivalent basis. It appears that this adjustment is better based on the figures obtained from the home herd rather than figures derived from an outside herd. It might be advantageous to adjust feed efficiency for size because pigs which grow faster become larger and, consequently, less efficient. This occurs when pigs are appraised at a given age. One way to overcome this would be to appraise the pigs at a common weight of 200 lb. Since it is generally not the practice to feed pigs individually but to obtain feed records on the individual litters, the appraisal should be made when the litter averages 200 lb. per pig.

With regard to feed efficiency in pigs, it was reported earlier that progress can be made in feed efficiency by selecting for more rapid post-weaning gains. It may not be worth the added effort to obtain records on feed efficiency, but if such records are needed for use in selecting breeding animals, then more progress can be made by feeding the animals individually rather than by feeding them by litters.

In scoring pigs for carcass desirability, one should keep in mind that a large amount of lean rather than fat is desirable. Also, the more important parts, such as the hams, rump, loin, back and sides, should be given more credit than minor points such as hair, set of ears, and head.

RABBITS

Each rabbit can be identified by an ear tattoo. The birth weight of rabbits is generally not considered, but larger rabbits may be weighed on a dairy scale or small platform scales which are set on a table. Market rabbits are usually produced as fryers and marketed directly from the doe at eight to nine weeks of age at a weight of 4 to 4.5 lb. each.

There may be a need for appraising the young rabbits for meat purposes at weaning (marketing) time. It has been shown (Bogart, 1953) that rabbits which are out of condition and lacking in desirable conformation make much less desirable carcasses. No score card has been developed for appraising carcass merit in the live animal, but this does not mean that one cannot develop his own system of scoring. One way to appraise and record differences in rabbits on the basis of meat animals is to use a point system of 5 to 1, with the most desirable rabbits receiving a score of 5 and the culls a score of 1.

A form for keeping a record of production on rabbits has been developed at Oregon State College. One card or sheet is used for the doe and one is used for the buck. The front side of the card is shown. In both cases the production record is continued on the reverse side of the card. It may be necessary to use more than one card for the buck but these can be clipped together to function as one card.

A very simple record card has been prepared for use by 4-H Club boys and girls. This does not have details which a breeder may want, but it may be useful for beginning breeders and for those who feel that more details are not worth the added time and effort.

DAIRY CATTLE AND POULTRY

Record-keeping has progressed so far with dairy cattle and poultry that the reader is referred to books on dairy cattle and poultry breeding, and to D.H.I.A. and Poultry Improvement Association methods of record-keeping.

PURPOSE OF RECORD-KEEPING

One point needs to be emphasized. An elaborate set of records adds nothing to an improvement program unless these records are used in the selection of animals. Sometimes a breeder has kept records, but when it comes to selecting the breeding animals, all that is considered is the appearance of the animals at the time of selection. One reason may be that the breeder is unaware of how much good records can contribute toward improving his herd or flock.

The best way to use performance records is by establishing an index and to apply it in conjunction with good sense. Such traits as suckling gains, feedlot gains, feed efficiency, litter size, and score can be used in an index. Abnormalities and fertility in cattle are not easily indexed but these traits can be guide points when culling. For example, a boar that is a cryptorchid or an animal with a hernia would be culled regardless of its record. The use of the selection index is discussed fully in Chap. 16.

EXERCISES

1. Prepare a record form to be used by a range beef cattle producer that will yield the most information of importance to selection and at the same time one that is sufficiently simple to make it practical for the producer to use it.

2. If cattle are not all weaned at the same age how can one obtain information from the weaning weights which will allow accurate comparisons of calves on the basis of this trait?

DOE RECORD

Breed _____ Date of Birth _____ Disposal _____

Ear No.

Sire _____ { Grandsire _____
                        { Grandam _____

Dam _____ { Grandsire _____
                      { Grandam _____

PRODUCTION RECORD

Sire No.	Breed	Date of Breeding	Wt.	Date of Kindling	No. of Young Dead	No. of Young Alive	Date of Weaning	No. Weaned	Young Weaning Record Sex	No.	Wt.	Sex	No.	Wt.	Comments
		1.							1.			6.			
		2.							2.			7.			
		3.							3.			8.			
									4.			9.			
									5.			10.			
		1.							1.			6.			
		2.							2.			7.			
		3.							3.			8.			
									4.			9.			
									5.			10.			
		1.							1.			6.			
		2.							2.			7.			
		3.							3.			8.			
									4.			9.			
									5.			10.			
		1.							1.			6.			
		2.							2.			7.			
		3.							3.			8.			
									4.			9.			
									5.			10.			

BUCK RECORD

Breed _____ Date of Birth _____ Disposal _____

Ear No.

Sire _____ {Grandsire _____ / Grandam _____

Dam _____ {Grandsire _____ / Grandam _____

PRODUCTION RECORD

Dam No.	Breed	Date of Breeding	Wt.	No. of Young Dead	No. of Young Alive	No. Weaned	Sex	No.	Wt.	Sex	No.	Wt.	Comments
		1.					1.			6.			
		2.					2.			7.			
		3.					3.			8.			
							4.			9.			
							5.			10.			
		1.					1.			6.			
		2.					2.			7.			
		3.					3.			8.			
							4.			9.			
							5.			10.			
		1.					1.			6.			
		2.					2.			7.			
		3.					3.			8.			
							4.			9.			
							5.			10.			
		1.					1.			6.			
		2.					2.			7.			
		3.					3.			8.			
							4.			9.			
							5.			10.			

Young Weaning Record spans the Sex / No. / Wt. columns.

OREGON 4-H CLUB: RABBIT PRODUCTION RECORD CARD

Name or No. of Doe __Peggy__ Breed __New Zealand White__

Birth Date __July 4, 1952__ Number in Litter __6__ Weight at 56 days __4.40__

| Litter Number | Date Bred | Date Due | Date Kindled | Number Born | | 56-day Record | | | |
				Live	Dead	Date	Number	Total Weight	Average Weight
1	2/14/53	3/16/53	3/17/53	7	1	2/12/53	7	29½	4.21
2	5/16/53	6/15/53	6/15/53	6	1	8/10/53	8	35	4.37
6/16/53 - Gave Peggy 2 baby rabbits from Josephine's litter									

Remarks on other side

16

EFFICIENCY AND USES OF
SELECTION METHODS

In general, one will find several rather than just one characteristic toward which selection pressure should be applied. If only one trait were desired and being selected for, a minimum culling level could be developed on the basis of the number to be maintained in the herd. For example, if a breeder had a herd of 100 females as his herd number and there were 40 young females, he could keep the top 100 animals, adults and young, from his total of 140, using the records for this trait as the basis for his selection.

SELECTION FOR ONE TRAIT

Where more than one characteristic is important, the desire is to increase the merit of the herd for each of these important characteristics. Those traits that are highly heritable will show the greatest genetic gains from selection. Where heritability is very low, progress from selection will be very slow because the phenotypic variations are largely due to environmental effects. If one is dealing with a trait in which heritability is approaching zero, very little progress can be made by mass or individual selection. From a practical consideration, more immediate progress might be made by improving the environment (better production practices) rather than by selection. In fact, the real danger in selecting for traits of extremely low heritabilities is that one reduces the amount of selection which can be done for the more highly heritable traits.

Progeny-testing might be an aid in obtaining a better estimate of the genotype. Certain breeding practices such as inbreeding and the conversion of inbred lines might assist in improvement. Keeping the animal under a more constant set of conditions would reduce the environmental variations, making heritability higher.

A breeder is concerned not only with how much progress he can make for each trait by selection, but also with how important each of these traits is economically. Perhaps the greatest net gain to him would be the product of expected genetic gain (heritability) $\times$ economic importance. If trait A is 80 per cent heritable while trait B is 40 per cent heritable, and the two are independent, it is evident that he would make twice the progress in genetic gain from equal selection for trait A as he could for trait B. However, if the improvement in B is three times as important as A, then he might want to apply 1.5 times the selection pressure for B as he did for A. When this pressure was applied to B improvement would be made, but performance in A would improve less rapidly.

The economic importance of the various traits is difficult to appraise. One factor that will influence the economic importance of a trait is the need for that trait in the herd. An example may be illustrated with two herds of swine. Suppose that in one herd the average number of pigs farrowed is six, while in the other the number farrowed is 13. Let us make the assumption that the heritability is the same in the two herds for number of pigs farrowed (this may be an erroneous assumption). It is obvious that the need for more pigs in the one herd is great but that increasing the number in the other would have little or no advantage. Sows on the average would not raise more than 13 pigs even though more were farrowed. Thus, the economic importance of larger litters in the one herd is high, whereas in the other it is very low.

The kinds of condition one operates under also influences the relative economic importance of the various traits. A cattle producer on sparse range will be engaged in the production of feeder calves. Survival of his cows and their ability to raise calves are more important. A grassland farmer of the Midwest may be producing baby beef, and therefore the importance of post-weaning gains and condition of his calves is very important. Survival of the cows and their ability to produce calves are not put to severe stress under these conditions. The demands of the market also influence the relative economic importance of the traits. The demand for highly finished beef in the eastern part of the United States is far greater than in the western section. An animal's ability to fatten, and thus to improve in grade, has greater economic value to eastern producers than it does to western producers.

SELECTION FOR VARIOUS TRAITS

The Tandem Method

When a breeder has several important characteristics which he wishes to improve, he has three general methods at his disposal. He may use the tandem method, which involves selecting for one trait until it is at a satisfactory level, then a second trait until its level is satisfactory, and then a third trait, etc. This method will have its greatest value when the different traits are entirely independent or when the desirability of one trait is associated with the desirability of another. Where the desirability of one trait is closely associated with the undesirability of another, a breeder would merely "teeter-totter" in his improvement of the two traits (Fig. 126). As he improved the herd in one of

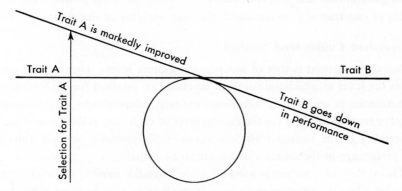

Fig. 126. Influence on trait B when selection is for trait A, and A and B are closely associated negatively.

these traits, the performance in the other would go down proportionately (Fig. 126) when he directed his attention to the second trait, the first would go down proportionately (Fig. 127). With only two traits in which this type of close association existed (desirable of one associated with undesirable of the other), he could continue indefinitely to use the tandem method and make little genetic improvement.

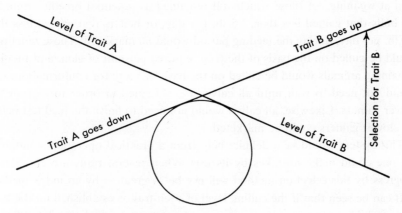

Fig. 127. Influence on trait A when selection is for trait B, and A and B are closely associated negatively.

When the traits under selection are entirely independent, the effectiveness of the method approaches that which can be made by other methods if the number of traits is small (2), but its effectiveness is much lower when the number of traits becomes greater. This method is the least desirable of the methods which will be considered. Even when the traits are independent, it is the least effective. It has the danger that one might select toward less important traits for too many generations, and it is completely ineffective for traits in which the desirability of one trait is associated with the undesirability of the other.

Independent Culling-level Method

A second method is that of independent culling levels. This method establishes the level at which animals will be culled or retained for each trait. The performance in one trait is considered entirely independently of performance in other traits. The basis for the culling level of each trait is determined by the heritability of the various traits, the economic importance of each trait, and the percentage of the animals which are to be culled.

This system of selection is most effective when the number of traits is small (2) and when the percentage retained is small (selection pressure is high). Its effectiveness goes down as the number of traits increases and when the culling pressure decreases.

From a practical standpoint it has one merit: animals can be selected at different stages of development and at different times of the year. For example, during the suckling period one could set a level of gains of 2.0 lb. per day for the bull calves and 1.8 lb. per day for the heifer calves. Any bull that gained less than 2.0 lb. per day during this period would be castrated at weaning. Any heifer that gained less than 1.8 lb. per day would be put into the fattening yard at weaning. Of those which still remained as potential breeding animals, the bulls that gained less than 2.5 lb. per day, or heifers that gained less than 2.0 lb. per day, during the feeding period would be marketed. Those remaining would be culled on the basis of the feed required per unit of gain, and the final remaining animals would be culled on the basis of score for conformation. One would not need to wait until all calves were weaned in order to castrate the slower gainers. Likewise, all calves would not need to finish the feed test before the slower gainers could be marketed.

This system would be a definite help from a practical operation standpoint, but one could make mistakes by its use. When several traits are considered, progress by this selection method will not be so great as by an index method.

It can be seen that if the culling level of each trait is established on the basis of heritability, economic importance, and percentage which can be culled, it would make no difference which trait was used first as a basis for culling. As this method is now practiced by most ranchers, culling by the first trait considered may be quite severe and may make it almost impossible to do any selecting for any of the other traits. Some of the beef cattle breeders often state that we should first cull all those calves which do not meet certain standards in type and conformation. After this is done, one could select for gains, feed efficiency, etc. However, this practice would eliminate a great majority of the animals, leaving little or no opportunity for selection for all the other traits. One of the big objections to this method is the fact that an animal which is outstanding in all traits except one in which he fell barely below the culling level would be culled. At the same time, one which was barely over the culling level in all the traits would be kept. Suppose one had established the following independent culling levels for young bulls in his herd:

Suckling gains	= 2.3	lb. per day.
Feedlot gains	= 2.6	lb. per day.
Feed per 100-lb. gain	= 500	lb.
Score	= B+	

Assuming that three bulls, shown in Table 9, were being considered and that one is to be kept for breeding purposes, the breeder must decide which is the best.

Table 9. COMPARATIVE RECORDS OF THREE BULLS

	Bulls		
	No. 1	No. 2	No. 3
Suckling gains	2.25	2.35	2.8
Feedlot gains	3.25	2.65	3.6
Feed per 100-lb. gain	400	498	380
Score	A+	B+	B

With the use of the independent culling levels bulls 1 and 3 would be culled because 1 showed gains that were too low during the suckling period and 3 did not score well enough. Bull 2 would be kept. It is evident from a casual glance that either 1 or 3 are superior to 2 in over-all merit.

The Index Method

The most effective method is the use of an index in which all the important traits of each animal are properly evaluated and combined into one figure with which all the animals may be compared (Hazel and Lush, 1942). This method prevents the culling of animals which are outstanding in all but one trait. This method accepts slight mediocrity in one trait in order to obtain high performance in others. It is a method of balancing all the traits and then keeping the animals which are superior in the over-all estimation.

In order to evaluate properly each of the traits so that a sound and effective index can be developed, the breeder must consider the heritability and economic importance of each of the traits, the need in his herd, and the genetic and environmental correlations existing between the traits. A selection index will be developed in Chap. 18 to illustrate how one is constructed.

There are some practical difficulties in using a selection index. In order to obtain all the information necessary for its use, it necessitates the keeping of every animal until each one has reached the stage in development where the last record is made. For example, with beef cattle in which gains during the suckling period, feedlot gains, feed efficiency, and conformation score are the traits used in the index, all calves must be kept until they have completed the test period and have been scored. None could be castrated or sold at weaning.

Another disadvantage of the index is that such traits as fertility in beef cattle show discontinuous rather than continuous variation. A cow either has one calf or she has no calf, but it is not possible to put such a trait into an index. What one would be most likely to do would be to cull on a minimum level for fertility and use the index for the other traits. With pigs, where the number in the litter obeys the law of continuous variation, fertility traits can be included in the index.

In some farm animals, such as pigs, it may be desirable to start the breeding season before some of the later pigs have finished the feed-test period. This brings up a real difficulty in establishing the index because one would need to calculate this for all the animals and then make his selections. Sometimes the mass of figures that must be computed to do this for a big herd is so large that much time is used. These calculations must be done quickly in order to facilitate the management program and if there are delays in calculating the index, it would mean that animals to be culled would be carried for an unnecessarily long period; this might be quite expensive.

Both the independent culling level and the index method of selection are subject to errors made in determining the relative economic importance of the traits or in estimating the heritability of the traits. It should be emphasized that, with either method, the overstress of any one character will reduce the selection which can be done for all the other traits. This is one reason why superficial and fundamentally unimportant characteristics should be ignored or, if considered at all, should be given only minor emphasis.

The index method is $\sqrt{n}$ times as efficient as the method of independent culling levels; where $n =$ the number of traits under consideration in the selection program. For two traits the index method would be 1.41; for four traits,

2.0; for six traits, 2.45; and for eight traits, 2.83 times as effective as selecting on the basis of independent culling levels. Where four traits are selected for, as much progress can be made in one generation by use of the index as would be made in two generations by selection on the basis of independent culling levels. The progress made for any one trait by use of the index would be $1/\sqrt{n}$ times that made by selection for that trait alone. If selection were made for four characteristics in an index, the progress for each would be $1/\sqrt{4}$, or ½, as great for each of the traits as compared with progress made when selection is applied only to that one trait (when the traits are given equal emphasis).

Linkage of desirable of one trait with undesirable of another, as has been postulated by Dickerson and Grimes (1947) in which superior sow productivity is associated with lowered rate and economy of gains, would need consideration in a selection index. About all that can be done in such a situation is to balance the selection pressure applied to each, so that improvement in one trait will not reduce performance in the other, and to attempt to improve the animals for other traits. If each of the traits showing such a linkage relation is under strong selection, it reduces the selection pressure which can be applied to all other traits. Consequently, the selection pressure applied to such linked traits would be minimized so that more emphasis could be placed upon other traits in which improvement is possible.

SELECTING FOR COMBINING ABILITY

The Montana station has one group of cattle which is being developed on the basis of specific combining ability by recurrent selection. The bulls are selected for specific combining ability by testing with cows of another line before they are used. An example of selection for this ability may be useful. If a breeder is developing a line in which the objective is a high level of general combining ability, the breeding stock would be tested on a large assortment of breeding material before it would be used in the line. Since it would not be feasible to test cows, only the bulls would be tested. Suppose we label this line as *A* and the cows of various breeding as the *tester herd*. Five to ten bulls of line *A* would be bred to the tester herd cows, and the one that sired the best group of calves would then be used in the line *A*. This would be repeated in each generation. If the objective were to develop two lines which would combine well (specific combining ability), one might label these two lines as *A* and *B*. Again, it would be feasible only to test the bulls, not the cows. Bulls from line *B* would be bred to cows in line *A,* and the one that sired the best calves would then be used in line *B*. All the calves produced by mating bulls of line *B* to cows of line *A* would be discarded. Bulls of line *A* would be mated to cows of line *B,* and the one that produced the best performing calves would be retained for use in line *A*. All calves produced by mating line *A* bulls to line *B* cows would be discarded. The tested line *A* bull would be used in line *A* to produce the next generation of line *A* cattle. Similarly, the tested line *B* bull would be used in line *B* to produce the next generation of line *B* cattle. This testing and use of tested bulls would be done for every generation. It would require considerable time to develop these lines because cow herds are used one-half the time for testing bulls of the opposite line and one-half the time for producing replacements for their own line.

EXPERIMENTATION ON BREEDING AND SELECTION METHODS

Some pilot experiments have been conducted at the central testing station of the Poultry Breeding Laboratory, using Drosophila as the experimental animal to test the efficiency of breeding methods. In addition, the effectiveness of selection while developing inbred lines has been investigated. Some consideration has been given the performance of inbred lines in relation to their performance in line crosses. Since these results are of vital importance in the field of livestock improvement, this work is presented here in some detail.

Bell et al (1953) used Drosophila for selection experiments because in one year results can be obtained which are equivalent to those obtained in 25 years with chickens or in 100 years with cattle. He developed six inbred lines as follows: (1) selected for high egg production; (2) selected for low egg production; (3) unselected for production control; (4) selected for large egg size; (5) selected for small egg size; and (6) unselected for egg size control. Full-sib matings were made and selection was entirely on the females. From the performance of 30 females in a line, one was selected to produce the next generation. There were two objectives in this study: (1) to determine the effectiveness of selection in inbred lines for two kinds of traits, one which is only slightly heritable (5 to 15 per cent) and the other which is highly heritable (30 to 50 per cent); (2) to determine what relationship exists between performance level of the inbred lines and performance level of line crosses.

After ten generations of inbreeding with selection there were marked differences between the lines, particularly for egg size, which is more heritable. Even for the less heritable trait of egg production, the line selected for high production was producing at a higher rate than the line selected for low egg production. The experiment was replicated and has been repeated so that one can consider the results not to be a matter of chance. It appears that, with vigorous selection, the depressing effect of inbreeding can be overcome in this species. One comparison should be made between Drosophila and large farm animals, however. In Drosophila, it was possible to use one out of 30 females, or approximately 3 per cent was needed for reproducing the next generation. In beef cattle, very little selection of females is possible because 40 per cent of the females are needed for replacements. Inbreeding would normally be increased at a slower rate in beef cattle because half-sib mating would be practiced. This should make it possible to select somewhat more in relation to increase in inbreeding than would be indicated entirely from the relative selection pressures which could be applied in the two species. Nevertheless, it is evident that selection that could be applied in the larger farm animals would be low when compared with that which is possible in Drosophila.

In the other phase of the study, all lines were crossed in all possible combinations to see if performance level of the inbred line was related to performance level of the line crosses. According to Hull (1945 and 1946), specific combining ability might be greatest where the performance of inbred lines is lowest if heterosis is largely due to overdominance. It was pointed out earlier that overdominance means that the heterozygote (*Aa*) is superior to either homozygote (*AA* or *aa*). It is assumed that greatest heterosis from crossing two inbred lines will result when the heterozygous state is produced in all the line-cross individuals. This will result when the two inbred lines are homozygous, one *AA* and the other *aa*. If the inbred lines are homozygous for the genes showing overdominance effects, they will, of necessity, be low in performance level within themselves. If quantitative characteristics in general are due to genes showing overdominance effects, then the inbred lines of lower performing levels can be expected to produce line crosses with the greatest heterosis. Some evidence for this relationship has been presented for corn (Hull, 1945; and Comstock, et al, 1949).

When the data on Drosophila were summarized by Bell according to performance level of the inbred lines for the less heritable trait (egg production), there was a clear-cut relationship between performance level of the inbreds and performance level of the line crosses (Table 10). Thus, high-producing inbreds × high-producing inbreds gave line crosses with an egg production level of 95, while low-producing inbreds × low-producing inbreds gave line crosses with an egg production level of 78. The line crosses in general produced 50 per cent more than the inbred lines, showing marked heterosis.

The data on egg size, a highly heritable trait, differed markedly from those on egg production because little heterosis for egg size results when inbred lines are crossed. It may be pointed out that selection for egg size was relatively more effective than selection for egg production while the inbred lines were

Table 10. EGG PRODUCTION OF INBREDS AND HYBRIDS IN FOUR
GROUPS OF COMPARISONS

	Daily Production per Female by Groups				
Types	I	II	III	IV	*Grand Mean*
INBREDS					
High inbreds	73	64	77	80	74
Medium inbreds	61	58	64	60	61
Low inbreds	42	44	50	50	46
GENERAL COMBINABILITY					
High × others	94	89	91	94	92
Medium × others	91	90	88	84	88
Low × others	92	85	82	80	85
PHENOTYPIC COMBINATIONS					
High × high	94	92	96	98	95
High × medium	93	92	94	93	93
High × low	93	86	89	91	90
Medium × medium	90	92	90	84	89
Medium × low	87	86	81	78	83
Low × low	90	83	74	66	78

being developed. This is due to the higher heritability of egg size and is also
related to lower heterosis for egg size when inbred lines are crossed.

As might be expected for a highly heritable trait (egg size), the performance
of the inbred was directly related to the performance of the line cross (Table
11).

Table 11. EGG SIZE SUMMARY ON INBREDS AND HYBRIDS IN FOUR
SETS OF COMPARISONS

	Mean Egg Size in Micrometer Units by Groups				
Types	I	II	III	IV	*Grand Mean*
INBREDS					
High inbreds	37.9	37.8	39.2	38.4	38.3
Medium inbreds	37.4	37.4	38.1	36.5	37.4
Low inbreds	36.2	37.2	35.8	33.7	35.7
GENERAL COMBINABILITY					
High × others	37.8	38.4	38.5	37.5	38.1
Medium × others	37.8	38.1	38.1	37.0	37.8
Low × others	37.4	38.0	37.4	35.7	37.1
PHENOTYPIC COMBINATIONS					
High × high	38.0	38.8	39.1	38.2	38.5
High × medium	38.0	38.2	38.6	37.6	38.3
High × low	37.6	38.1	38.1	36.8	37.7
Medium × medium	37.9	38.0	38.2	37.5	37.9
Medium × low	37.6	38.0	37.5	35.8	37.2
Low × low	36.7	37.8	36.5	34.6	36.4

All the results on performance of inbred lines in relation to performance of line crosses show clearly that for general combining ability, the better performing lines would be expected to give better performing line crosses. From these results both with a character of low and with one of high heritability, it appears that eliminating a line on the basis of its own low performance level is sound. However, there is the danger of eliminating a line which is not desirable in itself but which has great capacity for specific combining ability with some other line. The difficulty arises in detecting lines with high specific combining ability because of the large number of line crosses which are necessary for locating the lines which combine well. General combining ability is much easier to determine because a certain measure of general combining ability can be obtained by mating to outbred material or to a group of genetically divergent inbred lines.

To determine the relation of performance of inbred lines to the production of the "elite" hybrids, Bell determined the percentage of "elite" hybrids produced by combining lines of the various levels of performance. For the highly heritable trait, egg size, most of the good line crosses were produced by mating inbred lines of superior performance level. However, for the less highly heritable trait, egg production, more of the "elite" hybrids were produced when an inbred line of high production level was mated to an inbred line of medium production level. Very few of the "elite" hybrids resulted from mating high $\times$ high, and none resulted from mating low $\times$ low producing lines (Table 12).

Table 12. DISTRIBUTION OF "ELITE" EGG-PRODUCTION AND EGG-SIZE HYBRIDS AMONG PHENOTYPIC COMBINATIONS OF INBRED PARENTS

Phenotypes of Inbred Mating	Percent of Total Hybrids	Percent of "Elite" Hybrids Production	Egg Size
High $\times$ high	10	6	47
High $\times$ medium	23	61	35
High $\times$ low	26	17	12
Medium $\times$ medium	7	0	6
Medium $\times$ low	23	17	0
Low $\times$ low	10	0	0

It appears that there is little evidence that overdominance effects influence the highly heritable trait (egg size). Whether the greater proportion of "elite" hybrids resulting from crossing high- and medium-producing inbred lines can be the results of overdominance effects is not known. Certainly there has been no evidence for the superiority of line crosses resulting from crossing the most inferior inbred lines.

Bell also determined the percentage of "elite" hybrids which would be included if only the upper one-third, the upper one-half, and the upper two-thirds of the inbred lines were tested for combining ability. For the less heritable trait, egg production, only 6 per cent of the "elite" hybrids would have been located if only the upper one-third of the inbred lines, based on egg production, had been used for combining-ability tests. However, 44 per cent would have been located if the upper one-half of the inbred lines were tested, and 67 per cent of the "elite" hybrids would have been located if the upper two-thirds of the inbred lines had been tested for combining ability (Table 13).

Table 13. EFFECT OF RESTRICTING BY INBRED PHENOTYPE THE NUMBER OF INBRED LINES TESTED ON THE DISCOVERY OF "ELITE" HYBRIDS POSSIBLE IN FOUR GROUPS OF INBRED LINES, EGG PRODUCTION

Inbreds Tested	Percent of Possible "Elite" Hybrids Observed				
	I	II	III	IV	Grand Mean
High one-third	0	0	14	0	6
High one-half	33	67	43	40	44
High two-thirds	33	67	86	60	67

For the more highly heritable trait, egg size, 47 per cent of the "elite" hybrids would have been located by testing the upper one-third of the inbred lines for combining ability. By testing the upper two-thirds of the inbred lines, 90 per cent of the "elite" hybrids for egg size, the highly heritable trait, would have been located (Table 14).

Table 14. EFFECT OF RESTRICTING BY INBRED PHENOTYPE THE NUMBER OF INBRED LINES TESTED ON THE DISCOVERY OF "ELITE" HYBRIDS POSSIBLE IN FOUR GROUPS OF INBRED LINES, EGG SIZE

Inbreds Tested	Percent of Possible "Elite" Hybrids Observed				
	I	II	III	IV	Grand Mean
High one-third	0	33	70	40	47
High one-half	100	67	70	60	71
High two-thirds	100	100	86	80	90

Bell, et al (1952), discussed four systems of breeding: individual and family selection within a closed flock; recurrent selection, in which the breeding stock of a line is selected on the basis of the performance of offspring produced by tester-stock matings; reciprocal recurrent selection, in which the selection of breeding stock in each of two lines is based on the performance of the line-cross offspring; and inbreeding and line converging.

It was pointed out that how the trait is inherited influences the relative effectiveness of the systems of breeding. Dominance can be lacking, partial or complete, or there can be overdominance. The dominance effects will influence the changes in gene frequencies which will be brought about by different breeding systems. First, let us see what the phenotypic effects will be for the various genotypes when one pair of genes is involved with different degrees of dominance. If we let $K =$ the degree of dominance, then when dominance is lacking $K = 0$, with partial dominance $K < 1$, with complete dominance $K = 1$, and with overdominance $K > 1$. If d is a constant equal to the mid-point between the two homozygotes, then $AA = 2d$, $Aa = d + Kd$, and $aa = 0$ in phenotypic expression of the three genotypes. This has been well shown by Bell, et al (1952), in tabular form which is presented in Table 15.

Table 15. PHENOTYPIC VALUES FOR GENOTYPES UNDER VARYING DEGREES OF DOMINANCE

Genotype	Phenotypic value
AA	2d
Aa	d + kd
aa	0

AA —|— 2d	AA —|— 2d	Aa, AA —|— 2d	Aa —|— 3d
	Aa —|— 1.5d		AA —|— 2d
Aa —|— d	—|—	—|—	—|—
aa —|— 0	aa —|— 0	aa —|— 0	aa —|— 0
No dominance, k = 0	Partial dominance, k = 0.5	Complete dominance, k = 1	Over-dominance k = 2

From *Poultry Science*, **31** (1952).

Comstock, et al (1949), calculated the change in gene frequency expected from recurrent selection and from reciprocal recurrent selection. The general concept is that the gene A will be favored over the gene a in selection. Both recurrent and reciprocal recurrent selections will bring about an increase in frequency of A in a population under selection if the frequency of A in the tester line is less than $(1 + K)/2 K$, but selection will bring about a decrease in the frequency of A when the frequency of A in the tester line is greater than $(1 + K)/2 K$. For cases of partial dominance, $K < 1$, the frequency of A in both strains in reciprocal recurrent selection will move toward 1.0. If dominance is complete, $K = 1.0$, the frequency of A will increase in both strains until one is homozygous where all offspring in the strain cross would show the dominant effect, and thus the maximum phenotypic effect. In the case of overdominance, $K > 1$, there will be a tendency for fixing the two strains in opposite directions, one AA and the other aa, so that all cross-line progeny will be Aa and express superiority. If the frequency of A is low in both strains at the beginning of selection, there will be a tendency for A to increase for a time in both strains until the frequency of A reaches $(1 + K)/2K$ for one of the strains. After this frequency is reached in one strain, and if one strain has a higher frequency of A than the other, the tendency will be to increase the frequency of A in the strain in which A occurs more frequently, and to decrease the frequency of A in the strain in which A occurs less frequently.

In the closed flock in which selection is based on individual and family records, selection will tend to increase the frequency of A until it approaches a frequency of 1.0, except in the case of overdominance, $K > 1$, in which the frequency of A will increase until it reaches $(1 + K)/2K$, after which selection would be ineffective. This would mean that selection will favor Aa and that one-half the offspring will not be equal to the selected parents. This situation would prevent the population average from ever reaching the maximum; i.e., the level of the selected parents.

The potential limits of improvement will be the same for recurrent and reciprocal recurrent selection except in the case of partial dominance, $K < 1.0$, where reciprocal recurrent selection will be superior. With partial or complete dominance, selection on a closed flock basis will be equal to recurrent or reciprocal recurrent selection unless the closed flock is homozygous initially. If overdominance, $K > 1$, exists, either reciprocal recurrent selection or recurrent selection will be superior to selection in a closed flock.

If epistasis, the nonallelic interaction of genes, exists in two or more of the loci, selection in a closed flock on the basis of individual or family records will be relatively ineffective. The greatest gain can be expected from the formation of inbred lines for converging to produce hybrid vigor. Both recurrent and reciprocal recurrent selection will be more effective for epistatic genes than mass or individual selection in a closed flock.

The highly heritable traits will respond more to individual selection and will show little advantage from crossing inbred lines. Selection in a closed flock will be the most effective method for highly heritable traits.

Bell (1953) compared selection in a closed flock, recurrent selection, reciprocal recurrent selection, and crossing of inbred lines for obtaining maximum egg production and egg size in Drosophila. The closed-flock selection method gave better results than any one of the other three for the highly heritable trait, egg size. For example, after 16 generations of breeding with each of the four methods, egg size was 38.1 units (for the closed-flock method which was superior to that resulting from line crossing), 37.7, and 37.5 units. Only the recurrent selection method equaled the closed-flock method for increasing egg size (Table 16).

The less highly heritable trait, egg production, showed the least response of any of the breeding methods to selection on the closed-flock basis. Egg production was 86 by this method after 16 generations and 92 to 99 for the other methods. Both reciprocal recurrent selection and recurrent selection were superior to selection within a closed flock. Maximum heterosis was not obtained by either recurrent selection or by reciprocal recurrent selection for the less heritable trait, egg production, as shown by greater egg production when inbred lines were crossed, than when cross populations by recurrent or reciprocal recurrent selection were produced.

Table 16. COMPARISON OF FOUR METHODS OF SELECTION AFTER 16 GENERATIONS OF SELECTION

Method	Egg Size	Production	Index
Closed-flock selection	38.1	86	2248
Reciprocal selection	37.6	92	2249
Recurrent to tester	38.2	96	2297
Single cross I	37.7	99	2284
Single cross II	37.5	96	2260

Bell, et al (1953), concluded that for improving quantitative characteristics which are determined largely by additive genes, selection on the basis of individual and family records is superior to recurrent selection, reciprocal recurrent selection, or the crossing of inbred lines. The crossing of inbred lines is superior to any other method of breeding for obtaining maximum heterosis for a characteristic which is not highly heritable (Table 16).

A general summary of the studies that have been made by the Regional Poultry Breeding Laboratory demonstrates the importance of performance level of inbred lines for use in line-crossing when the traits are highly heritable. It appears that even with less highly heritable traits, culling of the lower one-third of the inbred lines is not likely to result in loss of much valuable genetic material. Some exceptions might be found if one or only a few epistatic genes caused poor performance of a line.

Highly heritable traits respond to individual and family selection, therefore the development of inbred lines to obtain maximum production of highly heritable traits appears unnecessary. Reciprocal recurrent selection and recurrent selection are less effective for obtaining maximum heterosis for a trait of low heritability than is line-crossing. Individual and family selection for a trait of low heritability results in very little progress. Reciprocal recurrent selection, recurrent selection, and crossing of inbred lines are all superior to selecting in a closed population for improving a trait of low heritability.

EXERCISES

1. What are the genetic advantages of selecting on an index basis compared with independent culling levels or tandem selection?

2. Under what conditions, few or many traits, would independent culling level and index selection approach equality?

3. What are the practical difficulties encountered when selecting on an index basis?

4. Discuss the relative effectiveness for obtaining maximum performance by crossing inbred lines and selecting on the individual or mass basis for traits that are (a) highly heritable, and (b) low in heritability.

5. Could one eliminate the less productive lines, keeping only the better performing ones for crossing, and still locate the "elite" hybrids?

6. What is the relation between performance of lines and their (a) general combining ability, and (b) their specific combining ability?

17

COMPONENT ANALYSIS, CORRELATION, AND HERITABILITY

By segregating variance and covariance into components which are attributable to sires, dams, etc., correlations and heritabilities can be calculated. The phenotypic, genotypic, and environmental correlations can all be obtained by such an analysis.

The estimates of these correlations and of heritability give us a keener insight regarding the response one might expect from selection. The heritability of a trait is an estimate of the progress one might expect from selecting for that trait. The genotypic correlations between traits show how changing the inheritance in one trait will affect the other trait. The environmental correlations affect all the traits in relation to one another.

It seems advisable to present a simple example, using two productive traits in rabbits. These data are not real but are chosen to avoid unequal numbers which would occur in natural data and which would complicate the analysis. For a review of analysis of data in which there are unequal numbers, the reader is referred to King and Henderson (1954).

In this example there are 3 sires and 12 dams, each producing 6 young. The dams were allotted to each sire at random until four females were bred to each sire. It is assumed that no difference is present in these two traits which is attributable to differences in sex of young. Since the females were allotted at random to the sires, it is assumed that there is no sire-dam interaction. There was no inbreeding in either the parents or the offspring; therefore no correction was needed for inbreeding. The number of young per doe was the same (6) and all young were produced at the same time; therefore, analysis can be made from sums of each trait for each dam within sires. The data are presented in Table 17. It should be kept in mind that the data used in this illustration are hypothetical because one would seldom obtain litters containing exactly the same number of young. However, these data were derived from figures obtained in a good rabbitry.

Table 17. SUM FOR EACH TRAIT BY DAM WITHIN SIRES

Dams Sires	Trait	Dam 1	Dam 2	Dam 3	Dam 4	Totals
Sire I	x_1*	54.1	53.8	50.0	44.9	202.8
	x_2*	1.93	1.95	1.76	1.57	7.21
Sire II	x_1	50.4	50.8	43.6	43.0	187.8
	x_2	1.71	1.80	1.50	1.48	6.49
Sire III	x_1	42.6	50.0	43.3	41.4	177.3
	x_2	1.52	1.81	1.50	1.38	6.21
						G.T.
Totals	x_1	147.10	154.6	136.90	129.3	567.9
	x_2	5.16	5.56	4.76	4.43	19.91

* Where x_1 equals score for meat animal merit and x_2 equals feed efficiency.
Note. The analysis used is similar to the one presented by Lerner (1950).

ANALYSIS OF VARIANCE

The analyses of variance and covariance were determined by the method of Snedecor (1946). These analyses are presented in Table 18.

Table 18. ANALYSIS OF VARIANCE AND COVARIANCE OF SCORE AND FEED EFFICIENCY

Source of Variation	Symbol	d.f.	x_1	x_2	$x_1 x_2$
Total	$a\text{-}bc\text{-}1$	71			
Between sires	$a\text{-}1$	2	6.843725	0.011088475	0.27250
Within sires					
Between dams	$a(b\text{-}1)$	9	2.069260	0.00298888	0.076462962
Between full sibs	$ab(c\text{-}1)$	60	0.85513266	0.0011725833	0.03067847

a = the number of sires
b = the number of dams per sire
c = the number of offspring per dam
x_1 = 8-week score—mean square
x_2 = feed efficiency—mean square

The variances and covariances were further broken down into their components, according to the method of Winsor and Clark (1940). These components are presented in Table 19. Although equal numbers in each cell simplify the calculations in this example, Winsor and Clark have presented the method for the general case in which unequal numbers are present.

Table 19. COMPONENTS OF VARIANCE AND COVARIANCE OF 8-WEEKS
SCORE AND FEED EFFICIENCY

Symbol	Source of Variation	x_1	x_2	$x_1 x_2$
V_S	Sire variance	0.1989360415	0.0003374828	0.0081682099
V_D	Dam variance	0.202354556	0.00030271745	0.007630748
V_I	Individual variance	0.855132666	0.0011725833	0.030678472

V_I = same value as the mean square for between full sibs

$V_D = \dfrac{\text{mean square for between dams} - \text{mean square for between full sibs}}{\text{number of offspring per dam}}$

or

$V_D = \dfrac{V_D - V_I}{c}$

$V_S = \dfrac{\text{mean square for between sires} - \left(\begin{array}{l}\text{mean square for between sibs} \\ + \text{ mean square for between dams}\end{array}\right)}{\text{number of dams per sire} \times \text{number of offspring per dam}}$

or

$V_S = \dfrac{S - V_I + c_D}{bc}$

From these components one can derive the phenotypic, genotypic, and environmental correlations.

PHENOTYPIC CORRELATIONS

The phenotypic correlations, using the individual, sire, and dam components of variances and covariances, are shown in the following equations:

Phenotypic Correlation between 8-weeks Score and Feed Efficiency

$$r_{x1x2} = \frac{{}^{cov}I_{x1x2} + {}^{cov}D_{x1x2} + {}^{cov}S_{x1x2}}{\sqrt{[(V_{I_{x1}} + V_{D_{x1}} + V_{S_{x1}})(V_{I_{x2}} + V_{D_{x2}} + V_{S_{x2}})]}}$$

$$= \frac{0.0464774299}{0.0477244589} = 0.97387023$$

With a phenotypic correlation of the magnitude obtained in this analysis, one would expect almost as much progress from selecting for either of these traits as from selecting for both. However, this high correlation might not continue to exist if selection were practiced for a considerable period of time. Also, one needs to make further studies to determine if this high phenotypic correlation is indicative of genetic relationships between these two traits. It would be possible for high phenotypic correlations to result from an environmental relationship. Any differences existing between animals that would give a large variation of environmental effects would tend to increase the phenotypic correlation without altering the genotypic correlation.

GENETIC CORRELATIONS

The genetic correlations are determined by one of three methods. The first method uses the dam components of variance and covariance. The analysis is based on the assumption that the full-sib component contains all the environmental and one-half of the additive genetic variance and covariance (Rae, 1950). The dam component contains one-fourth of the additive genetic variance and covariance. In addition, the dam component can contain maternal effects. The analysis, using dam components of variances and covariances, is calculated by use of the following equation:

1. Using Dam Components of Variance and Covariance,

$$r_{G1G2} = \frac{4 \, ^{cov}D_{x1x2}}{\sqrt{4V_{D_{x1}} \times 4V_{D_{x2}}}} = \frac{0.030522992}{\sqrt{(0.809418224)(0.00121087)}}$$

$$= \frac{0.030522992}{0.031306552} = 0.97497137$$

The second estimate of genetic correlation can be derived by using the sire components of variance and covariance. The effects of sex-linkage are contained in the sire components. The analysis, using the sire components of variance and covariance, is calculated by use of the following equation:

2. Using Sire Components of Variance and Covariance,

$$r_{G1G2} = \frac{4 \, ^{cov}S_{x1x2}}{\sqrt{4V_{S_{x1}} \times 4V_{S_{x2}}}} = \frac{0.9326728396}{\sqrt{(0.795744166)(0.0013499312)}}$$

$$= \frac{0.0326728396}{0.032774988} = 0.996888334$$

The same assumptions can be made by using the sire component analysis in the same way as in the dam component analysis. It is assumed that the sire component contains one-fourth of the additive genetic effects. The sire component would not be expected to contain any maternal effects but it could contain some of the effects of sex-linked genes.

The third method of calculating genetic correlations combines the sire and dam components of variances and covariances. Actually, this analysis is the average between the sire and dam estimates of genetic correlations. The analysis, using the sire and dam components of variances and covariances, is calculated by use of the following equation:

3. *Using Sire and Dam Components of Variances and Covariances,*

$$r_{G1G2} = \frac{2(^{\text{cov}}D_{x1x2} + {}^{\text{cov}}S_{x1x2})}{\sqrt{[2(V_{D_{x1}} + V_{S_{x1}}) \times 2(V_{D_{x2}} + V_{S_{x2}})]}}$$

$$= \frac{0.0315979158}{\sqrt{(0.802581195)(0.0012804)}} = \frac{0.0315979158}{\sqrt{0.00102762496}}$$

$$= \frac{0.0315979158}{0.03205658} = 0.985692042$$

It follows that analysis by this method is subject to the errors inherent in both the sire and dam component analyses, i.e., the maternal effects and the sex-linkage may both be included in part by this method.

All three methods can contain some of the nonadditive effects. Greater accuracy may be obtained in determining the relative amounts contributed by these sources of error by an analysis of diallele matings. However, this method calls for a special mating design which is not ordinarily used in farm animal breeding.

ENVIRONMENTAL CORRELATIONS

Environmental correlations are also determined by one of three methods. The first method uses the dam component analysis. It is based on the assumption that one-fourth of the dam component is due to additive genetic effects and that three-fourths of the dam component is due to environmental effects. The computation of the environmental correlations from the dam components of variances and covariances is made by use of the following equation:

1. *Using Dam Components of Variance and Covariance,*

$$r_{E_{x1}E_{x2}} = \frac{^{\text{cov}}I_{x1x2} + {}^{\text{cov}}S_{x1x2} - 3\ {}^{\text{cov}}D_{x1x2}}{\sqrt{[(I_{x1} - 3D_{x1} + S_{x1})(I_{x2} - 3D_{x2} + S_{x2})]}}$$

$$= \frac{0.0159544379}{\sqrt{(0.4470050395)(0.0006019136)}} = \frac{0.0159544379}{\sqrt{0.00026905841}} = \frac{0.0159544379}{0.016403}$$

$$= 0.9726536$$

The second method of calculating environmental correlation uses the sire component. The same assumption is made in this analysis as in the one in which the dam component is used. It is assumed that the sire component contains one-fourth of the additive genetic effects. The other three-fourths of the sire component is due to environmental effects. The analysis, using the sire components of variance and covariance for calculating the environmental correlation, is made by use of the following equation:

2. *Using Sire Components of Variance and Covariance,*

$$r_{E_{x1}E_{x2}} = \frac{{}^{cov}I_{x1x2} + {}^{cov}D_{x1x2} - 3\,{}^{cov}S_{x1x2}}{\sqrt{[(I_{x1} + D_{x1} - 3S_{x1})(I_{x2} + D_{x2} - 3S_{x2})]}} = \frac{0.0138045903}{\sqrt{(0.4606790975)(0.00046285)}}$$

$$= \frac{0.0138045903}{\sqrt{0.0002132253}} = \frac{0.0138045903}{0.014602236} = 0.945375$$

The third method of calculating the environmental correlation between these two traits is based on the combined sire and dam components of variances and covariances. It is based on the assumption that one-half of the additive genetic effects are included in the combined sire and dam components. The other half is assumed to be due to environmental effects. One might also assume that since the full-sib component contains one-half of the additive genetic effects, the removal of this genetic portion by subtracting the sire and dam components would also remove all genetic effects. The remainder is then assumed to be only environmental effects. The calculation, using the combined sire and dam components of variances and covariances for calculating environmental correlation, is made by using the following equation:

3. *Using Sire and Dam Components of Variances and Covariances,*

$$r_{E_{x1}E_{x2}} = \frac{{}^{cov}I_{x1x2} - {}^{cov}D_{x1\,x2} - {}^{cov}S_{x1x2}}{\sqrt{[(I_{x1} - D_{x1} - S_{x1})(I_{x2} - D_{x2} - S_{x2})]}} = \frac{0.014879514}{\sqrt{(0.4538420685)(0.000532383)}}$$

$$= \frac{0.014879514}{\sqrt{0.0002416178019}} = \frac{0.014879514}{0.01554405} = 0.957248207$$

HERITABILITY

Heritability can be estimated from the preceding data by either of two methods. The first method utilizes the component analysis of the variance by using the dam component, the sire component, or a combination of dam and sire components. The assumption is made in calculating heritability from components of variance that one-fourth of the additive genetic effects are present in either the sire or the dam component and that one-half of the additive genetic effects are in the combination of sire and dam components.

The estimate of heritability from the dam component for score is

$$h^2 = \frac{4V_{D_{x1}}}{V_{I_{x1}} + V_{D_{x1}} + V_{S_{x1}}} = \frac{0.809418}{1.256423} = 0.6442$$

The estimate of heritability from the sire component for score is

$$h^2 = \frac{4V_{s_{x1}}}{V_{I_{x1}} + V_{D_{x1}} + V_{s_{x1}}} = \frac{0.795744}{1.256423} = 0.63334$$

The estimate of heritability from the sire and dam components combined for score is

$$h^2 = \frac{2(V_{D_{x1}} + V_{s_{x1}})}{V_{I_{x1}} + V_{D_{x1}} + V_{s_{x1}}} = \frac{0.80258}{1.256423} = 0.63878$$

In estimating heritability for feed efficiency, the same analysis may be employed. The determination of heritability for feed efficiency from the dam component is

$$h^2 = \frac{4V_{D_{x2}}}{V_{I_{x2}} + V_{D_{x2}} + V_{s_{x2}}} = \frac{0.00121087}{0.0018127836} = 0.66796$$

The determination of heritability for feed efficiency from the sire component is

$$h^2 = \frac{4V_{s_{x2}}}{V_{I_{x2}} + V_{D_{x2}} + V_{s_{x2}}} = \frac{0.0013499312}{0.0018127836} = 0.74467$$

The determination of heritability for feed efficiency from the combination of the sire and dam component is

$$h^2 = \frac{2(V_{D_{x2}} + V_{s_{x2}})}{V_{I_{x2}} + V_{D_{x2}} + V_{s_{x2}}} = \frac{2(0.0006402)}{0.0018127836} = \frac{0.0012804006}{0.0018127836} = 0.706317$$

The second method for estimating heritability from these data is by use of path coefficients. Only one example will be presented because the same principle is involved regardless of whether the correlations are determined from one of the components or from the combined sire and dam components. The analysis derived from the combined components represent an average correlation; therefore, the correlations used for heritability estimation by path coefficient analysis are those obtained in this manner. The path coefficients are shown as illustrated on page 256. It should be noted that the heritability estimates obtained from analysis by path coefficients are exactly the same as those obtained from component analysis.

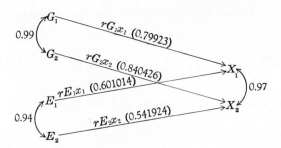

The genetic correlation equals 0.99, the environmental correlation equals 0.94, and the phenotypic correlation equals 0.97.

The genetic-phenotypic correlation $(r_{G_1 x_1})$ for score is calculated by the following equation:

$$r_{G_1 x_1} = \sqrt{\frac{\sigma_{G_1}^2}{\sigma_{x_1}^2}} = \sqrt{\frac{0.80258}{1.256423}} = \sqrt{0.63878168} = 0.79923$$

The environment-phenotype correlation $(r_{E_1 x_1})$ for score is calculated by the following equation:

$$r_{E_1 x_1} = \sqrt{\frac{\sigma_{E_1}^2}{\sigma_{x_1}^2}} = \sqrt{\frac{0.453843}{1.256423}} = \sqrt{0.3612183} = 0.601014$$

The genetic-phenotypic correlation for feed efficiency $(r_{G_2 x_2})$ is calculated by the following equation:

$$r_{G_2 x_2} = \sqrt{\frac{\sigma_{G_2}^2}{\sigma_{x_2}^2}} = \sqrt{\frac{0.0012804006}{0.0018127836}} = \sqrt{0.7063174} = 0.840426$$

The environment-phenotype correlation for feed efficiency $(r_{E_2 x_2})$ is calculated by the following equation:

$$r_{E_2 x_2} = \sqrt{\frac{\sigma_{E_2}^2}{\sigma_{x_2}^2}} = \sqrt{\frac{0.000532383}{0.0018127836}} = \sqrt{0.293682} = 0.541924$$

Heritability is calculated by squaring the genetic-phenotypic correlation in each case.

$$h^2 \text{ score} = (r_{G_1 x_1})^2 = (0.79923)^2 = 0.63878$$
$$h^2 \text{ feed efficiency} = (r_{G_2 x_2})^2 = (0.840426)^2 = 0.706317$$

When two traits exhibit a genetic correlation, as illustrated in this text, the change in the mean genotypic value of one trait will be accompanied by genetic changes in the other. If score were subjected to selection so that the average genetic merit of score for the population would be changed, the average genetic merit of feed efficiency would show a change proportional to $r_{G_1 G_2}$ and to the ratio between the square roots of the genetic variances of score and feed efficiency. Selection with the resulting change in genetic merit for score would influence feed efficiency in the following manner:

$$\Delta^* G_{x1} = r_{G_{x1} G_{x2}} \frac{\sigma_{G_{x1}}}{\sigma_{G_{x2}}} \Delta_{G_{x2}}$$

$$\Delta_{G_{x1}} = 0.99 \frac{0.89586}{0.035782} \Delta_{G_{x2}}$$

$$\Delta_{G_{x1}} = 0.99 \ (25.0366) \ \Delta_{G_{x2}}$$

$$\Delta_{G_{x1}} = 24.786 \ \Delta_{G_{x2}}$$

* Δ = change.

Thus a change in the genetic merit for score resulting from selection would cause a marked change in the genetic merit for feed efficiency.

Selection for feed efficiency with the resulting change in genetic merit for this trait would be expected to change score as follows:

$$\Delta_{G_{x2}} = r_{G_{x1} G_{x2}} \frac{\sigma_{G_{x2}}}{\sigma_{G_{x1}}} \Delta_{G_{x1}}$$

$$\Delta_{G_{x2}} = 0.99 \frac{0.035782}{0.89586} \Delta_{G_{x1}}$$

$$\Delta_{G_{x2}} = 0.99 \ (0.0399415) \ \Delta_{G_{x1}}$$

$$\Delta_{G_{x2}} = 0.03954 \ \Delta_{G_{x1}}$$

There would not be a large effect on the genetic merit for score resulting from a change in the genetic merit for feed efficiency due to selection.

EXERCISES

1. In determining heritability estimates by component analysis what is the basic assumption relative to the proportion of the additive genetic effects that are included in the sire component?

2. Calculate heritability by path coefficients where the genetic correlation is 0.61, the environmental correlation is -0.27, and the phenotypic correlation is 0.40.

18

USING AND DEVELOPING A SELECTION INDEX

There are two general kinds of index. One is needed to aid in the selection of a single trait expressed only in one sex, for the purpose of appraising the individuals of the sex in which the trait is not expressed, such as milk or egg production. The other index is needed to combine several traits into an overall estimate of merit so that comparisons of animals can be made. For example, it would be most difficult to compare animals A and B if A were superior to B in two traits, equal in one, and inferior in two. Actually, there could be a marked advantage of A over B when they were compared by index.

A selection index should have certain characteristics.

1. It should be simple. The average breeder may find it difficult to understand a complicated index. Unless the use of a more complex index is necessary to give a decided advantage in progress, it may be better to use a very simple one.

2. It must be based on accurate and comparable records. Records based on selected individuals rather than a random sample or all the individuals may result in bias. A marked change in environment from one generation to the next makes an index inaccurate for comparing animals of the two generations. Also, environments which are greatly different for two herds make an index inaccurate for comparing animals of the two herds. The most important considerations are accuracy and definiteness of records. Errors made in record-keeping will affect the accuracy of the results obtained from use of the index.

3. It should have a high efficiency. This means that progress is most rapid when traits that have a high heritability are properly emphasized in selection.

USE OF AN INDEX FOR COMBINING SEVERAL TRAITS INTO ONE FIGURE

In the selection of beef cattle, sheep, swine, and rabbits, it is necessary to select for more than one characteristic. Some of the characteristics, such as rate

258

of gain, feed efficiency, and grade, are expressed in both sexes; others, such as litter size and milking ability, are expressed only in the female.

The primary reason for using an index is to compare animals for over-all merit. Comparing animals for five or six characteristics at the same time without over or underemphasizing certain traits is extremely difficult. To give proper weight to each trait requires considerable judgment as well as a knowledge of heritability and the relative economic importance of the various traits. Lush (1943) pointed out that one needs the following information to properly construct an index:

1. Heritability of each trait
2. Economic importance of each trait
3. Genetic correlations between the traits
4. Environmental correlations between the traits
5. Standard deviation for each trait

Winters (1954) stressed the importance of the need for a particular trait in the herd or flock. For example, the average litter size in one herd of hogs may be 12 while in another herd it is 6. A breeder may have no desire to increase litter size in the first herd, but it is very important that litter size be increased in the second herd. This can be done in one of two ways: selection for litter size on an independent culling level basis and selection for the other traits by use of the index. More emphasis in the index for litter size in the second herd could be allowed on the basis that litter size will be of greater economic importance than it would if this weakness in it were not corrected.

Heritability and economic importance may be more important than genotypic or environmental correlations. For example, Lush (1943) reported an index developed for swine on the basis of heritability and economic importance in which weight at 180 days, score for market desirability, sow productivity, average litter weight, and average litter score were used. Later, it was changed to take into consideration the genetic and environmental correlations. The efficiency of the two indexes were 0.404 for the second and 0.364 for the first. This means that with the index based on economic importance and heritability alone, selection was 36 per cent of what it could have been had the genotype of the pigs been known, whereas the inclusion of genetic and environmental correlations so improved the efficiency of the index that 40 per cent was obtained.

In setting up an index for a particular ranch or for a certain herd or flock, it is best if all the information used in the index can be determined from that herd or flock. Heritabilities determined under one set of conditions may not be applicable to another. In case no data are available on the herd with which one is concerned, it may be necessary at first to use heritability estimates from some similar area and set of conditions. In the broad sense, heritability is the ratio of the variance due to genetic differences divided by total variance, or

$$\text{Heritability} = \frac{\text{genetic variance}}{\text{total variance}}$$

The genetic variance is made up of that which is due to additive genetic (σ_G^2), dominance (σ_D^2), and epistatic (σ_I^2) effects. Total variance includes all the genetic variance plus environmental (σ_E^2) variance. Thus, in a broad sense, heritability is

$$\frac{\sigma_G^2 + \sigma_D^2 + \sigma_I^2}{\sigma_G^2 + \sigma_D^2 + \sigma_I^2 + \sigma_E^2}$$

It is often the practice to use heritability in the narrow sense, i.e., the ratio of the variance due to additive genetic effects divided by the total variance, or

$$\frac{\sigma_G^2}{\sigma_G^2 + \sigma_D^2 + \sigma_I^2 + \sigma_E^2}$$

The strictly additive genetic variations are the ones that are easiest to improve by selection if the heritability is high because they respond to any type of selection program used.

Let us now understand the reason for determining heritabilities for traits in the herd or flock with which we are working. If there is not much genetic variation due to homozygosity or some other cause, the additive genetic effect σ_G^2, the numerator in the ratio, will be small. This will give a low heritability. If the environment fluctuates greatly and differs from animal to animal, σ_E^2 will be large and will make the denominator in the ratio large. This will also give a low heritability. If we are dealing with a trait that is highly homozygous and has a consequent low heritability, selection will be relatively ineffective. Selection for some other trait of higher heritability would be much more effective. If environmental factors account for most of the variations in a trait, little can be done toward improving this trait until a more uniform environment is created. When this has been accomplished, heritability will be increased and selection will be more effective. Many mistakes are made in selection when environmental variations are large. Therefore, one should strive in an improvement program to reduce these variations to a minimum or to make corrections for these differences. This means that conditions should be standardized as much as possible, but it does not imply that conditions necessarily need to be improved.

PROCEDURE FOR CONSTRUCTING AN INDEX

In order to use a phenotypic scale of merit, one has to have knowledge of how much each of the components contributes to the economic value of the total or aggregate phenotype. The example that has been used thus far has an aggregate phenotype X_P which is made up of two components, trait X_1 and X_2, in such a way that its value is determined by

$$X_P = m_1X_1 + m_2X_2$$

where m coefficients represent the economic weights of the component traits.

The aggregate genotype (Hazel, 1943) corresponding to X_P, which shall be referred to as H, is then determined by

$$H = m_1G_1 + m_2G_2$$

where G_1 and G_2 are the expected values of the x_i due to additive gene effects.*

One can see from the preceding equation that the variance of H is entirely genetic and consists of the sum of the variances of its components, plus the co-variance between the two traits.

$$\sigma_H{}^2 = m_1{}^2G_{11} + m_2{}^2G_{22} + 2m_1m_2G_{12}$$

The genetic variances and covariances between the traits were estimated to be (from sire component)

$$G_{11} = 0.7957 \qquad G_{12} = 0.0326728 \qquad G_{22} = 0.0013499$$

With these variances, covariances, and m values, the right-hand sides of the equations can be computed $(i, j = 1, 2 \cdots n)$.

$$\varepsilon_j m_j G_{1j} = m_1G_{11} + m_2G_{12} = 15\,(0.7957) + 3(0.0326728) = 12.0335$$
$$\varepsilon_j m_j G_{2j} = m_1G_{21} + m_2G_{22} = 15\,[0.0326728 + 3(0.0013499)] = 0.4941$$

The relative economic weights to be used are

$$m_1 = 15 \text{ units}$$
$$m_2 = 3 \text{ units}$$

* x_i = expected values of G_1 and G_2. $G_1 = X_1$ and $G_2 = X_2$ for the additive effects of traits of 1 and 2.

in which m_i are the relative economic values which measure the amount by which profit is expected to increase for each unit change in x_i.

The phenotypic variances and covariances are found to be

$$X_{11} = 1.65083 \qquad X_{12} = 0.0633513$$
$$X_{21} = 0.0633513 \qquad X_{22} = 0.0025225$$

The equations to be solved are then formed from the phenotypic variances and covariances; thus,

$$b_1 (1.65083) + b_2 (0.0633513) = 12.0335$$
$$b_1 (0.0633513) + b_2 (0.0025225) = 0.4941$$

or in symbolic terms,

$$b_1 X_{11} + b_2 X_{12} = \varepsilon_j m_j G_{i_j}$$
$$b_1 X_{21} + b_2 X_{22} = \varepsilon_j m_j G_{2_j}$$

The above matrix can be solved by using the abbreviated Doolittle method; (Dwyer, 1942) thus,

1.65083	0.0632513	=	12.0335
	0.0025225	=	0.4941
1.65083	0.0632513		12.0335
1.0	0.038375		7.28936
	0.00009139		0.0323144
	1.0		353.5879

$$b_2 = 353.5879$$
$$b_1 = 7.28936 - (353.5879 \times 0.038375) = -6.279575$$

The index resulting from the solution of these equations is

$$I = -6.279575X_1 + 353.5879X_2$$

The variance of I is

$$\sigma_I^2 = b_1^2 X_1 X_1 + b_2^2 X_2 X_2 + 2b_1 b_2 X_1 X_2$$
$$\sigma_I^2 = 39.43306 (1.65083) + 125,024.403 (0.0025225) - 2(2220.3817)$$
$$(0.0633513) = 99.1429$$
$$\sigma_H^2 = m_1^2 G_{11} + m_2^2 G_{22} + 2m_1 m_2 G_{12}$$
$$\sigma_H^2 = 225 (0.7957) + 0.012149 + 2(45 \times 0.0326728)$$
$$\sigma_H^2 = 181.985199$$

The correlation between I and H is

$$r_{HI} = \sqrt{\frac{\sigma_I^2}{\sigma_H^2}} = \sqrt{\frac{99.1429}{181.985199}} = \sqrt{0.5447855} = 0.738$$

The correlation between the aggregate genotype and the selection index gives a measure of the efficiency of a selection index. In other words, the correlation r_{HI} expresses the accuracy of identifying the genotypes.

DAIRY-SIRE INDEXING

Let us now consider the use of an index based on one trait which is expressed only in one sex. In dairy cattle it is very desirable to estimate a bull's transmitting ability. Since he produces no milk, one has to consider the production of his ancestors, the production of his half-sibs, or the production of his daughters. Estimating a bull's transmitting ability on the basis of the production of his daughters is a progeny test, and it is on this basis that most sire indexes of dairy cattle have been developed. Since it is assumed that the production of the daughters is determined by the inheritance from the sire and the dams, knowledge of the production of the dams and of the daughters makes possible the construction of an index.

Some basic factors must be given consideration.

1. A young cow will not produce as much milk as she will when she becomes mature, and to allow for this, correction factors have been determined. It is best to use a factor that has been developed for a particular breed for cattle of that breed. For example, a Jersey breeder would be wise to use a factor for converting production to a mature equivalent which was developed for Jersey cattle rather than for another breed or for all breeds combined. In fact, a large breeder might do well to develop a correction factor for his own herd based on production records of his herd. An illustration of the importance of age as a factor that influences milk production can be shown by the conversion factors which have been determined for cows of different breeds (Table 20).

Table 20. CONVERSION FACTORS FOR ADJUSTING MILK PRODUCTION
TO A MATURE EQUIVALENT BASIS

Age at Freshening	Jersey, Guernsey and Ayrshire	Brown Swiss and Shorthorn	Holstein
2	1.262	1.538	1.377
3	1.141	1.286	1.203
4	1.063	1.136	1.077
5	1.020	1.052	1.017
6	1.000	1.012	1.000
7	1.000	1.000	1.006
8	1.012	1.000	1.018
9	1.024	1.006	1.054
10	1.047	1.030	1.090
12	1.112	1.114	1.192

If a two-year-old Jersey cow produced 8,000 lb. of milk, this production of 8,000 lb. × the conversion factor of 1.262 would give 10,096 lb. as the corrected mature equivalent production of this cow.

2. Cows that are milked more often will give more milk than those milked only twice per day. It has been the practice to convert the production of all cows to a basis of twice-a-day milking. If a cow has been milked three times a day for the entire lactation period of 305 days, her production would be multiplied by 0.8333 to adjust it to the basis of milking twice a day. The production of a cow milked four times a day for the entire lactation period of 305 days would be converted to twice-a-day milking by multiplying by 0.7407.

3. The length of the lactation period must be known. Most records are on the basis of a lactation period of 305 days. If records are not obtained during a lactation period of 305 days, they should be converted to 305 days (or some constant period) for proper index comparisons.

Although a sire index is a valuable tool for estimating the breeding value of an animal in which the trait is not expressed, it may be subject to errors. Differences between the estimated and the actual breeding value of a bull may be great because of discrepancies between the phenotype and true breeding value of the females to which the bull is mated or of the daughters sired by the bull.

1. The level of environment under which the record of the dams was established may differ markedly from the environment under which the record of the daughters is established. This error is likely to be large if the dams and daughters are producing at two different farms where management, etc., are under different personnel. It can be also large where marked improvements are made in management and feeding on the same farm, particularly if the record of the dams is made long before the record of the daughters. It is easy to see that a bull would show a desirable index if the records of the dams were made under a severe environment and they averaged 8,000 lb. while the records of the daughters were made under a very favorable environment and their adjusted average was 11,000 lb., even though the general productive ability of the dams and the daughters may have been the same. Other errors can be made when such conditions as disease or a severe season which lowers production affect either the dams or the daughters but not both. Corrections may be attempted where such discrepancies exist. The difficulty arises in being able to make corrections without introducing error which may be as great as that existing where no corrections were made. Also, many differences in environment between the dams and the daughters may not be known.

2. The daughters for which records are available may be a selected group rather than a representative sample of all daughters sired by the bull under test. The best or ideal method is to take the entire population sired by a bull. A breeder could be anxious to get the bull indexed and might take the first six to ten daughters. This would be sound if the matings to the bull had been to a random group of cows.

3. The dams of the daughters may have been a selected group. This can introduce some error, but it is likely to be less than the errors due to environmental differences or selected daughters.

The discrepancies resulting from dominance or epistatic effects are likely to be random and, consequently, should tend to pull the index of a bull up and down with about equal force. There can be some error from these effects, but it would be difficult to make adjustments to compensate for it. If one or a very few epistatic genes are involved, there could be considerable error.

Several methods have been proposed for indexing a bull. Pearl, et al (1919), were among the earlier workers to present an index. They suggested the quartile method which is based on dividing the Advanced Registry records into quartiles and then classifying the offspring of a sire in terms of percentage on the basis of the relative standing of each dam with her daughter. The method may become very complicated. Furthermore, it fails to give an index on the basis of milk production in pounds so that it is difficult to compare the index of one bull with that of another.

Yapp (1924) proposed the index $X = 2A - B$, where X is the index of the sire's transmitting ability, A is average production of the daughters converted to a 4 per cent butterfat basis, and B is the production of the dams, also converted to 4 per cent butterfat. If a bull is bred to cows with average production of 4 per cent milk of 8,000 lb., and the adjusted production of the daughters is 10,000 lb. of 4 per cent milk, then

$$\text{Sire's index} = 2\,(10,000 - 8,000) = 20,000 - 8,000 \text{ or } 12,000 \text{ lb.}$$

This index is based on the assumption that milk production ability is inherited equally from the sire and dam. It does have two important advantages. In the first place, it is relatively very simple. In the second place, the converting of milk production to a basis of 4 per cent butterfat removes the necessity for having a separate index for milk and for butterfat production. Also, this index permits direct comparison of two bulls. It combines the average of the daughters plus the average increase or minus the average decrease of the daughters over the dams. It is expressed in the same production terms as the cows are producing; therefore, one can compare an index with cow production. It can be affected by selected daughters or selected dams being used. Although a more accurate index will be discussed later, this index is one of the better ones, and where random matings to cows is practiced and the daughters are representative of the production of the sire, it has real value on a given farm where management is generally constant.

Turner (1925) suggested that a sire's transmitting ability equals the daughter's fat production minus 0.15 of the dam's fat production divided by 0.85. If the dams averaged 400 lb. of butterfat and the daughters average 440 lbs.

$$\text{Sire's index} = \frac{440 - (400 \times 0.15)}{0.85} = 447 \text{ lb.}$$

This implies partial dominance on the part of the bull or gives him more importance than the cow. One would not be inclined to agree with this implication because the general evidence supports the assumption of equal inheritance from sire and dam. Sex-linked genes would not be inherited equally in all the offspring (both sons and daughters) from sire and dam. However, one would expect the daughters to inherit sex-linked genes equally from the sire and dam.

Graves (1926) suggested that the difference between the record of the dams and that of the daughters equals the bull index. It would not be difficult to make the index positive for all bulls by adding a given amount to the index of each. This index is not expressed in general production figures and might be difficult to understand. It is probably less affected by environment than any other index. It does not take into account differences in the average production level of the dams to which different bulls might be mated. This would be unfair to bulls mated to high producing cows and too generous to bulls mated to cows of low production. For example, if two bulls that actually had a transmitting ability of 10,000 lb. of milk were mated, one to dams averaging 6,000 lb. and one to cows averaging 12,000 lb., the results would differ. The first bull would have +2,000 while the second would have −1,000 (or approximately these figures), with a difference of 3,000 lb. of milk in favor of one bull over the other.

Goodale (1927) proposed the Mount Hope index for milk production and for butterfat percentage. He based his index on crossbreeding studies (Gowen, 1920) done at Mount Hope Farm and other Jersey sires used at the Maine station, as well as on sires of different breeds used by the U.S.D.A. It is based on the assumption of partial dominance for high milk production and for low fat percentage.

The Mount Hope milk index compares the mature equivalent production of the dams and daughters. If the production of the daughters exceeds that of the dams, three-sevenths (0.4286) of the difference is added to the average production of the daughters to obtain the sire index. If the mature equivalent of the dams is 8,000 lb. and that of the daughters is 9,000 lb., then the index of the bull is 9,000 + 0.4286 (1,000) = 9,429 lb. If the average production of the daughters is below that of the dams, seven-thirds (2.333) of the difference is subtracted from the average production of the daughters to obtain the index of the bull. Therefore, if the mature equivalent production of the daughters is 8,000 lb. and that of the dams is 9,000 lb., the index of the bull = 9,000 − (1,000 × 2.333) = 6,667 lb.

The Mount Hope index of butterfat percentage is calculated in a similar manner to that of milk production but different constants are used. If the percentage of butterfat is higher in the milk produced by the daughters than that produced by the dams, three-halves (1.5) of the difference is added to the percentage produced by the daughters to obtain the bull's index. If the percentage of butterfat is lower in the milk produced by the daughters than that produced by the dams, two-thirds (0.6667) of the difference is subtracted from the percentage of fat which is in the milk produced by the daughters to obtain the index of the bull.

One objection to this index is that bulls must be compared on the basis of two indexes rather than one. How to get the two into one figure so that bulls can be compared directly is an additional problem.

Gifford (1930) proposed an index based on a study of Guernseys made at the University of Missouri. This is the simplest, and perhaps one of the best for comparing bulls in the same herd where they are randomly mated to cows. The bull's index will be the average production of his daughters, with the production of the dams ignored entirely. However, the index is highly influenced by differences in environment from herd to herd, and unless herd averages are used in adjusting for these differences, it will be useful only for selecting bulls within a given herd.

Wright (1931) distinguished between three types of matings. In a mating of a bull to an individual cow, the results are best predicted by multiple regression, provided all the necessary correlation coefficients are known. If the bull is mated to cows in the same herd, the results are best predicted by records from daughters by this bull when mated to cows in the herd. Thus, Wright confirmed the usefulness of the average production of daughters of a bull, as suggested by Gifford, as a good index when the bull is tested in the same herd in which he is to be used later.

To determine the general transmitting ability of a bull when he is mated to a random group of cows within the breed, Wright took into consideration the number of dam-daughter pairs and the breed average. Where the number of dam-daughter pairs is small, the breed average will be more important, but where the number of pairs is large, the dam-daughter comparisons will become more important.

This index is quite complicated but prevents large errors with small numbers, which could be made with other indexes. It is perhaps the most accurate but the most complicated index to use.

Rice (1944) proposed a regression index which is obtained by adding to the breed average the difference between the daughters' actual and "normally expected" production.

Regression index $= W + (d-e)$ where $W =$ breed average, $d =$ daughters' actual production, and $e =$ daughters' expected production. The expected production of the daughters would be approximately halfway between the production of the dam and the breed average. This index moves very low or very high equal-parent indexes halfway back to the breed average. It probably has merit in reducing the effects of these extremes.

One should give attention to the records of other animals, besides the records of the daughters of a bull, in order to evaluate him most accurately. If the records of his dam and sisters or half-sisters are considered in addition to the records of his daughters, greater accuracy will result. However, the complexity of taking into consideration all the relatives of a bull is so great that one may not want to consider the more remotely related animals.

Lush (1931, 1933, 1935, and 1943) gave careful consideration to such factors as number of daughters necessary to test a bull and the errors that may be made by use of the different indexes. He recognized that greater accuracy is obtained with more dam-daughter comparisons, but he also saw the need for a valid test on a minimum number and suggested that perhaps six to ten daughters could be considered sufficient. He emphasized the effects of environmental differences between herds or between one generation and the next. He also pointed to the errors that can be introduced into an index when the dams or the daughters are a selected group.

Hayden (1946) showed that it is difficult to maintain a high producing herd by selecting unproven sires on the basis of their line of breeding and the production of their dams.

Hall, et al (1948), stated that young unproven bulls are a gamble. One out of four young bulls sired by bulls with an index of 500 lb. butterfat and out of dams with production records of 500 lb. of butterfat will sire daughters that average below 400 lb. of butterfat.

These studies demonstrate the need for a sound indexing program. Since it is very difficult for a small breeder to prove bulls himself, he is faced with the problem of locating highly indexed bulls his small operation can justify. One method of obtaining the inheritance of bulls that have proven their transmitting ability is to cooperate with other small breeders in the ownership of such animals. Some small breeders make use of semen from outstanding bulls through artificial insemination. Outstanding older bulls may be used by a small breeder to advantage.

The small breeders who are giving a great deal of thought to improving the herd because their living depends upon good production make a great contribution to the over-all improvement of livestock. In addition, these small breeders help to maintain desirable genetic diversity. When the selection of breeding stock is left in the hands of a few people, as it would be if all cattle were bred through artificial insemination, all mistakes would be very serious. The loss of genetic diversity resulting from such a program might make it impossible to rectify mistakes. Therefore, it is even more important that bulls used in artificial insemination should be selected with the greatest care.

One bit of caution is needed. A bull that has been proven may or may not be the one to use. Too often a breeder may have the impression that a proven bull will surely be the one to use. If the animal has proven himself to be only average or below, he is still a proven bull but not one to be used in a good herd. The level of the index is very important, but one should remember that a bull with a high index may not always transmit high production which is equal to his index. If several proven bulls are used, it is fairly certain that their average transmitting value will be approximately equal to the average index. This gives us a good indication that indexed bulls in general will transmit in accordance with the index but that a particular bull may index much higher or lower than he transmits. Small differences in indexes probably do not mean much.

One could at first assume that, since milk and butterfat production is the reason for keeping dairy cattle, the only consideration in selecting dairy cattle would be milk and butterfat production. However, there are other points to be considered. Records may be established early in the life of an animal that are quite high. However, she must be able to continue at a high rate of production over a long life time. Replacing young cows that do not have the vigor to hold up in high production is very expensive. A good cow must be a regular breeder to assure that she is not out of production unduly. Vigor in early life is necessary for raising the calf and getting it into production at an early age. All these factors need consideration in addition to production records on the cows and indexes on the bulls.

EXERCISES

1. What characteristics should a selection index possess in order to be most effective?

2. In an over-all merit index what information is needed for its construction?

3. By use of equations, define heritability in (a) the broad sense, and (b) the narrow sense.

4. Explain how the differences in (a) environmental variations and (b) genetic variations can influence heritability. What can a producer do to influence these genetic or environmental variations?

5. In dairy-sire indexing what are some of the basic considerations that must be given attention?

19

GENETIC CONTROL POPULATIONS

Studies regarding the effectiveness of selection or systems of breeding for bringing about improvement in animal performance are difficult to evaluate because of probable changes in environment which may occur. Some investigators have attempted to overcome the effects of environmental changes by selecting one group in the positive direction and another group in the negative direction. Evaluation of the effects of selection are made by the two groups, and the difference between them is accepted as the measure of the effectiveness of selection.

SELECTION IN OPPOSITE DIRECTIONS

The selection of hogs by the Illinois station was made in both directions; one line was selected for heavier weight while the other line was selected for lighter weight at six months of age. Similarly, Warren and Bogart (1952) selected rats for early and for late sexual maturity based on age at time of vaginal opening. In both selection experiments, the difference between the lines which were selected in opposite directions was considered as due to genetic change resulting from selection. Both experiments could be subject to chance variations, since only one line was developed by selection in each direction. It would have been better if two or more lines of rats had been selected for early maturity and a similar number of lines for late sexual maturity so that some estimate of the variation between lines selected for the same trait could have been made. Also, because selection was applied in both directions, no information was obtained on the relative response to selection in the two directions. It is possible that selection for earlier sexual maturity might have been entirely ineffective for a larger number of lines, while selection for late sexual maturity might have been quite effective.

It could be concluded from the difference found that selection by use of

270

differences between lines in opposite directions would result in developing animals which mature sexually at a younger age. This conclusion might be entirely invalid because of a certain physiological limitation which would prevent sexual maturity at an early age.

The inspection of the data on selecting rats shows that those selected for later sexual maturity responded, whereas those selected for earlier sexual maturity did not show this characteristic at a younger age. In fact, even those selected for early sexual maturity were older at sexual maturity after three generations of selection than were the original stock. The two lines did separate markedly in age of sexual maturity. These data do not provide information from which a decision can be reached relative to the response of selection in opposite directions.

The logical comparison would have been made from a genetically stabilized group of animals. Such a genetic control group could have shown the environmental changes which were occurring, and from this comparison the studies could have determined how effective selection in each direction could be in influencing age at sexual maturity.

Various attempts have been made for providing a control group. At the Oregon station selection of sheep has been made for high and low fertility in two inbred lines. The change in fertility in each of these two lines is compared with changes in fertility which occur during the same time in the college flock of the same breed. The results indicate that selection for high fertility is less effective than the depressing effect of inbreeding in a one-sire herd. Even though selection for greater fertility in the "high" line was applied, fertility of the line steadily decreased. Selection for reduced fertility for three generations in the "low" line, in addition to the depressing effect of inbreeding on fertility, reduced fertility in this line to such a level that no further selection could be practiced because of sterility. At the same time that fertility changes occurred in the two lines, there were no general changes occurring in fertility in the college flock. However, this college flock of sheep was not a genetically stabilized group of animals, since selection pressure was being applied on it for several traits.

COMPARISON OF SELECTION METHODS

If one wishes to appraise improvement made by developing and combining inbred lines with selection in a noninbred population, this can be done directly by comparing the two programs. However, measurement of the amount of improvement made by either program will require a genetically controlled population for comparison. Certainly, the fact that performance level from selection was equal to performance level from combining inbred lines can be only of limited value. Suppose no improvement resulted from either program; then they would be equal but neither would offer much in the hands of a breeder.

DEVELOPING A GENETICALLY STABLE POPULATION

A genetically stable population would be quite desirable as a control group for measuring the genetic progress being made by selection or by various breeding methods. This population, in which inheritance showed no general change, either up or down, would reflect by phenotypic expression general environmental changes that were occurring. A comparison of another group with this genetically stable group would make it possible to determine how much change in the genetically changing group was due to genetic and how much was due to environmental changes.

A genetically stable population should be one in which no selection is occurring and one in which homozygosity or heterozygosity is not increasing. Intentional selection may be prevented from occurring by randomly choosing replacement animals to continue the population. This does not prevent natural selection from operating. It can be seen that if our objective in breeding farm animals is opposed to the natural forces, when selection by man is no longer practiced then natural selection will bring about genetic changes. Suppose that the kind of animal that has been considered desirable in a prior selection program shows this desirability because of an endocrine unbalance. When selection is no longer practiced for this endocrine unbalance, natural selection will tend to favor the balanced endocrine condition. Poultry breeders have studied changes that took place in a previously selected population when selection was discontinued (Lerner and Dempster, 1951). One might generalize that for those traits in which selection has been in line with natural selection, no change should occur, but that when selection has been opposed to natural selection, natural selection can be expected to bring about genetic changes when artificial selection is discontinued.

Two factors might cause a noninbred, genetically constant population to be inadequate controls for comparing with inbred animals. In the first place inbred strains may react much more violently to adverse conditions than do noninbreds. In the second place, noninbreds can be expected to fluctuate genetically with changes in the environment. The first of these factors would be very important in large-animal research. The second factor would not be expected to play an important role where generation interval requires such a long period of time as it does with most of our farm animals.

The discussions by several workers (Dickerson, 1955; Lerner and Dempster, 1951; Robertson, 1955) show that genetic changes are probably to be expected when rigorous selection is relaxed. There is a tendency for the selected population to slip in performance when this relaxation of selection occurs. Consequently, the genetically constant population group would need to be established for control purposes well in advance of its need. In this way the relaxation in selection pressure could allow the control population to become stabilized. After a population is stabilized genetically, its shortcomings are largely concerned with the less violent reaction it will express as a result of adverse conditions.

If we assume that changes from natural selection will not be great, a genetically stable population could be bred, providing certain conditions are met, although a relatively large number of breeding animals would be necessary in the control population. This large number would tend to prevent increases in homozygosity which would result from inbreeding in a very small group and might also prevent chance selections, either up or down, that might occur if the population were small and only a few replacements were kept. It would be necessary to use a relatively large number of males in this control population to hold down inbreeding and to give random selection of the males a better chance for sampling the entire population.

In order to prevent natural selection from operating too strongly, probably only one replacement female from each dam would be kept. However, this practice could not be followed continuously because female replacements for those dams which produced no female offspring would have to come from some dam that was being replaced by one of her daughters. If this were not done, the control group in succeeding generations would grow smaller in size.

Replacement males and females would be selected at random from those raised to breeding age. Sterile animals leave no replacements, and therefore these animals and the offspring that die, because of accidents or because of inheritance which does not enable them to cope with their environment, would not contribute genetic material for the next generation. This is selection imposed by nature which is operating in the control population. This same type of natural selection should be operating in the groups which are to be compared with the control group; consequently, the bias from natural selection should not be extreme.

There are some differences of opinion as to whether males are to be mated to females entirely on a random basis or if the mating of close relatives is to be prevented. Certainly, the mating of close relatives increases the inbreeding and brings about increased homozygosity. However, the prevention of close matings might tend to maintain greater heterozygosity, which would give more heterosis than would be expected in a freely breeding population.

It would be preferable to allot at random the females to the males during each breeding season rather than to mate the females to the same males for several seasons. Some researchers assert that a definite attempt should be made to assure that no female is bred to a male for any two seasons. Others are of the opinion that breeding for each season should be strictly at random.

So far only general observations have been presented on how a genetically stable population could be maintained. Poultry research personnel consider a population of 250 females and 50 males as adequate for maintaining a genetically stable population. A group of animals of this size certainly should be sufficient in animals that have such a high reproductive rate, and there should be no difficulties from increasing homozygosity when so many males are used. With this number of females and with a high reproductive rate, the population should be quite stable and should serve well as a control population. For our larger farm animals the cost of maintaining such a large control population would be great. Furthermore the reproductive rate in the larger farm animals is low, and it would be difficult to maintain a genetically stable population because of expense, facilities needed, etc., over the longer period required. Therefore the objective with large animals is to maintain the minimum size population in the controls which will offer reasonable accuracy.

It seems logical to suppose that genetic control in cattle would require a herd of minimum size equal to that needed in sheep. For the latter Terrill (1951) considers that a breeding flock of 50 ewes and 10 rams is the minimum for a control flock that will function as a genetically stable population. (A flock twice this size would be better.) But in cattle this would mean a herd of 50 breeding cows and 10 bulls. In such a program the heifer and bull replacements would be selected randomly and the females would be randomly allotted to the males for breeding. Some care might be given before randomizing to prevent males and females by the same sire from being allotted to the same breeding groups. Young bulls could be used for breeding so that the cost of maintaining bulls could be reduced by one year. The productivity of this genetically stable group should be satisfactory, and the only added costs in maintaining such a group over any other group of commercial cattle would be due to the large number of males needed.

A college might find such a genetically stable herd quite valuable for teaching purposes as well as useful for evaluating progress made by selection or by different breeding methods. It appears, however, that only the larger experimental units will be in a position to maintain a genetically stable herd of beef cattle, swine, or sheep for control purposes. One way that such a control herd of flock could be made available to smaller research units would be to maintain the control herd or flock at a central testing station. Breeding material from the cooperating research units could be sampled and tested for performance at the central testing station. This could be done either by using breeding stock from the cooperating units on females at the central testing station or by bringing young animals to the central testing station for performance test purposes.

Unless a central testing station can be established, it appears that the only evaluation which can be made by smaller research stations will be the comparison of the performance of one generation with that of another after adjustments for year effects are made. Obviously this is not the most accurate way to evaluate progress made, but it may be the only means available.

EXERCISES

1. Determine the number of males and females necessary and how they are to be mated in order to create and maintain a genetically stabilized population acting as a control.

2. In a population previously under intense selection for a trait, what will occur in this trait when selection pressure is released?

20

GENETIC-ENDOCRINE INTERRELATIONS

ENDOCRINE PHYSIOLOGY

The endocrine or ductless glands produce hormones which affect the development and function of the animal. A hormone is a chemical substance which is secreted by a ductless gland into the blood stream, which in turn carries the hormone to some other part of the body where it has an effect. There are two general types of abnormal condition for most endocrine glands: one, the hyper- or overactive endocrine gland, and the other, the hypo- or underactive endocrine gland.

Hormones are considered to have specific target organs on which they act, but every hormone may directly or indirectly affect the secretions of the other endocrine glands or may affect the response of the target organs or glands to the secretions of the other glands. Thus, the endocrine system is very complex, and simple alterations may induce many varied and complicated changes throughout the organism.

The pituitary, or hypophysis, is located at the base of the brain (Fig. 128)

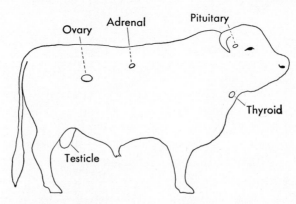

Fig. 128. Outline drawing of a beef animal showing the location of some major endocrine glands.

and is composed of three general regions: the anterior lobe, the posterior lobe, and the intermediate region, called the *pars intermedia*. The anterior lobe is the one about which much is known. The *anterior pituitary* secretes:

1. Growth hormone which controls the general growth of the soft tissues and the long bones.
2. The lactation hormone, known as *prolactin, galactin,* or *lactogen,* which stimulates milk secretion.
3. The follicle-stimulating hormone (F.S.H.) stimulates follicular development in the ovary and spermatogenesis in the semeniferous tubules of the testes. The luteinizing hormone (L.H.) stimulates corpus luteum formation in the ovary and androgen output by the interstitial cells in the testes.
4. Thyrotropic hormone, which stimulates the development and function of the thyroid gland, thus causing the thyroid gland to secrete its hormone, thyroxine.
5. Adrenotropic hormone, which stimulates the adrenal cortex to function in the secretion of its hormone.

There are some other hormones secreted by the anterior pituitary, but their functions are not so well known and will not be discussed fully.

The *posterior pituitary* secretes (1) *pitocin,* or oxytocin, which stimulates contraction of smooth muscle such as that in the uterus (it is used to speed up delivery of young); and (2) *pitressin,* the pressor and diuretic-antidiuretic principle.

The *thyroid* gland, which is located on each side of the trachea posterior to the larynx or Adam's apple (Fig. 128) secretes thyroxine, which regulates metabolic rate.

The *ovary* consists of two glands, the *follicle,* which secretes *estrogen,* and the *corpus luteum,* which secretes *progesterone.* The estrogens (estrone, estradiol, and estriol) stimulate the epithelial lining of the vagina to thicken and become cornified, the epithelial lining of the uterus to thicken and start preparation for receiving the egg, the liquefaction of the mucous plug of the cervix so that sperm may pass from the vagina to the uterus, the motility of the oviducts (Fallopian tubes) and their fimbriated ends. The estrogens also cause the female to become receptive (estrus); they stimulate duct development of the mammary glands, either acting directly on the mammary tissue or through the pituitary by stimulating the production of mammogen.

Progesterone stimulates progestational proliferation of the uterus (final preparation of the uterus for receiving the egg, including the production of uterine milk, a fluid from which the egg may obtain nutrient material prior to implantation), quiets the motility of the uterine tubes and oviducts, and stimulates alveolar development of the mammary gland, either acting directly on the mammary tissue or indirectly through the pituitary and causing it to produce a mammogen material.

The *testes* (Fig. 128) secrete *testosterone,* which stimulates the development and function of the accessory reproductive organs such as the Cowper's glands, the prostate, and the seminal vesicles. It also causes the development of secondary sexual characters and gives sex drive to the male.

The *parathyroids* (located near the thyroid gland) secrete *parathormone,* which is concerned with calcium metabolism.

The *adrenal* glands (Fig. 128), also called the *suprarenal* glands, are located anterior and somewhat mesially to the kidneys. The adrenals are really two glands in one. The *medulla* of the adrenal produces *epinephrine* or *adrenaline,* which brings about excitability of the animal. The *cortex* of the adrenal produces the steroid hormones which are necessary for life. They function in carbohydrate metabolism, electrolyte balance, and nitrogen retention.

The estrogens act on the pituitary to reduce its output of F.S.H. and initiate the output of L.H. Thyroxine acts on the pituitary to reduce the output of thyrotropin. If for some reason the thyroid is incapable of secreting thyroxine, the pituitary continues to secrete large amounts of thyrotropin. This may result in proliferation of thyroid tissue to the extent that a goiter is produced. Thyroxine also acts on the metabolism of all the body. If a hypothyroid state exists, the tissues of the body may not respond to hormones produced by the other glands.

This very brief review of the hormones is presented as a background so that inherited dysfunctions of the endocrine glands can be understood.

A disturbance in the function of the pituitary may affect the individual directly or through its effects on some other glands such as the thyroid gland or the gonads. Similarly, an observed disturbance in the function of the thyroid gland or the gonads may be due to an abnormality of these glands or may be caused by a pituitary disturbance expressed through the thyroid or gonads.

Dwarfism may be due to a reduced output of the growth hormone or to a reduced output of thyroxine by the thyroid gland. The age at which a disturbance occurs in the pituitary or thyroid glands affects the way the disturbance will be expressed. For example, a hypothyroid condition early in life results in cretinism, a disproportionate dwarf condition in which the animal is short-legged, is broad through the shoulders, and has a broad, bulging forehead. A hypothyroid condition later in life results in myxedema in which metabolism is low, the skin is dry and the hair dull, the animal is lethargic, and there may be a tendency to become fat.

The age at which a hyperpituitary condition develops influences its effects. A hyperpituitary condition in the young animal results in giant development, whereas in older animals there is an overgrowth of the long bones.

GENETIC ASPECTS OF ENDOCRINE DISTURBANCES

The most thoroughly studied inherited endocrine disturbance in which the pituitary is the gland involved is that of the dwarf mouse. Snell (1929) reported that the dwarf is inherited as a simple recessive. The dwarfs reached about one-fourth the size of the normals, although growth was normal up to about the fourteenth day. The dwarfs were proportional in structure but they were sterile. De Beer and Gruneberg (1940) found a lack of eosinophils (acidophilic cells) in the anterior pituitary.

Smith and MacDowell (1930 and 1931) found that the thyroids and adrenals of the dwarf mouse were reduced in size and showed structural derangement. These workers proved that the dwarf gene affected the growth-hormone output of the pituitary. Implants of anterior pituitary from normal animals stimulated growth in the dwarf mice. Bio-assay of the pituitaries from dwarf mice showed a high concentration of gonad-stimulating hormone but a complete lack of growth hormone. There was a great similarity of the dwarf mouse with a hypophysectomized nondwarf. In both cases growth was absent or far below normal. However, the reproductive tracts of the dwarf and the hypophysectomized mice were entirely different. The reproductive tracts of the dwarf mice showed the influence of stimulation from the pituitary, whereas the hypophysectomized animal showed gonads completely lacking in pituitary stimulation. A cytological study of the pituitary showed a complete lack of eosinophils. There may be some diminution in the thyrotropic and adrenotropic output by the pituitary of dwarf mice. The thyroid and adrenal glands of these mice were not normal. Bates, et al (1942), reported that the silver dwarf mouse is due to one gene in a chain reaction system. Injection of anterior pituitary fractions into these dwarfs caused a 30 per cent increase in body weight in 30 days.

Mollenbach (1941) described a dwarf mouse which reaches one-fourth to one-third the normal size. These animals differed from those previously described in that they were sterile, while the ones described by Smith and Mac-Dowell were partially fertile. The mice described by Mollenbach had a reduced metabolic rate (60 per cent of normal), and the anterior pituitary was hypoplastic. There was a marked reduction in, or complete lack of, eosinophils in the pituitary. Mollenbach, as well as Mirand and Osborn (1953) found that the dwarf mice were very sensitive to insulin. It appears that the growth, gonad-stimulating and adrenotropic hormones were insufficient in these dwarf mice. The hormones from the adrenal cortex give an animal a higher insulin tolerance. These dwarf mice, which are very susceptible to insulin shock, were expressing a reduced hormone output from the adrenals. Since adrenotropic hormone increased the resistance of the dwarf mice to insulin, it showed that their adrenals were capable of functioning but lacked the stimulus from the pituitary to produce the hormone.

King (1950) reported on a sterile dwarf mouse called "pygmy." This is a simple recessive, with the heterozygotes producing 3 normal:1 dwarf. Both the male and the female dwarfs were completely sterile. It is assumed that the anterior pituitary was abnormal in this case also.

The first case of hereditary dwarfism was described by Sollas (1914) in the guinea pig. His matings of dwarf-producing families gave 192 normal and 64 dwarfs, a ratio which closely approximates 3:1. This is undoubtedly a simple recessive. The dwarf guinea pigs were sterile and reached only one-half the normal size. Many of them died in early life. No analysis was made on the endocrine disturbance, but from the description of the animals, pituitary and/or thyroid disturbances can be assumed.

Castle (1940) reported a dwarf rabbit, which is due to a dominant gene. The heterozygous animals were dwarf even from birth but they were fertile. The dwarf rabbits were about two-thirds the size of the normals at birth and remained dwarf throughout life. When dwarfs were mated together, they produced one normal:2 dwarf:1 homozygous dwarf, which died soon after birth. The homozygous dwarf animals had abnormal jaws and often died of starvation due to inability to obtain food. It was concluded that the dwarf condition resulted from a reduced growth hormone production by the anterior pituitary.

Greene, et al (1934), described a dwarf condition in Polish rabbits. This breed of rabbit is normally very small, but the dwarf gene in the homozygous state reduced the size to one-third the normal for the breed and to two-thirds the size of the heterozygotes. The homozygous dwarfs died shortly after birth, and the heterozygous animals became progressively more afflicted with age. They showed some reproductive disturbance but were not completely sterile. This condition appears to have resulted from a pituitary disturbance.

Greene (1940) gave a more detailed description of the dwarf rabbit. The homozygous dwarfs always die. If the birth weight of the largest litter mate equals 100 per cent, the homozygous dwarf is 35 to 45 per cent, the heterozygotes are 75 per cent, and the normal sibs are 94 per cent as large as the largest litter mate. The heterozygous females tend to become overfat at maturity and are quite susceptible to toxemia of pregnancy during succeeding pregnancies. This is an example of an incompletely recessive character.

Gregory and Goss (1933) found a relationship between racial size and glutathione concentration of the blood in rabbits. They indicated that races differing in size might have resulted from differences in glutathione concentration.

Several cases of inherited disturbances in thyroid function have been reported in farm animals. Bogart and Dyer (1942) described dwarf lambs which showed symptoms of thyroid deficiency such as short legs, thick shoulders, and bulging foreheads. The lambs were born alive but died within five weeks. A histological study of the thyroid showed it to be abnormal. Administration of thyroxine increased the length of life of a dwarf lamb but only for a limited time before it died. There was some evidence that other conditions as well as the thyroid were abnormal.

Dwarfism, which is due to an inherited thyroid hypofunction, was reported in the chick by Mayhew and Upp (1932) and by Landauer (1929). These studies showed a disproportionate growth which was quite retarded. The afflicted birds were susceptible to diseases and had very reduced length of life.

Riddle (1929) reported that thyroid size was inherited in ring doves, and he was able to establish races which differed in thyroid size. However, body weight was not necessarily connected with thyroid size, and it is possible that thyroid size and function in these doves were not associated in all cases.

Dwarfism in beef cattle has been reported by several investigators. Craft and Orr (1924) reported a dwarf calf in which the thyroid gland was only one-fifth the normal size. The pituitary gland was also small, being only one-half the normal size. Lindley (1951) found the thyroid and pituitary glands of dwarf cattle to be almost normal histologically. Carroll, et al (1951), found that pituitaries of dwarf cattle were smaller than those in normal cattle. Also, the content of thyrotropic hormone in the pituitaries from dwarf beef animals was much lower than that found in pituitaries of normal cattle. There was also an indication of normal growth and gonad-stimulating hormones in the pituitaries of the dwarf animals. This would indicate that reduced growth rate and fertility level were the result of the hypothyroid state rather than the direct effect on these traits of a pituitary dysfunction. Very likely the hypothyroid condition resulted from the reduced output of the thyrotropic hormone by the pituitary rather than being due to an inherent defect of the thyroid gland.

Turner (1939) and Adams (1946) found that pituitaries from dairy cattle contain much more thyrotropic hormone than pituitaries from beef cattle. Elijah and Turner (1942) also showed that pigs which grew more rapidly had a higher content of thyrotropin in the pituitaries than the slower gaining pigs. These studies tend to show that a high content of thyrotropin in the pituitary, with its stimulation of greater thyroid activity, is associated with less fattening and greater milk output. That these conditions are under genetic control is suggested by breed and type differences.

Many other examples of inherited endocrine disturbances might be presented here, but the examples given are sufficient to show that many of the disturbances in metabolism, growth, and reproduction are due to inheritance of hypo- or hyperfunction of one or more endocrine glands. The discussions have dealt largely with hypofunction, but disturbances due to hyperfunction of endocrines are also important. Hyperthyroidism is quite serious and family studies show marked differences in incidence. It appears that this condition is under genetic control but not so simple in its inheritance as some of the examples given for inherited hypothyroidism. Hyperpituitarism causes giants if it occurs early in life and overgrowth of parts if it occurs later in life. Some cases of this affliction appear to be under genetic control while others appear to arise from other causes.

The very marked cases of endocrine disturbances have received much attention. Increasing evidence indicates that mild disturbances in endocrine function are also genetically influenced.

EFFECT OF ENDOCRINES ON GENETIC EXPRESSIONS

There is evidence for endocrine influences on genetic expression of characters. Baldness in man in the heterozygous state can be halted by removal of testosterone (castration). When the testosterone is later provided, there is a prompt response in the resumption of hair recession. There are several studies which show that the genes affecting growth are influenced by testosterone. The administration of testosterone into steer and heifer calves at the Oregon station has caused a marked increase in growth rate (Table 21). Whether there are genetic differences in output of testosterone by the testes, which would account for some of the differences in rate of gain in males, is not known. Certainly this is a possibility.

Table 21. THE EFFECT OF TESTOSTERONE ON AVERAGE DAILY GAINS
OF HEIFER AND STEER CALVES

	Gain per day in pounds	
Treatment	Heifers	Steers
Testosterone	2.61	2.74
Control	2.09	2.65

Much of the work which has been reported on endocrine disturbances affecting reproduction is presented in Chap. 22, to which the reader is referred.

EXERCISES

1. Describe the effect of (a) hypo- and (b) hyperpituitarism in (1) younger and (2) older animals.
2. Cite examples of inherited thyroid and pituitary disturbances.
3. How do endocrines influence the way genes may express themselves?

21

NUTRITION AND METABOLISM STUDIES IN FARM ANIMALS

GENETIC-NUTRITION RELATIONS

Inheritance is important in its relation to nutrition because the two are quite interdependent. Nutritional deficiencies may tend to mask potential genetic differences. Hammond is of the opinion that, for us to identify the animals of superior genotypes, it is essential that the nutritional level permit the better genotypes to express themselves. He points out that it would have been impossible to develop the enormous production of our present-day milk cows had selection depended only on cows that had been fed nothing but fodders. The idea is that good genotypes under such conditions would not have performed any better than less-productive genotypes.

It might also be pointed out that under ideal nutritional conditions, the inherent inabilities to cope with borderline deficiencies would not be detected. A great deal of evidence has been obtained which indicates genetic variations in response of animals to nutritional deficiencies. Some of this genetic variation may arise from differences in abilities to assimilate and utilize certain nutrients.

Gowen (1936) found that 11 inbred lines of rats varied greatly in survival time on a rachitic diet. The mean ages at death of male rats varied from 132 days for the line most severely affected to 344 days for the line least affected by the deficient diet. These lines had been established by nine or more generations of full-sib matings prior to the study of survival on the deficient diet. This amount of inbreeding could have caused considerable genetic diversity between the lines, although about one-half of the variation in survival time could be accounted for by line differences. It was estimated that survival on the deficient diet was 59 per cent heritable. This would suggest that the vitamin D requirement in these rats was definitely under genetic control, but whether it was under genetic control directly or associated with other factors, such as growth rate, which are genetically influenced is difficult to know. However, there was an association of vitamin D requirement with rate of growth.

Johnson and Palmer (1939) found that breeds of swine differ greatly in the time required to deplete the body of vitamin D. Poland-China, Duroc Jersey, and many of the Hampshire hogs were readily depleted of their vitamin D stores and soon developed severe rickets. This condition could be cured by giving them irradiated yeast. The Chester White pigs and one of the Hampshires which was largely white did not show vitamin D deficiency symptoms either by low calcium and phosphorus levels of the blood or by external symptoms. It was found that the store of vitamin D was greater in the white pigs and that its depletion was more difficult. Also, the actual vitamin D needed by the white pigs was much less than for the colored ones. A white pig should have considerable advantage over colored pigs where reduced sunshine prevails. The dark-skinned pigs have an advantage over white pigs in bright sunlight because the white pigs may sunburn at times.

Ellis, et al (1936), reported a type of lameness in pigs in which the rear legs of the growing pigs were involved. Certain litters had many affected pigs while others had few or none. In the inbred litters about 50 per cent were affected, whereas in outbred litters only 3 per cent of the pigs showed lameness. Later, Ellis and Madsen (1941) found that they could produce the condition at will in outbred as well as inbred pigs by heating the ration at a temperature of 115° to 120°C. for 30 to 40 hr. They concluded that the cause was nutritional rather than genetic in nature. It would appear more logical to conclude that this was an example of genetic-nutritional interaction. With only a low quantity of the needed nutrient in the feed, the pigs of one genotype could do satisfactorily while those of another genotype were affected. When all this needed nutrient was destroyed by long heating, pigs of all genotypes were affected.

Landauer (1934) found that creeper chickens react more severely to a vitamin-D-deficient diet than normal chickens, although their requirement for the vitamin may be no higher. His study was made by putting 20 creeper chicks on a deficient diet at hatching and comparing them with 20 control chicks on a deficient diet; he also put 20 creeper chicks on a vitamin-D-deficient diet at five weeks of age and compared them with 20 controls on a deficient diet (Table 22).

Table 22. PROGRESSIVE INCIDENCE OF RACHITIC SYMPTOMS

Chicks on Diet from Hatching			Chicks on Diet at 5 Weeks of Age		
Days	Normal	Creeper	Days	Normal	Creeper
24	0	1	24	1	1
31	2	11	29	3	3
43	5	12	42	7	14
47	13	15	50	12	17
64	19	19	55	15	19
			61	17	19
			71	20	20

Nichita, et al (1934), and Lamoreaux and Hutt (1937 and 1939) found breed differences in thiamin requirement of chickens. White Leghorn chickens consistently showed a greater resistance to the thiamin-deficient diet than Rhode Island Reds or Barred Plymouth Rocks (Table 23).

Table 23. SURVIVAL OF CHICKS ON A THIAMIN-DEFICIENT DIET

| | Breed of Chickens | |
| | White Leghorn | Rhode Island Red |
	Age in Days at Death	
Chicks on deficient diet from hatching	12.8	10.8
Chicks on deficient diet at 2 weeks of age	22.1	16.9

The Barred Plymouth Rocks were the most susceptible to thiamin deficiency as shown in Table 24.

Table 24. COMPARATIVE SURVIVAL TIMES OF THREE BREEDS OF CHICKENS ON A THIAMIN-DEFICIENT DIET

	Leghorns	Reds	Rocks
At 8 weeks of age	50.8%	23.1%	15.8%
At 13 weeks of age	32.0%	20.5%	8.0%
At 17 weeks of age	30.5%	12.8%	0%

Rhode Island Red females $\times$ white Leghorn males produced F_1 that were intermediate between the two breeds in susceptibility to thiamin deficiency.

Serfontein and Payne (1934) found that chicks differ in incidence of slipped tendon (perosis), which is caused by manganese deficiency. A strain of "normal" chicks, in which no slipped tendon had ever been observed, was compared with chicks which had been affected with slipped tendon but recovered sufficiently so that matings could be made. The offspring from the "normal" chicks were compared with offspring from the "affected" chicks by putting all the offspring on a manganese-deficient diet (Table 25). Over twice as many afflictions occurred in the offspring when the parents were more susceptible to manganese deficiency than in the offspring where the parents were more resistant to the deficiency.

Table 25. NUMBER OF NORMAL AND SLIPPED TENDON CHICKS FROM "NORMAL" AND "AFFECTED" MATINGS

| | "Normal" Matings | | |
Leg Involved	Male	Female	Both Sexes
Right leg only	4	2	6
Left leg only	2	0	2
Both legs	9	2	11
Total crooked legs	15	4	19
Total normal legs	40	43	83
Per cent crooked	27.3	8.5	18.6

Table 25—*Continued*

| | *"Affected" Matings* | | |
	Male	*Female*	*Both Sexes*
Right leg only	5	6	11
Left leg only	3	6	9
Both legs	17	19	36
Total crooked legs	25	31	56
Total normal legs	22	34	56
Per cent crooked	53.2	47.7	50.0

There is some evidence that certain breeds of cattle are more susceptible to milk fever than others. This condition may result from either a greater need for certain minerals and/or vitamin D or a reduced ability to assimilate and mobilize the minerals which is inherited by these more susceptible cows.

Guernsey cattle at one time were selected for yellow skin color and for the production of yellow butterfat. This selection had a tendency to develop in the Guernsey breed the inability to convert carotene, one of the yellow materials, into vitamin A, a colorless substance. Ward, et al (1940), reported a higher carotene requirement by Guernsey than by Holstein cows. However, when the vitamin A needs were provided by cod liver oil instead of carotene, there was no difference in requirements between the breeds. This study suggests that selection favored the inability of the animal to convert carotene into vitamin A but that it did not increase the vitamin A requirement.

The organism which causes molding in sweet clover hay also produces a hemorrhagic agent which lowers the prothrombin of the blood. Cattle that are fed such hay will die of hemorrhage. The rabbit is frequently used to test moldy hay to determine if it contains the hemorrhagic material. However, some rabbits are not affected by this material, while others are quite susceptible. The tendency appears to be a breed difference which is genetically controlled. No studies have been made to determine whether genetically controlled differences are present in cattle.

The inability to utilize cystine and methionine results in cystinuria. Although not common, it has been reported by Martland and Robison (1929) to be a hereditary abnormality. The inability to utilize these amino acids is a disadvantage to the afflicted person. There is also the danger of cystine calculi formation when these amino acids are not properly utilized.

Some of the studies indicate that differences in digestibility are slight and probably account for little or none of the differences in feed efficiency between strains of animals. Also, in some studies the more efficient strains seem to store more fat than the less efficient strains. However, some studies have shown that differences in feed efficiency result in part from differences in digestibility of the feed. Baker, et al (1951), found that more efficient beef cattle digested the crude fiber of the ration more effectively than the less efficient cattle. Digestion of other food nutrients was not related to feed efficiency. Craft and Wilham (1936) found that inbred and outbred pigs differed in their ability to digest feed, particularly protein and nitrogen-free extract (Table 26).

Table 26. COMPARISON OF DIGESTABILITY COEFFICIENTS OF INBRED AND OUTBRED PIGS

Kind and number of pigs		Digestion Coefficients, in Per Cent			
	Protein	Ash	Fat	Fiber	N.F.E.
Outbred, 39	74.28	44.04	58.51	41.94	87.64
Inbred, 39	71.93	40.42	55.13	38.49	86.28
Difference	2.35	3.62	3.68	3.45	1.36
Standard deviation	1.08	2.53	2.04	2.11	0.66

Significant differences occurred between inbred litters from inbred sows but not between outbred litters from outbred sows. This indicated that digestion efficiency had been fixed by inbreeding, resulting in certain groups differing from others in ability to digest food.

If strains of animals differ in efficiency of converting feed into gains, this difference can be caused by one or more of the following:

1. Differences in digestibility of the food.
2. Differences in activity, with more nutrients needed for the more active animals.
3. Differences in basal metabolism. The ones with higher metabolic rates would have a higher maintenance cost.
4. Increased food intake, with a resulting shorter time required to gain a given amount and thereby reduce maintenance per unit of gain.
5. Storage of less costly materials such as water and protein as contrasted with fat.
6. Greater efficiency of storage.

Some studies directed at separating lines differing in feed efficiency have used selection. Morris, et al (1933), selected rats for high and low efficiency of food utilization. After six generations the high line was 40 per cent more efficient than the low line. In a thorough study of the two strains of rats, Palmer, et al (1946), showed that even on the same food intake, the high-efficiency line was much more efficient. The high-efficiency line stored more fat and less protein than the low-efficiency line. There was no difference between the two lines in the coefficients of digestibility of the food, with the exception of lower apparent energy digestibility of the high-efficiency males compared with the low-efficiency males. The high-efficiency line showed much greater efficiency in storage of food energy. The low-efficiency strain of rats had a higher energy requirement for maintenance than the high-efficiency strain. The two strains had about the same activity, but basal metabolism was higher for the low-efficiency strain, even though rectal temperature was higher for the high-efficiency strain.

It appears that selection had separated the two lines primarily in their fat metabolism. Greater energy digestion and storage and a lower energy requirement were established in the high-efficiency line. There was some indication that the high-efficiency strain had a lower secretion of thyroxine by the thyroid gland.

Hess and Jull (1948) showed that there are hereditary differences in feed efficiency of chickens. In general, the faster gaining birds were the more efficient ones. However, there were differences in feed efficiency which could not be explained on the basis of body weight, rate of gain, or time. It was concluded that these differences are inherited. Sire groups differed materially in feed efficiency.

Dickerson and Gowen (1947) found that the yellow mouse, which stores large quantities of fat and gains weight more rapidly than its nonyellow litter mate, eats only slightly more feed. These yellow mice are much more efficient feed utilizers and yet they store great quantities of fat. The difference between the yellow and nonyellow mouse is due to one gene or a group of very closely linked genes. This study, as well as studies with pigs (Dickerson, 1947), demonstrates that differences in efficiency of food utilization are not the result of storing less fat and more protein and water (the less costly, energy-producing materials). The pigs that made the most efficient gains were the ones which stored more body fat as revealed by carcass studies. They were the pigs that ate more and gained more rapidly and were generally the less active animals.

Falconer and Latyszewski (1952) selected mice for large size, with one line developed under *ad libitum* feeding and the other line fed only 75 per cent as much as the first line consumed. Feed efficiency improved with selection for faster rate of gain. When the lines were later compared under the ideal feed level, both performed quite satisfactorily. When both lines were compared on the lower nutrition level, those developed on the high nutrition level performed at a lower level than the ones developed under the lower nutrition level.

Krider, et al (1946), reported that two lines of pigs developed by selecting for weight at 180 days of age, one line for high and one line for low weight, differed markedly in feed efficiency. The pigs selected for the larger weight were more efficient and were storing more body fat than the pigs selected for lower weights.

The estimates of heritability for feed efficiency have been calculated in the selection experiments on the basis of progress that was made. In other studies, heritability of feed efficiency has been calculated on the basis of greater similarity of related animals than of unrelated animals. Feed efficiency is heritable in all the species studied (mice, rats, chickens, pigs, and beef cattle), but there is variation from one class of animals to another and from one herd to another within a class of animals.

Results at the U.S. Range Livestock Experiment Station (Knapp and Nordskog, 1946) indicated that feed efficiency is approximately 50 per cent heritable in beef cattle. In pigs the heritability of feed efficiency is lower. Dickerson and Grimes (1947) selected pigs for high and low efficiency of feed utilization. From the progress made in selection in the two directions and by parent-offspring regressions, they found feed efficiency to be 24 and 26 per cent heritable. Their results indicated that one could make about as much progress in improving feed efficiency by selecting for fast rate of gain as by selecting the more efficient pigs.

Weaver and Bogart (1944) showed that lines of swine differ in feed efficiency. In addition, the better performing lines produced highly efficient pigs when crossed among themselves or when mated to another breed. This was not the case when inferior lines were used in line-crossing or crossbreeding.

Selecting beef cattle for greater efficiency at the Oregon station for one generation has resulted in improvement, even though the cattle were slightly inbred at the end of this generation and not inbred when the original data on feed efficiency were obtained (Table 27).

Table 27. PROGRESS IN FEED EFFICIENCY OF BEEF CATTLE FROM SELECTION FOR ONE GENERATION

| | | *Initial* | | *After One Generation* | | |
| | | *Number of Animals* | *Feed per 100- lb. Gain lb.* | *Number of Animals* | *Feed per 100- lb. Gain lb.* | *Inbreeding %* |
Line						
Angus	Bulls	15	400	17	371	10.5
	Heifers	7	565	21	559	
Lionheart	Bulls	5	460	9	341	9.9
	Heifers	7	572	12	505	
Prince	Bulls	8	366	12	370	8.4
	Heifers	4	480	11	455	
David	Bulls	4	428	9	363	16.7
	Heifers	2	500	11	483	

Few data are available on feed efficiency in sheep. It has been the general practice to evaluate lambs at weaning time off pastures rather than to wean them and put them onto feed tests. Where animals are produced in this manner, feed efficiency has less importance and other characteristics have greater importance. This is in line with the custom of sheep production in which farm-flock lambs are marketed at weaning time.

All the studies show clearly that selection for greater efficiency of feed utilization will result in improvement of this trait. In some animals, progress should be quite rapid because of the high heritability of feed efficiency (beef cattle), while it will be somewhat slower in others since heritability of feed efficiency is lower (swine).

Rate of gain is very closely associated with feed efficiency in both swine and beef cattle. It would appear that where it is quite difficult to obtain results on feed efficiency, a breeder may improve his swine or beef cattle for this trait by selecting the faster gaining animals. Animals could be fed in groups and accurate figures on rate of gain could thereby be obtained. This should not necessitate the individual feeding that is required for obtaining figures on feed efficiency.

In summary, evidence has been presented to show that animals inherit a higher vitamin or mineral requirement. There is also evidence that some animals are less capable of utilizing the vitamins and minerals present in their feed. These are specific nutrient requirements which vary for animals of different genotypes. Evidence has also been presented that animals which are more efficient may possess the ability to digest certain nutrients more effectively than animals of lower efficiency. The evidence suggests, however, that a large portion of the differences in feed efficiency must be explained on some basis other than increased ability to digest feeds.

It has been shown that animals which have greater feed efficiency store more fat with less protein and water. It appears that even if fat is a more costly material to store, the more efficient animals can still store greater amounts of it.

Feed efficiency is highly heritable in beef cattle and moderately heritable in swine, and rapid progress can be made by selecting for this trait. Where it is not feasible to feed-test animals individually, progress can be made in improving feed efficiency by selection for greater rates of gains, since the two are closely associated. Selection on the basis of performance of the individual should be more effective, and it should not be necessary to progeny-test or to use any specific breeding system for obtaining maximum results in feed efficiency. Commercial producers who use sires from highly selected herds should obtain excellent results.

METABOLISM STUDIES

One of the big needs in livestock improvement is the development of effective methods of appraisal whereby techniques require only a short time for determination and can be applied at any time during the life of the animal.

Fundamental data on metabolism of the animal through chemical determinations of constituents of blood and urine should give us basic knowledge of normal body functions and the possible consequences of slight or marked aberrations in certain functions.

Some preliminary studies at the Oregon station indicate that faster gaining and more efficient beef calves have greater ability to draw nitrogenous substances from the blood stream for building body tissues. These faster gaining and more efficient calves have lower values for blood amino acids and excrete smaller quantities of nitrogenous materials. It appears that the slower gaining calves accumulate amino acids in the blood stream, since they are not used rapidly in building body tissues. These materials are de-aminated, with the carbonaceous fraction being used for fattening, while the nitrogenous metabolites are excreted, primarily as urea.

Other studies at Oregon State College have shown that the faster gaining and more efficient calves have higher heart rates and body temperatures. Both heart rate and body temperature are higher in younger, growing animals than in those which show more maturity. It appears that the higher pulse rates and body temperatures of faster gaining calves is indicative of their continued growth. Unfortunately, heart rate and body temperature vary from day to day and even with different periods within the day. This reduces the value of these measurements for use in predicting fast and economically gaining animals. Detailed studies on blood and urine chemistry of calves have been made at the Oregon station. Normal values have been established at 500-lb. and at 800-lb. body weight for glucose, haemoglobin, urea nitrogen, amino acid nitrogen, creatinine, and uric acid of the blood (Table 28).

Table 28. NORMAL VALUES FOR BLOOD CONSTITUENTS OF CALVES AT
500-LB. AND AT 800-LB. BODY WEIGHT.
(ALL VALUES PER 100 ML. BLOOD.)

	Hereford	Angus	Females	Males	All Animals
At 500 lb.					
Glucose	58.00 mg.	58.00 mg.	59.00 mg.	58.00 mg.	58.00 mg.
Haemoglobin	11.80 gm.	12.20 gm.	12.10 gm.	11.80 gm.	12.00 gm.
Urea nitrogen	16.90 mg.	18.90 mg.	19.00 mg.	15.80 mg.	17.70 mg.
Amino acid nitrogen	6.90 mg.	7.40 mg.	7.40 mg.	6.70 mg.	7.10 mg.
Creatinine	1.51 mg.	1.69 mg.	1.57 mg.	1.59 mg.	1.58 mg.
Uric acid	1.84 mg.	2.31 mg.	1.98 mg.	2.06 mg.	2.02 mg.
At 800 lb.					
Glucose	67.00 mg.	63.00 mg.	67.00 mg.	64.00 mg.	66.00 mg.
Haemoglobin	12.20 gm.	12.90 gm.	12.70 gm.	12.20 gm.	12.40 gm.
Urea nitrogen	15.20 mg.	15.70 mg.	16.20 mg.	14.30 mg.	15.40 mg.
Amino acid nitrogen	7.10 mg.	17.60 mg.	7.60 mg.	6.80 mg.	7.30 mg.
Creatinine	1.61 mg.	1.05 mg.	1.41 mg.	1.37 mg.	1.39 mg.
Uric acid	1.76 mg.	2.39 mg.	2.06 mg.	1.92 mg.	2.00 mg.

Blood glucose increases markedly as calves approach the stage of growth plateau. Amino acid nitrogen is very much lower in the faster gaining cattle and there is also a correspondingly low level of urea nitrogen. It appears that the slower gaining cattle do not remove the amino acids from the blood for tissue building; therefore, the levels of blood amino acids become higher in calves that do poorly. There is probably de-amination with corresponding increases in urea formation. This would give higher urea nitrogen levels for the slower gaining animals.

The detailed urine studies conducted at Oregon State College established normal values at 500-lb. and at 800-lb. body weight for daily urine volume, total urinary nitrogen excretion per day, daily urinary nitrogen excretion per kilo body weight, daily urinary urea nitrogen excretion per calf, urinary urea nitrogen excretion per kilo body weight, daily ammonia nitrogen excretion, urea nitrogen:ammonia nitrogen ratio, daily urinary creatinine excretion, creatinine coefficients, daily urinary uric acid excretion, and uric acid coefficients.

Urine volume for a 24-hr. period increased from an average of 3,472 ml. at 500-lb. body weight to 6,992 ml. at 800-lb. body weight. Likewise, urinary nitrogen excretion for a 24-hr. period increased from 46.2 gm. at 500-lb. body weight to 97.2 gm. at 800-lb. body weight. The increase in nitrogen consumed in the feed accounted for only a part of this nitrogen excretion. It appears that as the calves approached the growth plateau, less nitrogen taken in by the feed was used for tissue building and more was excreted. The animals that were gaining at a lower rate excreted much more nitrogen than the faster gaining animals. This was true for both total daily urinary nitrogen excreted on the "per calf" and on the "per kilo" bases. Since most of the nitrogen was excreted as urea, this excretion could serve as an index of the use an animal was making of the nitrogenous materials of the feed. This could be done either from blood or urine analyses because blood amino acids and urea levels can be taken as a guide to the amount of amino acids stored in the body in relation to that which is de-aminized. Low blood levels of amino acids and urea are indicative of greater use of the amino acids in growth, whereas high blood amino acid and urea values may be indicative of reduced use of amino acids in growth, with a consequent higher de-amination. The same animals, the fast gainers, that have low blood levels of amino acids and urea excrete less total nitrogen, particularly urea. Also, those animals, the slow gainers, that have high blood levels of amino acids and urea excrete larger amounts of total nitrogen. This suggests that either blood levels of amino acids and urea nitrogen or urinary excretion of nitrogen could be used as an index of the use made by the animal of the protein material eaten for growth purposes.

Colby, et al (1950), presented figures on blood levels of urea nitrogen, non-protein nitrogen, creatine, creatinine, and glucose for calves. They found a correlation of blood urea nitrogen with rate of gain of —0.55, which was non-significant. Apparently, their failure to find significance was due to lack of numbers. It appears that their findings and those of the Oregon station are in good general agreement.

Endocrine studies show that pituitaries from faster gaining animals contain and produce more thyrotropic hormone. This stimulates the thyroid gland to the greater activity which is probably conducive to growth.

Several studies have been made on protein-bound iodine of the blood in relation to rate and efficiency of gains. The idea is that protein-bound iodine is a reflection of the thyroid output of the animal. According to the work at the Oregon station, one might expect greater thyrotropin output from the pituitary, which causes greater thyroid activity, to be associated with more rapid and economical gains. Elijah and Turner (1942) found that faster gaining, bigger types of hog had a higher thyrotropic content of the pituitary glands. However, the work of Stokes, et al (1953), and Kunkel, et al (1953), indicates that there is an optimum level of protein-bound iodine associated with gains and feed efficiency. Too much or too little protein-bound iodine are both associated with lower gains and reduced feed efficiency.

The general relationship of protein-bound iodine to growth rate and feed efficiency (Kunkel, et al, 1953) showed that there was an optimum level of protein-bound iodine and that slower rates of gain and reduced feed efficiencies were associated with both lower and higher than optimum levels of protein-bound iodine. This study was made on ten individually fed calves for feed efficiency studies and on additional animals for the gain studies.

Stokes, et al (1953), used 150 calves of 8 to 14 months of age and found that the best gaining cattle had a level of protein-bound iodine of 5 to 6.8 mg. per 100 ml. of serum. There were some animals with normal protein-bound iodine values which gained at a low rate, however.

The results of Carroll, et al (1951), showed that pituitaries from dwarf animals contained some thyrotropic hormone but much less than pituitaries from normal animals. This difference in the thyrotropic content of the pituitary between the dwarf and the normal was considered enough to account for the difference in growth rate of the two kinds of cattle. Feed tests at the Oregon station compared a dwarf bull and a dwarf steer with a normal bull and steer for gains and feed required to make 100 lb. of gain. These tests showed marked differences between the dwarf and normal (Table 29).

These results show very low rates of gain and inefficient feed utilization in dwarf calves as compared with normals. Whether the lower thyrotropic content

Table 29. RATE OF GAIN AND FEED EFFICIENCY OF DWARF AND
NORMAL CALVES

Kind of Calf	Weight	Gain per Day	Feed per 100-lb. Gain
Normal bull	800	3.12	510
Dwarf bull	416	0.30	820
Normal steer	758	2.60	635
Dwarf steer	403	0.28	915

of pituitaries can account for all this difference in gains is not known. It may
indicate that low output of thyrotropic content of the pituitary accounts for
reduction in gains and feed efficiency. Marlowe and Chambers (1954) determined the thyrotropic, adrenotropic, growth, and gonadotropic contents of
pituitaries from dwarf and normal calves by assay. They found no difference
in thyrotropic or adrenotropic content of pituitaries from dwarf calves and
those from normal calves. The pituitaries from the dwarfs contained more
growth and gonadotropic hormone than pituitaries from normal calves. Fransen
and Andrews (1954) found the same level of thyrotropic hormone in the
pituitaries of dwarf calves as in pituitaries of normal calves. However, the administration of thyroprotein, a material which has thyroxine activity, to the
dwarfs resulted in increased gains and general well-being. It did not stimulate
bone growth.

Crenshaw and Turner (1954), by use of I^{131}, found that pituitaries of dwarf
calves secrete at least some thyrotropin and that this secretion could be inhibited
by introducing large amounts of thyroxine into the animal. Thus, the pituitary
of the dwarf shows the same thyroxine-thyrotropin interaction as in the normal animal. It was also found that the thyroids of dwarf calves have the capacity to respond to thyrotropin stimulation. It would appear that there may be
hormonal imbalance in dwarf calves but no complete absence of a hormone
and no complete inability to respond to a hormone.

Gawienowski, et al (1955), found that higher protein-bound iodine levels
in growing swine were associated with lower rates of gain. Also, the pigs with
higher levels of protein-bound iodine were shorter in body. Although it can be
assumed that greater thyroxine output is associated with higher levels of protein-bound iodine, this study might be interpreted to indicate just the opposite
relation between the two.

One interesting relationship of hormone level and metabolism of a specific
vitamin compound is found with thyroxine and vitamin A. If the organism is
hyperthyroid, there is increased metabolism of vitamin A and consequently a
higher vitamin A requirement. However, with a hypothyroid state, there is a
reduced ability to convert carotene into vitamin A. With either a hyper- or

hypothyroid state, one might find evidence for vitamin A deficiency. This type of condition may operate with many nutrients. It appears likely that requirements for several nutrients, and particularly for energy-containing foods, would be increased with a higher metabolic rate. However, the proper digestion and assimilation of nutrients would be impaired by a hypothyroid state. It seems, then, that an inherited metabolic optimum is desired so that proper use of the feeds can be made. Unfortunately, this metabolic optimum may exist at one stage of development and not at another.

Most workers (Brody, 1945) find that efficiency is related to physiologic age. An animal that matures early in life may show high efficiency in early life but may lose efficiency earlier because of the early maturity. An animal that matures later in life may show higher growth efficiency for a longer period of time but might not make a desirable finished product. It appears that active metabolism in early life, with a decrease in metabolism which permits later rapid fattening, would be desirable in our meat-producing animals. Since it appears unlikely that we can breed for greater metabolism in early life, followed by reduced metabolism when a desired weight is approached, it seems that our efforts should be aimed at a compromise. It may be necessary to consider the over-all rate and efficiency of production to the marketable stage rather than to try for extreme rate and efficiency of production at any particular growth phase.

We may liken an animal to a machine, as Kleiber (1936) diagrammed one. The food material taken in is regulated by appetite and capacity. The first source of loss is through the feces as the undigested portion. Some of the digested material is lost through excretion, some by oxidative process, katabolism, etc., while some can be used for growth, milk production, etc. It can be seen from the diagram (Fig. 129) that genes may influence appetite, food capacity, digestibility of food, capacity for food absorption, assimilation, excretion rates, katabolic losses, etc. With this also is the inherited ability to grow or to produce milk. Certainly an animal that eats only a little more than is needed for the general metabolic processes will have little food left with which to grow or to produce milk. Very likely an animal that has great capacity to build large body stores will not, at the same time, be one which has the capacity to produce large quantities of milk. The regulation points indicated in the diagram are probable enzyme complexes and very likely are under genetic control. Enzymes are chemical substances which affect certain chemical reactions but which do not ordinarily become a part of the product of these reactions.

It has been observed that individual rabbits differ in the ability of their blood to hydrolize the plant alkaloid atropine. It is known that this reaction

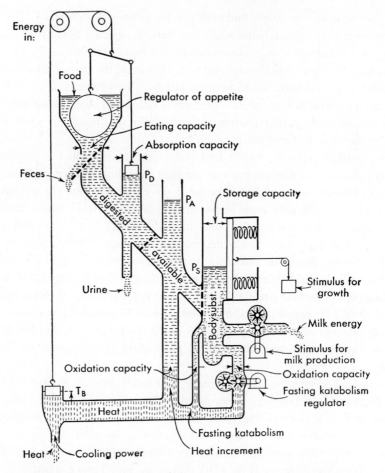

Fig. 129. Schematic diagram of energy metabolism. *(From Kleiber, Proc. Amer. Soc. Animal Production, 1936.)*

is enzymatically catalyzed, and it has been demonstrated that the enzyme concerned, atropinesterase, is dependent for its presence on the dominant allele of a specific gene. Ability to hydrolyze atropine is therefore inherited as a simple Mendelian dominant trait (Sawin and Glick, 1943).

A Mendelian recessive trait known in the rabbit is one in which the fat is yellow rather than white, as in normal rabbits. This, apparently, is the result of inability to oxidize ingested carotenoid pigments, which are then accumulated in the fat. If homozygous yellow-fatted animals are fed on a carotenoid-free diet, they have white fat. The dominant allele of the gene concerned is apparently in control of a specific enzyme which has been referred to as xanthophyllase (Castle, 1933).

In some of the lower forms of animal life it has been possible to make studies which are not possible with farm animals. For example, Neurospora can be grown in media that can be altered to meet the needs of certain mutants which have a specific requirement. In this way, one can study mutants which are incapable of carrying on a certain synthesis necessary for life. These mutants may be either the result of blocking a certain reaction or the failure to produce an enzyme necessary for that reaction.

Only one example will be given of Neurospora, though many have been studied. It is assumed that a failure occurs when there is an accumulation of material in the cycle at one point. This can be verified by adding the material that is normally produced in the next step. If the organism can now grow, it indicates that there was a failure to produce an enzyme necessary for this reaction.

In Neurospora, as in the mammalian liver, arginase is present and catalyzes the splitting of arginine into ornithine and urea. Unlike the animal which excretes the urea, Neurospora further degrades it into carbon dioxide and ammonia under the influence of the enzyme urease. It is clear that the only reasonable interpretation of the combined genetic and biochemical data involves the assumption that in Neurospora there is an ornithine "cycle" (Fig. 130). In the ornithine or arginine cycle, seven genetically distinct types have been identified, each differing from the original by a single gene but in each case by a different gene. Four of these grow if supplied with ornithine, citrulline, or arginine and are presumed to be unable to synthesize ornithine from the constituents of the basal medium. Two grow if supplied citrulline or arginine but do not respond to ornithine. They apparently cannot convert ornithine to citrulline. One strain requires arginine for growth and cannot make use of either ornithine or citrulline. It evidently cannot carry out the reaction by which citrulline is transformed to arginine (Beadle and Tatem, 1945).

There is a great deal of evidence, particularly with some of the lower forms of life such as Neurospora, a mold, and with the higher mammal, the human, that genes control certain enzymes. In man, for example, the classical hereditary disease, alcaptonuria, results from the inability of the afflicted individual to oxidize 2.5–dihydroxyphenylacetic acid (alcapton) in the normal fashion (Beadle and Tatem, 1945). As a consequence, the compound accumulates in the body and is excreted through the urine. In the presence of oxygen this compound (alcapton) oxidizes to form a black substance which is a striking symptom of alcaptomuria—the darkening of urine on exposure to air. It appears that one gene, a mutation from the normal, accounts for this inability to metabolize alcaptons.

Another inherited defect in humans is that in which phenylpyruvic acid is

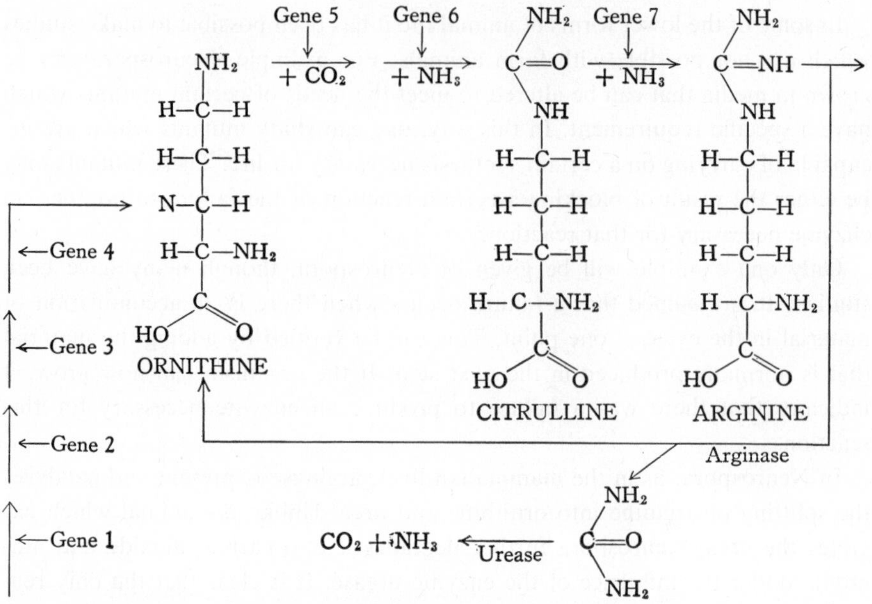

Gene 5   Gene 6 NH_2 Gene 7 NH_2
↓   ↓   ↓   ↓

NH_2 $\xrightarrow{+ CO_2}$ $\xrightarrow{+ NH_3}$ $C=O$ $\xrightarrow{+ NH_3}$ $C=NH$ →

H—C—H   NH   NH

H—C—H   H—C—H   H—C—H

N—C—H   H—C—H   H—C—H

H—C—NH_2 H—C—H   H—C—H

C   H—C—NH_2 H—C—NH_2

HO   O   C   C

ORNITHINE   HO   O   HO   O

                                            CITRULLINE   ARGININE

←Gene 4

←Gene 3

←Gene 2   Arginase

←Gene 1 $CO_2 + NH_3$ $\xleftarrow{\text{Urease}}$ $C=O$

                                                 NH_2

                                                 NH_2

Fig. 130. Ornithine cycle in Neurospora.

not oxidized to its parahydroxy analogue as is done in normal individuals. The inability to oxidize phenylpyruvic acid results in its accumulation in the body and excretion through the urine. Here, however, more serious consequences arise because this compound causes impairment of the central nervous system, a disease known as oligophrenia phenyl-pyrivica. This mutant, which prevents the individual from carrying on one chemical reaction, causes a serious mental impairment.

In addition to alcaptonura and phenylpyruvic oligophrenia in the human there are several other examples of gene-controlled enzyme deficiencies. The absence of tyrosinase, an enzyme which is necessary in melanin pigment formation, results in albinism. Von Gierke's disease results from an inherited failure of the individual to break glycogen, the animal polysaccharide, down to glucose. This results in a piling up of glycogen in various body tissues, particularly the liver and heart. The normal individual has phosphorylase which carries glycogen through glucose-1-phosphate and glucose-6-phosphate to glucose and phosphoric acid (H_3PO_4). Due to this one gene mutation, certain individuals lack this enzyme and as a result develop the excessive amounts of glycogen. Other examples of disturbances in carbohydrate metabolism in the human which are under genetic control are diabetes, pentosuria, and fructosuria. Cases of inability to metabolize lipids are also found in humans. The failure to oxidize sphyngomyelin results in paralysis, blindness, and death of afflicted infants. This, as well as inability to metabolize cholesterol, resulting in xanthomatosis, are inherited disturbances in metabolism.

The studies with Neurospora and humans has lead some biochemical geneticists to conclude that there is a one-gene–one-enzyme relationship. Obviously, the data at hand are not sufficient to prove or to disprove such a theory, but there are cases in which one mutation results in a lack of one enzyme. However, this is not sufficient to prove that each enzyme is under the control of only one gene, nor does it preclude the possibility that one gene may affect more than one enzyme or even may affect an entirely different enzyme system. All the evidence so far points to the fact that enzymes are under genetic control and that it is through the genetic control of enzyme systems that genes express themselves in character development.

Since genes appear to express themselves in character development through enzyme control, it becomes apparent that in a series of reactions where there are several enzymes involved, the one which operates in the initial reactions would have far greater effects than those which operate toward the end of the series of reactions. Thus, some genes have very marked influences, whereas the effects of other genes are extremely minor. An example of the extreme effect is that causing albinism, in which no pigment is produced. This can be contrasted to the effect of a gene operating later in the reaction series in which the shade of dark pigment is altered.

So many gene-controlled enzyme inabilities are known in man, Drosophila, and in Neurospora that one is inclined to the view that many of our inherited differences in growth rate, feed efficiency, milk production, egg production, and other productive characteristics in farm animals are the result of inherited metabolic differences. The more drastic disturbances in metabolism are likely the result of lack of enzymes which bring about reactions early in a series of reactions, whereas the minor differences are likely the lack of enzymes which control reactions later in this series of reactions. This concept points to the possibility through studies of metabolism, blood and urine analyses, etc., of finding criteria which are indicative of superior productive ability. Chemical analyses may some day form a routine method for indexing animals and may make it possible for us to make selections in early life of the animal without having to put it through laborious and expensive feed tests or other production-test procedures.

EXERCISES

1. Assume that the evidence is sufficient to establish a genetic-nutrition interrelationship. Under what level of nutrition would you select animals to develop outstanding herd performance for a specific set of conditions?

2. When selection is practiced under optimum and under suboptimum nutritional conditions and the two herds are later placed under (a) the optimum and (b) the suboptimum conditions, how will the two herds differ in performance?

3. Suppose animals are selected under very adverse nutritional conditions. For what is selection actually being made under such conditions?

4. In metabolism studies there are some examples of a one-gene–one-enzyme relationship. Cite some examples. Does this prove that all genetic expressions are of this nature? Explain.

22

INHERITANCE OF FERTILITY LEVEL

It must be recognized that fertility is not an all-or-none condition but that there are levels of fertility ranging from complete sterility to very high fertility.

In classes of animals such as cattle and horses, in which one young is the rule, expressions of fertility level are found in variations in the estrous cycle, interval from delivery of offspring to first estrus, and ease of settling at breeding. In polyparous animals (those having litters, such as swine and rabbits) fertility can also be expressed by number of eggs ovulated, number of eggs fertilized, implantation of fertilized eggs, and survival of young in the uterus, all of which influence litter size.

HOW INHERITANCE AFFECTS FERTILITY

There are three general ways in which genes may influence fertility:

1. Lethals, which cause death of embryos or make the germ cells not viable or fertilizable. Evidence for the existence of this condition is found by a relatively large percentage of cows which apparently settle, but which, after two or more heat periods have been skipped, come back into heat. In polyparous animals, one evidence of the action of lethal genes is the very large number of eggs which are produced in relation to the number of young born.

2. Inherited endocrine disturbances. Reproduction is under the control of hormones from the pituitary, thyroid, and gonads (testes in the male and ovaries in the female). Each endocrine has its specific effect and also interacts to cause variations in the output of the other endocrines. Lethals and inherited endocrine disturbances are closely related. Some lethals are the result of endocrine disturbances.

3. Heritable effects in which many genes, each with a small effect, influence fertility in a way similar to gene effects on heritability of growth and vigor.

One example of an inherited condition, cryptorchidism, which may affect fertility of the male, was presented by McPhee and Buckley (1934). Their analysis showed that this sex-limited character is probably due to one pair of recessive genes. The bilateral cryptorchid is sterile because the testes must be at a lower temperature than that of the body in order to function in sperm production. When both testes are retained in the abdomen, they are maintained at body temperature and sterility is the result.

A sex-limited sterility in dairy cattle, in which the females were sterile, was described by Gregory, et al (1945 and 1951), as sterility attributed to a simple autosomal recessive. No study of the reproductive organs was reported by the authors. A report similar to that of Gregory, et al, was made by Fincher and Williams (1926) and by Jones (1946). Fincher and Williams found that the reproductive tract was not properly developed in the sterile cows. Jones showed that one cow born in 1923 had 30 female descendents which were all good breeders, whereas a second cow born in 1923 had three out of four daughters which were sterile. The fertile daughter transmitted low fertility to four of her descendents.

Gregory, et al (1951), presented evidence for reduced fertility in bulls which is due to a recessive autosomal gene but different from the one causing female sterility. This gene in the homozygous condition causes the bulls to produce semen which is low in concentration and which contains sperm many of which are misformed. The conception rate from these affected bulls ranged from almost zero to 30 per cent, with the general range of 1 to 10 per cent.

Donald and Hancock (1953) reported a hereditary sex-limited sterility in bulls in which the spermatozoa had an abnormal formation of the acrosome which was designated "knob" by the authors. They reported that it was due to an autosomal recessive.

Eriksson (1943) reported arrested development in the gonads of both the male and the female due to an autosomal recessive in Swedish Highland cattle. Since there are other deviations associated with this sterility, such as alteration in growth, it is possible that this is another example of an inherited endocrine disturbance.

The white-heifer disease has been reported, in which the inheritance of abnormal structure of the female reproductive tract causes sterility. This trait is linked with the roaning gene that causes white when homozygous. It is another example of a sex-limited character which results in sterility.

A clear-cut example in which a lethal reduces fertility is found in the yellow mouse. When two yellow mice are mated, one-fourth die in the uterus, one-half are yellow, and one-fourth are nonyellow. This gives a ratio of 2 yellow:1 nonyellow for the mice that are born. Litter size is about three-fourths as large as when yellow mice are mated to nonyellow mice.

An example of sterility in the mouse, resulting from a disturbed endocrine system, was reported by Snell (1929). This type is due to a simple recessive and is the result of the mouse inheriting an abnormal pituitary gland. Also, the "pygmy" mouse, reported by King (1950), is due to an inherited endocrine abnormality. Since the pituitary, thyroid, and gonads are so closely associated with reproduction, it follows that any inherited condition in which one or all these glands are involved will influence fertility. At the Missouri station some pigs were produced which had no ovaries. This condition appeared to be a sex-limited recessive.

Numerous instances of hypo- or hyperthyroid conditions have been reported in the medical literature. The same is true for under- and oversecretion by the pituitary. The inheritance of these conditions has not been determined in many cases. Some endocrine disturbances are the result of genetic-environmental interactions rather than being chiefly and directly under genetic control. Research with mice at Oregon State College has provided evidence for interactions. Strain crosses were obtained which failed to reproduce unless more vitamins were added to what was considered an adequate diet.

HERITABILITY OF FERTILITY

In the farm animals in which one young is the rule (monoparous) the evidence indicates that conditions involving fertility level are not highly heritable. The examples of inherited low fertility are generally cases in which one or two genes with major effects are involved. Legates (1954) reported that services per conception in dairy cattle were not heritable, which means that environmental factors account for all the variation in this trait. Calving interval was so low in repeatability (0.133 ± 0.026) that no great importance could be given this measure of fertility. His findings are in agreement with those of Olds, et al (1949), and Olds and Seath (1950) in which they found correlations for services per conception between dams and their daughters of zero and correlations between number of services required per conception for a cow in two successive years to be only 0.08. Berge (1942) reported a higher repeatability (0.22 ± 0.05) in a Norwegian herd. Dunbar and Henderson (1950), in a study of nonreturns from first services, found a repeatability to be 0.024 and a heritability to be 0.004. They also found calving interval to have zero heritability.

On the basis of an index of reproductive efficiency, Spielman and Jones (1939) found a dam-daughter correlation of 0.546 ± 0.118. Gaines and Palfrey (1931) found the correlation between successive calving intervals to be 0.088. Ostergaard (1946) found intra-cow repeatability to be 0.13 for the first three calving intervals. Chapman and Casida (1937) found repeatability of the period from parturition to first estrus to be 0.19, and Olds and Seath

(1953) obtained a value of 0.29. Lasley and Bogart (1943), working with a group of range Hereford cows in which there had been no artificial selection for fertility, found that 80 cows requiring 1.78 services per conception in 1940 required 1.27 services per conception in 1941, with respective calving percentages of 74 and 89 for the two years. A group of 40 cows requiring 2.77 services per conception in 1940 required 3.32 services per conception in 1941 and had respective calving percentages of 65 and 58 for the two years. On the basis of these figures, they recommended that dry cows or those which require several services per conception be considered for culling. Lasater, a rancher in Colorado, has adopted a severe policy with his Beefmaster herd in which he culls all cows that are dry or calve late. He has shown a steady increase in calf crop and in early calving for the eight years that this culling procedure has been followed. It would appear that fertility in beef cattle may be more heritable than it is in dairy cattle.

Selection for increased fertility and weaning weights in a herd of Hereford cows, along with stocking the range in accordance with its carrying capacity at the New Mexico station, has resulted in marked improvement. One may question how much of the improvement in fertility in the Lasater cattle and the New Mexico herd is due to improved management, how much is due to culling barren cows, and how much is due to genetic improvement. From an inspection of the ranges in the two places, a high fertility level could not be attributed to luxuriant pasture conditions since drought had been recently severe in both areas. If the removal of barren cows from the herd can change the fertility level of a herd, it implies a high repeatability of reduced fertility, a part of which might be genetic.

Warnick found that dry cows coming from pastures and ranges in Oregon in the fall, following a summer breeding program, were mostly pregnant. He concluded from this that culling open cows in the fall from a determination of pregnancy by palpation would be more economical than culling dry cows in the fall. Apparently some cows can produce a calf every year under these conditions while other cows must take frequent rests.

In swine and other polyparous animals in which litters are produced, there is a continuous variation in number of offspring per litter. Heritability estimates of fertility in swine have varied from 5 to 44 per cent. Rommel (1906) was among the earlier workers concerned with inheritance of fertility in swine. His data can be used to obtain an estimate that is very close to that of Lush, et al (1933), of 14 per cent; Lush and Molln (1942) of 17 per cent; and Stewart (1945) of 17 per cent. These estimates, 15 to 17 per cent for heritability of fertility in swine, are lower than those reported by others.

Blunn and Baker (1949) obtained heritability estimates on total pigs and on live pigs per litter by intra-sire regression of daughter on dam and by re-peatability of sow performance (Table 30).

Table 30. HERITABILITY ESTIMATES FOR TOTAL PIGS AND LIVE PIGS
PER LITTER (BLUNN AND BAKER)

Heritability Estimated from:	Total Pigs per Litter	Live Pigs per Litter
Intra-sire regression of daughter on dam	0.251	0.237
Repeatability of sow performance	0.235	0.212
Average	0.243	0.224

The estimate by Blunn and Baker for live pigs farrowed is higher than that of 0.136 obtained by Stewart (1945).

It is evident that fertility in swine (litter size) is in part under genetic control because of the breed differences which exist. For example, Robertson, et al (1951), studied 49 Chester White and 37 Poland China gilts very extensively and found that although no differences between the breeds in age at time of puberty was present, the Chester White gilts produced more ova of which a greater number were fertilized and fewer lost from embryonic death than in the Poland China. The average number of pigs farrowed was 10.27 for the Chester Whites and 6.48 for the Poland China gilts.

Keith (1930) found that sows produce larger litters than gilts and that first litters were more variable than second and later litters. The second litter farrowed by a sow was found to be highly correlated with the average size of later litters. This agrees closely with the findings for rats reported by Asdell, et al (1941), in which they found that the size of the second litter produced by a female was a good indication of what she would produce in succeeding litters. The first litter was more variable and less under genetic control than later litters.

STUDIES OF IMPAIRED FERTILITY

Hauser, et al (1952), found that line-cross boars reach puberty earlier and develop larger testes than inbred boars. It appeared that as long as boar semen contained live sperm, fertility was good. Therefore the boar had little to do with litter size of fertile matings and would generally cease to mate before the semen quality became impaired from overuse.

Squiers, et al (1952), studied the fate of ova in inbred, outbred, and cross-bred gilts. They found that most of the ova were fertilized (only 5 per cent were infertile) but that 7 per cent of those fertilized degenerated by the twenty-fourth day and that 23 per cent could not be found, making a total loss of 35 per cent on the twenty-fifth day as compared with those recovered on the second day after breeding. Litter comparisons with embryo recoveries showed that an additional 1.4 embryos, or 11 per cent, had been lost. Breeding twice during estrus increased conception rate but had little effect on litter size. Variations in litter size were determined more by ova mortality than by number of ova shed. Number of ova shed was more affected by strains and crosses than ova survival. Ova mortality did not seem related to breeding. Crossbred gilts reached sexual maturity 30 days earlier, ovulated 1.9 more eggs, and had 1.85 more embryos per sow at 25 days gestation than the inbreds. Only 7 per cent of the 359 females showed gross abnormalities of the reproductive tract. The abnormality found in greatest number was cystic follicles.

In an attempt to determine why sows and gilts do not settle, Warnick, et al (1949), studied the reproductive tracts of 63 females. These were "problem" sows collected from farmers whose efforts were unsuccessful in getting the sows pregnant. They found that failure to settle was due to failure of fertilization in 53 per cent of the gilts and 33 per cent of the sows. Embryonic death was responsible for repeat breeding in 24 per cent of the gilts and 67 per cent of the sows. They concluded that abnormalities of the reproductive tract account for a large portion of the repeat breeders in gilts, whereas embryonic death is the primary cause of repeat breeding in sows. One might suspect that inheritance was important in the abnormal reproductive tracts, but it would be difficult to imagine such a high embryonic mortality to be the result of genetics alone, for this would be expected to cause death in only a few pigs in the litter rather than all. It is possible that permanent environmental effects or genetics could result in such physiological abnormalities of the sows that it would not be possible for the sows to provide a suitable environment for embryo survival.

Sheep are generally more prolific than cattle, and twins occur frequently, and triplets and quadruplets are not rare. Definite breed differences are found in fertility level of sheep. Even among the mutton breeds, there is a lower fertility in Southdowns than in Dorset Horns.

Heape (1899) studied the fertility of sheep, using records on 120,000 sheep for his analysis. He concluded that the differences in fertility level of certain breeds are so great as to constitute racial characteristics. Marshall (1904, 1906, and 1908) and Hammond (1914 and 1921) found that the number of young differs only slightly from the number of eggs ovulated. Thus, fetal atrophy may not be very important in sheep. However, the failure of ewes to lamb, which may be considered as nonpregnancy, might be caused by fetal death rather than low fertility. Differences in fertility level of the breeds would then be attributable to differences in number of eggs ovulated. Marshall states that some farmers have raised fertility level through selection to the point that a 200 per cent lamb crop is produced.

Castle (1924) analyzed the work of the Bell flock, in which selection for twinning had been practiced, and concluded that heredity has a minor role in determining the occurrence of twinning.

Numerous studies have shown that even though sheep have a breeding season which is restricted to the fall of the year, breeds vary greatly in the time of onset of estrus. Generally, the breeds that come into heat earlier also have an extended breeding season and show anestrus much later than those breeds in which onset of estrus is late in the season (Hafez, 1951; Kelly and Shaw, 1939 and 1943; and Kelly, 1937 and 1946).

de Baca, et al (1954), in two studies found that breeds of sheep differed in the onset of estrus, with Hampshires earliest, Romneys intermediate, and Southdowns latest. When rams of Hampshire, Romney, Cheviot, and Border Leicester breeds were mated to Lincoln $\times$ Rambouillet ewes, the first cross ewes showed no significant effect of breed of sire on onset of estrus. However, the second cross ewes, which were 75 per cent respectively of the various four breds indicated above, showed marked breed differences in time of estrous onset. The rank of the breeds according to onset of estrus in the second crosses was: Hampshire, earliest; Border Leicester and Romney, intermediates; and Cheviot, latest.

A study of repeatability of time of onset of estrus within breeds was very low (de Baca, et al, 1954) in spite of the very marked breed differences. This would indicate that selection for twinning or for early lambing within a breed would not result in rapid improvement. The fact that breeds differ so markedly indicates that genes affecting fertility are associated with other genes that have been used to separate the breeds. Selection for the genes that characterize the breeds of sheep has had more to do with differences in fertility than selection for increased fertility itself.

If fertility in sheep is not greatly influenced by genetics, it follows that the large variations that exist result largely from environmental variations. This suggests the importance of providing a good pasture just before and during the breeding season in order to encourage a large lamb crop. In fact, the work at the Utah station would indicate that proper nutrition after the breeding season will influence the lambing percentage. Ewes that had no feed except the range delivered fewer lambs than those which received added supplement, even though both groups were under the same conditions during the breeding season. This indicates that feed conditions may influence the survival of the developing young.

It has been shown that rams of some breeds are highly fertile early in the breeding season while others which are influenced more by high temperatures may not regain a high level of fertility until later in the breeding season. Such breeds as Southdowns and Shropshires are generally more susceptible to high summer temperatures than such breeds as the Rambouillet.

GENETICS OF FERTILITY AND HATCHABILITY IN POULTRY

Egg production, which certainly would influence the number of offspring that could be produced by a hen, has been selected for and studied by many investigators. This differs from fertility as defined by poultrymen. Fertility is the ability of the eggs to be fertilized. Hatchability is the ability of the fertilized egg to develop into a chick and hatch. Egg production is the ability of a hen to produce eggs. Early postulations on the inheritance of egg production were based on the concept that egg production during the first year of production was determined by five different characteristics:

1. Age at sexual maturity. Two pairs of genes were assumed; one, sex-linked E and e, and the other, autosomal E' and e'. The dominant in each case brought about early sexual maturity.
2. Intensity of rate of laying. Two pairs of autosomal genes which are complementary, R and r, and R' and r', were postulated. The dominant genes give higher rate of production, but R and R' in the same bird would have more effect than the sum of R and R' each alone.
3. Broodiness. This is due to two dominant genes, A and C, acting complementarily. A bird that is $A? cc$ or $aaC?$ would not be broody but could transmit broody genes to the offspring. Only the bird of the genotype $A-C-$ is broody. These genes are autosomal.
4. Winter pause (not the pauses due to broodiness). This is conditioned by M and m, with winter pause M dominant. Birds that continue to lay without a winter pause would be mm.
5. Persistency. This is due to one autosomal pair of genes, with persistency P dominant and lack of persistency p recessive. Persistency has been shown to be associated with early sexual maturity.

Although no doubt there are genes of which each has major effects, evidence has shown that egg production, intensity or rate of production, persistency, and winter pause are also influenced by many genes, each having a small effect. Munro (1937) gave 31 per cent as the heritability of egg production. Lerner and Taylor (1943) estimated heritability of egg production to be 22.5 per cent. Lerner and Taylor (1943) gave estimates of heritability for intensity of production as 21 per cent, persistency as 5 per cent, and winter pause as 10 per cent.

The individual research studies which have contributed so much to improvement in egg production will not be cited. The reader is referred to Jull (1940) and to Lerner (1950). It should be pointed out that great improvements have been made through selection for greater egg production. However, Gowell selected hens which produced 200 eggs or over and mated them to cocks whose dams produced 250 eggs or more, but after nine years no improvement was evident. Pearl (1912) progeny- and sib-tested and selected on winter egg production. On the basis of this study he postulated that two pairs of genes were involved in winter egg production. It was Goodale (1918) who developed the concept that yearly egg production is determined by the five characteristics, age of sexual maturity, persistency, broodiness, winter pause, and intensity or rate. Later, Lerner and Taylor (1936) postulated that spring and summer pause (not broodiness) is another character affecting egg production.

The age at sexual maturity is affected by the environment as well as by genetics. Kempster and Parker (1936) showed that later hatched chicks reach sexual maturity at an earlier age than early hatched chicks.

Taylor and Lerner (1939) found that, in addition to the time at which the chicks are hatched, the feed given will influence age of sexual maturity. There is no question about the importance of genetics in age of sexual maturity (Pearl, 1912; Hays and Sanborn, 1926; and Warren, 1934), for the genes are both sex-linked and autosomal. Some evidence indicates that extremely early sexual maturity is associated with small egg size and may actually reduce total egg production (Hays, 1936, and Knox, 1930).

Although it was postulated by Hays that winter pause is due to a dominant gene M, one can see quite readily that there should be no more birds with winter pause if this were the case, because selection against an undesirable dominant should be quite effective. There is a great deal of evidence showing that the environment has a large influence on pauses.

Broodiness was postulated by Hays (1940) as being due to two complimentary, dominant genes. One might think that dominant genes for broodiness would be easily eliminated by culling, since they are dominant. However, since both these genes are necessary for broodiness (complementary action), one could have a strain $AA\ cc$ (which is not broody) mated to a different strain $aa\ CC$ (which also is not broody) and get all $Aa\ Cc$ (which are broody). Progeny-testing of birds to two strains, $AA\ cc$ and $aa\ CC$, could be used to detect the presence of broody genes in nonbroody chicks. If the nonbroody chicks carried C, the mating to the $AA\ cc$ testers would reveal this. If the nonbroody chicks carried A, the mating to $aa\ CC$ would reveal this also.

Persistency may be measured by the length of the biological year (Hays and Sanborn, 1926), production in August and September (Knox, et al, 1935), or date at last egg (Goodale, 1918, and Lerner and Taylor, 1937). Selection for persistency by use of any of these criteria should result in marked improvement. It must be understood, however, that some other characteristics are involved when persistency is measured by these criteria. Such factors as age of sexual maturity and intensity of production would be included in the measure of persistency by use of some of the criteria listed.

Intensity or rate of production has been measured by length of clutch by Hays and Sanborn (1932). Rate of production can be measured over a relatively short period of time. This reduces the need for year-round trap nesting and is certainly more practical.

Fertility and hatchability do not appear to be related (Hays and Sanborn, 1924). The hatchability was postulated by them to be due to one pair of genes. However, Landauer (1941) showed that lethal genes affect hatchability. Taylor and Lerner pointed out that much of the variation in hatchability is due to nutritional conditions. Hays (1950) found evidence for sex-linked genes which affect fertility in chickens. The males grouped as low in fertility on the basis of fertility of their daughters sired daughters of low fertility when mated to hens of high fertility. Males of high fertility sired daughters which were high in fertility irrespective of fertility level of the hens to which they were mated.

Fertility seems to be influenced very little by inheritance (Hays and Sanborn, 1924). In fact, it has been difficult in some studies to demonstrate any heritability of fertility in chickens. A character of this type could be improved more rapidly by environmental changes which will increase fertility. It is often noted that some hens in pen matings never lay fertile eggs but when switched to another pen, mating occurs and fertility is high. In turkey production, increased fertility can be obtained by artificial insemination once per week during the hatching period, even though sufficient males are constantly with the females. An increase of 10 per cent or more in fertility by artificial insemination as a supplement to natural breeding is not uncommon.

Sexual maturity in male chickens and turkeys, as indicated by age at which semen is first produced, has been shown to be under genetic influence by Lorenz, et al, (1946). Clark, et al (1944), reported that crossbreeding did not increase fertility to any great extent (5 per cent advantage for the crossbreds) but did increase hatchability by 8 per cent. If hatchability is more highly heritable than fertility, one might expect more advantages from crossbreeding to show in fertility. However, lethal genes should not be expected to bring about death in crossbreds to the same extent as in straightbreds.

STUDIES WITH LABORATORY ANIMALS

In rabbits, Sawin and Curran (1952) reported a range of 4.5 for hybrids to a high of 64 per cent sterility in different strains. They divided the causes of sterility into two main categories: (1) primary, the inability to produce viable gametes; and (2) secondary, either low inherent viability of the embryos or endocrine unbalance which interferes with implantation and proper fetal development. Their studies have been concerned with this second type of sterility. One strain in which there was 39 per cent sterility showed late sexual maturity or no sexual development at all. Injections of pituitary gonadotropins corrected this condition. It was not certain whether or not this infertility was influenced by the gene *dw,* which causes pituitary dwarfism. It is a case of inherited reduced fertility which is due to an endocrine unbalance.

In one line of rabbits the average litter size had declined to 4.9, although prolificacy was initially high in the line. A rigid selection program, in which a litter size of 8 was the least acceptable, was practiced for eight years, at the end of which time litter size had increased to an average of 9.1 young.

Fig. 131. Fertility is important to the producer both because of greater income and because of greater selection opportunities with larger litters. There can be more than twice as much selection practiced with this litter of 8 as from a litter of 3 rabbits. *(Courtesy Oregon State College.)*

Studies with laboratory animals are quite numerous and reveal a wide difference in age of sexual development (Long and Evans, 1920 and 1922; Freudenberger, 1932; Engle, et al, 1937; and Asdell, et al, 1941). Blunn studied two strains of rats which differed in growth rate and age at sexual maturity. He found that growth rate and age at sexual maturity were associated but not inseparable. Inheritance had more to do with age at sexual maturity than with weaning size of litter in which they were raised. The F_1, when the two strains were crossed, was intermediate, but the back-cross population showed some segregation into early and late sexually maturing groups.

Warren and Bogart (1952) selected rats for late and early puberty as revealed by age at time of vaginal opening. The two lines were separated by three generations of selection. Heritability of age at puberty was estimated at 17 per cent, based on the comparison of progress attained in relation to selection pressure applied. The females in the early sexually maturing line were more fertile and reached puberty at an earlier age. However, they were not equal in milking ability to the late sexually maturing line. The two groups were bred to deliver their first young at the same age so that the early line would not be penalized by bearing young at a younger age than the others.

Gluecksohn-Schoenheimer, et al (1950), studied semisterility in the mouse by examining eggs and the uteri from mated female mice. They found that mice homozygous for two of the three recessive mutations, t^0, t^1, or t^3, were either partially or completely sterile. Embryos and eggs from female mice that had been mated were examined to see if pre- or post-implantation death of the embryos was the cause of sterility. Fifty-five females examined during gestation showed no embryo formation or live young. Examination of the uteri of 57 females at time of implantation yielded only 20 embryos. A total of 756 eggs obtained prior to implantation time showed only 44 to have cleaved; the remainder were uncleaved and degenerating. It appears that this semisterility is due to a lack of fertilization rather than to fetal death.

Although fertility is low in heritability in most farm animals, other types of inheritance appear to play an important role. Numerous studies have shown that single genes have a marked effect upon fertility. Also, everyone is aware of the importance of environment on fertility.

With a low heritability of fertility, one would not expect rapid progress to be made from individual or mass selection. Progeny-test results would be more accurate than individual records for appraising inherited fertility level. The commercial breeder should consider a breeding system for obtaining maximum fertility. Crossbreeding or rotational use of highly selected breeding stock from different closed herds would be highly effective. The purebred breeder should consider culling animals which inherit endocrine disturbances.

EXERCISES

1. In what ways can inheritance influence fertility?
2. Most analyses indicate that the various aspects of fertility are low in heritability. How effective will mass selection be in improving fertility? What breeding methods might be most effective for obtaining maximum fertility? What type of selection would be most effective for improving a herd for fertility level?

23

INHERITANCE OF GROWTH RATE AND ADULT BODY SIZE

Growth could be regarded as protein synthesis, but in actual studies that are being made with farm animals, most of the work is based on gains in body weight. Because of this practice there is a great chance for some error to be made when gains in weight are interpreted as growth. Some gain in weight can be made without any increase in body tissue simply by an accumulation of water. Fattening, which might not be considered as growth, can result in increased gains. True growth can be accomplished only by an increase in cell size, by an increase in cell number, or by a combination of the two.

Growth begins as soon as the egg is fertilized and continues until maturity is reached. Growth in animals is normally considered to be in three phases: prenatal, nursing, and post-weaning. It has been considered that the mother has a marked influence upon growth of her young during the prenatal and nursing periods, but that post-weaning growth reflects the individual's inherited capacity for growth.

PRENATAL GROWTH

There is evidence that genetic differences in growth are expressed very early in life. Castle and Gregory (1931) reported differences in rate of cell divisions of large and small rabbits as soon as 4 hr. after fertilization. There was a marked increase in number of cell divisions in fertilized eggs of the large breed over that of the small breed 40 hr. after conception. Genetic factors controlling body size may operate through differential stimulation of protein anabolism. Blunn and Gregory (1937) found indications in the chick for the expression of inherited growth differences at various stages of development. It appears quite evident that genes for growth rate express themselves from fertilization until maturity. Whether the same genes are effective throughout growth or whether certain genes are effective at one stage of development, with others effective at

313

other stages, is not known. If birth weight is taken as a measure of prenatal growth, it can be seen that at least two factors are operating. The size of the mother appears to have a large effect on birth weight of those young in which only one offspring is the rule. In cattle and horses, larger females have larger young. This could be due to a transmission to her offspring of genetic factors which caused the mother to become large and which would cause her offspring to grow more rapidly during prenatal life.

Some evidence points to other causes. For example, reciprocal crosses of Shire and Shetland horses should produce F_1 foals possessing similar geno- types. The crossbred foals produced by Shire dams, however, were much larger at birth than foals produced by Shetland dams (Hammond, 1938). The foal resulting from mating a Shire mare to a Shetland stallion weighed 53 kg. at birth, while the foal resulting from mating a Shetland mare to a Shire stallion weighed only 17 kg. at birth. One might consider that these differences in birth weight were due to differences in fetal nutrition. Certainly the Shire mare has a larger uterus in which a foal can develop and should be capable of supplying the foal with a larger amount of nutrients. However, there is the possibility of cytoplasmic inheritance, and the large mare may produce an egg containing cytoplasmic material which results in rapid growth.

Another explanation for the difference in prenatal growth of these two kinds of F_1 foals may be the difference in the hormonal constitution of the two breeds of mares. It is conceivable that a greater amount of growth hormone secreted by the pituitary of the Shire mare stimulates a foal carried by her to grow more rapidly.

Whatever the cause of greater size of young at birth from larger females, there appears to be some influence other than the genetic constitution of the young. This means that prenatal growth is affected by genetics but that, in addition, other forces are operating. These other forces may be environmental in nature, but they have a marked influence on production because an animal which has greater size at birth generally makes faster post-natal gains. The crossbred Shire $\times$ Shetland horses which had a Shire dam weighed 458 kg. at 38 months of age, whereas the crossbreds which had the Shetland dam weighed only 329 kg. at this age. Certainly there must have been some perma- nent environmental effects during the prenatal and nursing periods which caused this difference in size of the crossbred horses because they should have been approximately equal genetically.

A type of environmental effect which may occur in animals in which litters are produced is a reduction in size of each individual in the very large litters. Numerous workers have shown that birth weight is associated with future rate of gain. If the reduction in birth weight by large litter size reduces future growth rate, this would be an example of permanent environmental effects. It would be logical to assume that an animal which gets a good start in early life would do better during the rest of its development than one which had a poor start in life. This should be true whether the good and poor starts in life are due to differences in environment or to differences in inheritance.

Prenatal growth is controlled in part by additive genetic influences. The heritability of birth weight was reported by Knapp and Nordskog (1946) for calves as 23 per cent by intra-sire correlations and 42 per cent by sire progeny regressions. Burris and Blunn (1952) report a heritability of 22 per cent for birth weight. Dawson, et al (1947), obtained a heritability estimate of 25 per cent by half-sib correlations in beef Shorthorns. These investigators, and also Yao, et al (1953), found that calves which were larger at birth grew more rapidly, particularly during the post-weaning period, and required less time to reach a weight of 900 lb. than smaller calves at birth. Dahmen and Bogart (1952) and Pierce, et al (1954), found an association of birth weight with post-weaning gains. This would indicate that genes which influence prenatal growth are operating strongly during the post-weaning period.

Knapp and Clark (1950) obtained an estimate of 53 per cent for heritability of birth weight in Hereford cattle. Gregory, et al (1950), reported heritabilities of 45 and 100 per cent for birth weight. This would indicate that genetic influences in these cattle were greater than environmental influences as factors affecting prenatal growth. One fact that tends to support a high heritability of prenatal growth is found in the variation in average birth weight of sire groups. Quesenberry (1950) reported a range from 73 to 92 lb. in average birth weight of sire groups of calves. This variation would not be expected unless the bulls used differed in the inheritance they contributed for prenatal growth.

Age of dam, sex of calf, and inbreeding all influence prenatal growth. Two-year-old cows produce smaller calves at birth than more mature cows. Bull calves are generally heavier at birth than heifer calves. Inbreeding in dairy and beef cattle has been found to reduce birth weight. An excellent study was made on the normal prenatal development of the bovine by Winters, et al (1942). These normal values are presented here so that one may see how rapidly the calf grows during prenatal life (Table 31).

Heritability estimate for birth weight of lambs, as given by Nelson and Ven-Katachalan (1949), is 61 per cent from weighted averages of two methods of determination. Birth weight in lambs is highly related to rate of gain. Donald and McLean (1935) reported a correlation of 0.50 between birth and 70-day weights. This relationship varied with breeds, being higher in faster-growing breeds. Cadmus (1949) found that each pound of increase in birth weight was associated with 2.5-lb. increase in weaning weight, indicating that prenatal

Table 31. PRENATAL GROWTH OF THE BOVINE FETUS

Measurements of Bovine Fetuses by Age

Age of Fetus (days)	Weight (gm)	Forehead to Rump Length (cm)	Head Length (cm)	Head Breadth (cm)	Forearm Length (cm)
45	2.77	3.08	0.50	0.825	0.475
50	4.94	3.85	0.60	0.850	0.500
60	13.78	6.60	1.15	1.450	1.150
70	37.25	9.40	3.30	2.000	1.900
90	159.80	16.40	5.00	3.300	2.700
100	317.20	18.80	6.00	3.900	3.300
120	820.00	27.10	8.40	5.000	5.000
140	1807.00	32.60	11.00	6.100	7.200
160	3562.00	43.70	13.20	7.500	9.100
185	6685.00	54.00	16.60	8.300	13.200
200	10433.00	58.50	18.20	9.400	18.500
230	18144.00	73.00	18.50	10.200	20.000
260	31298.00	87.00	23.00	11.500	23.000

and post-natal growth rates are controlled by the same genes in sheep. Carter and Henning (1951) found very little advantage of crossbreeding reflected in birth weights of lambs.

Birth weight in pigs is influenced greatly by the number of pigs per litter. Since number of pigs and gains are more important than birth weight, most of the studies have been concerned with these traits.

POST-NATAL GROWTH

Post-natal growth has received a great amount of attention because of its importance in meat production. Hammond (1935 and 1940) stated that the vital organs used for maintenance of life develop first, while other parts develop later. The order of development is: (1) digestive and endocrine systems, (2) skeletal system, (3) musculature, and (4) fat deposition. Hammond suggested that a continuous and rapid growth rate in early life will result in greater protein (muscle) development. In fact, McMeekan and Hammond (1940) proposed a method for obtaining greater lean in pigs by feeding on a high level in early life and on a lower level near the time of slaughter. Their data showed that the proportion of lean-to-fat can be altered by plane of nutrition. Pigs that were fed sparingly in early life and thereafter fed at a high level developed great amounts of fat. Pigs that were fed well in early life and then fed either reduced or full feed allowance developed a greater proportion of lean. Guilbert, et al

(1944), also reported an advantage in beef cattle of rapid and continuous growth in early life. The percentages of the more valuable wholesale cuts were increased by having the calves on a continuous growth following weaning. Hogan (1929) showed that a beef animal has the capacity to grow until six years of age. Retardation in growth does not produce abnormal development in conformation. However, as others have shown, the slower gains in early life may lead to a greater fat-to-lean ratio in carcass composition.

Brody (1921, 1926, 1927, 1928) in numerous studies, and Kleiber (1947) showed that metabolism is related to size. Brody (1921) found two peaks in post-natal growth of cattle; one is reached at five months of age while the second is reached at about 20 months of age. One can assume that the first is a peak in muscle growth, whereas the second is the peak in fat deposition. Brody (1946) pointed out that more rapidly growing animals produce carcasses with a greater tenderness. He stated also that sexual development marks the point of decline in growth rate and the increase in rate of fat deposition. From this it can be assumed that in early life the pituitary is secreting growth hormone at a high rate, whereas later the pituitary secretes gonadotropins rather than growth hormone.

Growth During the Nursing Period

Growth during the nursing period is the result of a combination of the animal's genetic capacity to grow and the milk provided by its dam. The effect of milk production of the dam is great; therefore, heritabilities of suckling gains or weaning weight have generaly been shown to be low. Woodward and Clark (1950) did not find significant differences between sires for weaning weight of the calves. Koger (1948) divided cows into five groups on the basis of weaning weight of their calves and then compared the weaning weight of subsequent calves produced by these groups of cows. These data show a high repeatability in weaning weight of calves, but this reflects the repeatability of milk production by the cows as well as their ability to transmit high growth capacity to their calves (Table 32).

Table 32. THE RELATION OF INITIAL WEANING WEIGHT OF CALVES BY COW GROUPS TO SUBSEQUENT WEANING WEIGHTS

Groups of Cows	Average Weight of First Calf, lb.	Average Weight of Next Four Calves, lb.
1	321	404
2	349	417
3	383	430
4	409	443
5	441	456

The heritability of weaning weight or gains during the suckling period in cattle has been reported on the basis of intra-sire correlations as 12 per cent, and on sire-progeny regression as zero, by Knapp and Nordskog (1946). Gregory, et al (1950), obtained zero and 45 per cent as estimates of heritability of suckling gains by paternal half-sib correlations and 26 and 52 per cent as the heritability for weaning weights of cattle. Knapp and Woodward (1951) and Knapp and Clark (1950) obtained a heritability estimate of 28 per cent for weaning weight.

Heritability was estimated for weight at six months of age for Holstein and Ayrshire cattle by Tyler, et al (1946). They reported figures varying from 15 to 35 per cent. One might expect greater heritability of early growth if all calves were on the same quality of diet and were allowed all they would consume. It was necessary at the Washington station to raise beef calves from birth on a prepared ration in order to clear up a disease. Inheritance accounted for more of the variations in rate of gain in early life under these uniform conditions. Dawson, et al (1954), obtained zero for heritability of six-month weight by the methods of sire-offspring regression and paternal half-sib correlations in a Brahman-Angus population. Paternal half-sib correlations among daughters gave a heritability of 19 per cent in weight at six months of age.

Botkin and Whatley (1953) estimated cow repeatability for weaning weight of calves to be 43 per cent. Knapp and Black (1941) reported that most of the differences in suckling gains were due to milking ability of the dams. Gifford (1949) was of the opinion that milk production of beef cows is more determined by the calf's ability to take the milk in early lactation than by milking ability of the cows.

Five factors influence weaning weight of calves: inbreeding, sex of calf, age of dam, size at birth, and milking ability of the dam. Koger and Knox found that steers had an average weaning weight, corrected for age, of 32 lb. more than heifers. Bulls would have even more of an advantage than steers over heifers in weaning weight. Koch (1951) found that bulls are 31 lb. heavier than steers at weaning and that steers are 13 lb. heavier than heifers. In a herd where some males are to be kept as bulls (data used by Koch), it is obvious that heifers would have an advantage over steers, in contrast to one in which the entire male group was steers (data used by Koger and Knox). Burgess, et al (1954), developed adjustment factors for age of dam, sex of calf, and inbreeding. Sawyer, et al (1948), found that two-year-old cows wean calves which are 75 lb. lighter at 30 weeks of age than those produced by mature cows. These data have been generally in agreement with data from New Mexico and the U.S. Range Livestock Experiment Station. One would need to adjust weaning weights for sex, age of dam, and inbreeding for making accurate comparisons.

The Oregon station has found that time of calving is important even when breeding is restricted to a three-month period because earlier calves gain more rapidly than later calves. Under other conditions, earlier calves might be at a disadvantage when compared with late calves.

Weaning weight in sheep is also influenced by the milking ability of the ewe as well as the inherited growth capacity of the lamb. Hazel and Terrill (1943) obtained an estimate of 30 per cent heritability for weaning weight in sheep. Since lambs in farm flocks are normally marketed at weaning time, the heritability of weaning weight is very important. This estimate would indicate that considerable progress could be made by selecting larger lambs at weaning time. If one also selects breeding stock from sire groups of ewes possessing the ability to wean heavy lambs, progress will be increased.

There appears to be breed differences in heritability of weaning weight (Hazel and Terrill, 1946) because the estimates of heritability for Corriedales of 32 per cent, for Columbia of 16 per cent, and for Targhee of 8 per cent show marked differences. Blunn (1945) found large yearly variations and breed-year interactions for weaning weight of lambs. The Navajo lambs showed less yearly variation than Navajo crossbreds, which indicated that inheritance rather than environment was limiting growth in the Navajo lambs.

Nelson and VenKatachalan (1949) and Karam, et al (1953), emphasize the importance of sex, twin and single births, and year as factors influencing weaning weight of lambs. By the method of parent-offspring regression, heritability of weaning weight was estimated at 29 per cent by Nelson and VenKatachalan. The estimate of heritability for weaning weight by half-sib correlations was 42 per cent. Certainly one would need to correct for type of birth (twin or single) in order to compare lambs for weaning weights. One would also need to correct for birth type. This could be done by comparing lambs within a sex or by adjusting to a basis of one sex.

Heritability of weaning weight in swine is low. Lush and Molln (1942) studied data from various stations and found a low repeatability of weaning weight. Certainly the heritability would not be high where repeatability is low. Hazel, et al (1943), obtained an estimate of 15 per cent for the heritability of weaning weight of swine.

Since gains in cattle during the suckling period are largely under environmental rather than genetic influences, one would not expect a high relationship between suckling and post-weaning gains. Dahmen and Bogart (1952) and Pierce, et al (1954), have found only slight, if any, relationship between the two growth rates. There may be some indication that genes affecting growth during the suckling period are also effective in later growth. Wheeler (1944) found a low correlation of 0.12 between suckling and feedlot gains. However,

Kidwell (1954) found no relation of weaning weight with later gains. Knapp and Black (1941) found no relation between gains before and after weaning. Koger and Knox (1951) found no relation of weaning weight with pasture gains on the range.

Rollins, et al (1952), analyzed growth during the periods from birth to four months of age and from four to eight months of age. They concluded that the mechanism and genetic factors affecting growth of the calf for the period from birth to four months of age are significantly different and independent of the mechanism and genetic factors operating for the period from four to eight months of age.

The relationship between weaning weight and growth following weaning in pigs is somewhat higher than the same relationship in beef cattle. Although Dickerson (1947) found that genes which cause rapid fattening and efficiency of feed utilization also cause low sow productivity, numerous workers have obtained a positive relation of gains during the suckling period to gains during post-weaning. This indicates that sows which gain rapidly and convert feed into gains in an efficient manner are less desirable as mothers. But pigs within a litter that gain rapidly before weaning will also gain rapidly during the post-weaning period.

POST-WEANING RATE OF GAIN

Rate of gain in the feedlot is one of the most highly heritable traits that has been estimated for beef cattle. Numerous workers have reported heritability for post-weaning gains in beef cattle. A summary of these data is given in Table 33.

Table 33. HERITABILITY ESTIMATES FOR POST-WEANING GAINS IN BEEF CATTLE

Method of Estimation	Heritability, per cent	Investigators
Intra-sire correlation	99	Knapp and Nordskog
Sire-progeny regression	46	Knapp and Nordskog
Half-sib correlation:		
Male	26	
Female	30	Patterson, et al
Half-sib correlation	65	Knapp and Clark
Sire-offspring regression	77	Knapp and Clark
Paternal half-sib correlations	63	Kohli, et al
Half-sib correlation:		
Pasture	75	
Feedlot	42	Flower, et al
Paternal half-sib correlations	59	Schott, et al
Paternal half-sib correlations	44	Dawson, et al
Not stated	65	Quesenberry

Several workers have shown that rate of gain on pasture is negatively related to gains made the previous winter. However, most of these studies were concerned with one group which was fed to gain more than the other group during the winter period. In this case, the group that gained the most during the winter gained the least during the following summer. When one compares the gains of calves during the two periods when all calves are treated the same during the winter period, the calves which gain the most during the winter are the ones which gain the most during the summer (Flower, et al, 1953, and unreported work from the Squaw Butte station in Oregon). It appears that heritability of gains for beef cattle is high whether they are fed or pastured, as long as feed supplies will permit expression of genetic differences between animals.

In general, rate of gain is not altered by individual feeding as compared with group feeding. Therefore, if rate of gain is obtained under either system of feeding, its heritability is high.

Several investigators have been concerned with the influence of age, previous rate of gain, and condition on post-weaning gains. The effect of age when a calf is placed on test and of gains made during the suckling period on feedlot gains are slight and would not have a pronounced effect. Dahmen and Bogart (1952) and Pierce (1953) found very little effect of age on the gains made during the time when a calf was placed on test. The calf that gains the most during the suckling period may make these rapid gains because of its own growth capacity or because of a greater milk production by its dam. If the more rapid gains were the result of greater growth capacity of the calf, the post-weaning gains would likely be great. If the greater gains during the suckling period were the result of more milk produced by the dam, the calf would probably not show greater post-weaning gains. A higher condition of the calf at weaning may be reflected in lower gains during the post-weaning period, particularly if the better condition is due to early maturity that leads to fattening rather than to growth.

Williams (1955) found that if calves are accustomed to handling, only a short adjustment period is needed in order to get the calves ready for the feed test. On the other hand, if they come from a range and are wild, a month to six weeks may be required to get them adjusted to conditions of the feedlot.

Bulls grow much more rapidly during the post-weaning period than heifers. Burris, et al (1954), found that injected testosterone would increase gains. It is likely that the difference in gains between bulls and heifers is due to the hormone difference between the two sexes.

There is a close relationship in beef cattle between rate of gain and feed efficiency. The more rapidly gaining animals require less feed to make a unit of gain than the slower gaining ones (Winters and McMahon, 1933; Bogart and Blackwell, 1950; Knapp and Baker, 1944; Roubicek, et al, 1951; Black and Knapp, 1936; and Pierce, et al, 1954). Pierce observed that an increase in gain per day of 0.1 lb. resulted in a saving of 23 lb. of T.D.N. per 100 lb. of gain. Knapp and Baker (1944) concluded that the correlation between rate and efficiency of gain is reduced in a time-constant as contrasted with a weight-constant feed period. Gain per day during the early post-weaning period shows either no relation to weight or increases as weight increases, whereas feed efficiency is definitely related to weight of the animals and declines as weight increases.

Post-weaning growth in swine shows a lower heritability than for beef cattle. Hazel, et al (1943), obtained estimates of heritability for: the period from weaning (56 days) to 112 days of age, 28 per cent; and the period from 112 to 168 days, 17 per cent. Nordskog, et al (1944), obtained estimates of heritability for gains; from weaning (56 days) to 84 days, 18 per cent; from weaning to 112 days of age, 28 per cent; from weaning to 140 days, 39 per cent; and from weaning to 168 days, 45 per cent. These estimates indicate that accuracy of measuring growth increases as the length of the period increases. One might also interpret the results to indicate that growth is less heritable than fattening, as was suggested by Dickerson (1947). Nordskog, et al (1944), estimated the heritability of gains from birth to a weight of 200 lb. as 21 per cent and from weaning (56 days) to 200 lb. as 40 per cent.

There is a positive relationship of rate of gain with feed efficiency in pigs. In fact, the relationship is such that Dickerson and Grimes (1947) postulated that more progress could be made in feed efficiency by selecting for rate of gain than if selections were made for feed efficiency itself.

There has been some indication that breeders are willing to pay for rate of gain when buying breeding stock. Johnson and Aegerter (1952) found breeders gave more consideration to condition and conformation of bulls than to feedlot gain when buying bulls but that some attention was also given to gains. Willson, et al (1953), have stated that Midwest feeders are showing preference, expressed in premium prices, for steers sired by bulls that are rapid and efficient gainers. Winters (1936) has stated that there is a correlation of 0.8 for daily gain and sale index with net profit.

Rate of gain in beef cattle is not only highly heritable but is also greatly variable, and therefore a big reach for increased gains by selection is possible (PanTech Farms, 1950–1953; Willson, et al, 1950; and Pahnish, 1951). Several studies indicate that considerable progress has been made by selecting for greater rate of gain. Gerlaugh and Kunkle (1950) compared steers produced at the U.S. Range Livestock Experiment Station from production-tested sires with selected steers obtained at the stockyards. The steers sired by the production-tested bulls gained 9 per cent faster and 8.5 per cent more efficiently than those obtained from the market. There is some evidence that cattle which eat more will be the ones which gain the fastest. However, Carpenter (1953) raised the question as to whether the animal eats more because of its faster gains or gains more because of its greater food consumption. If the appetite of an animal is highly related to rate of gain, then fast and economical gains result largely from the increased conversion of feed into meat, thereby reducing the period of time necessary for maintaining the animal.

Grade or score seems to show no relation to rate of gain (Durham and Knox, 1953, and data from the Oregon station). This statement indicates that one can have animals that will make desirable carcasses and which also will gain rapidly. It could mean, however, that selection for both is necessary, because it is not possible to increase rate of gain by selecting on conformation score. In fact, the opposite might be true if the compact type were selected for, since many studies show that the more compact animal grows at a slower rate than conventional type cattle (Hultz, 1927; Chambers, et al, 1951; Woodward, et al, 1947; Willey, et al, 1950; Knox and Koger, 1946; Stonaker, et al, 1950–1952; and Schleicher, et al, 1950). There is some evidence that feed efficiency of the compact animals equals that of conventional type when the two are carried to the same degree of finish, but when they are fed to a given weight, the conventional type is much more efficient.

The work at New Mexico station indicates that compact cattle score higher as live animals but carcasses from the conventional type animals are equal to those from the compact cattle. Certainly the finish-constant basis for comparing the animals favors the smaller type of animal, whereas the weight-constant basis favors the conventional type of animal. Life-time production at the New Mexico station has been in favor of the conventional over the small type of cattle. This is one of the primary reasons for favoring a certain amount of size in beef cattle.

The "comprest" character is due to one major gene. It can be seen that this gene has a very marked effect on growth rate and also on length of the growing period. It appears that the comprest cattle reach a cessation of growth and begin to fatten at a very small size and at a young age.

Selection for More Rapid Rate of Gain

Some selection experiments for fast and slow rate of gains have been conducted both with laboratory and with farm animals. MacArthur (1944) selected mice for large and small size at 60 days of age for eight generations. At the end of the eighth generation, there were marked differences in adult body size and in other characteristics (Table 34).

Fig. 132. Large body size is important in beef cattle. Larger cattle grow more rapidly and are more efficient feed users than smaller type cattle. This bull, Atok Lionheart, weighs over 2200 lb. under irrigated pasture conditions. *(Courtesy Oregon State College.)*

Table 34. THE EFFECT OF SELECTION FOR LARGE AND SMALL SIZE IN MICE

	Weight of Mice in Grams			
	Selected for Small Size		*Selected For Large Size*	
Generation	*Males*	*Females*	*Males*	*Females*
0	18.5	13.9	18.5	13.9
8	10.8	10.6	27.5	18.7

MacArthur stated that the increase by selecting for increased size and the decrease from selecting for smaller size on a percentage basis were about equal. The normal is the same percentage larger than the ones selected for small size as the percentage of those selected for large size are larger than the normal. Thus the effect of size genes depends on the size and are relative rather than absolute.

The secondary effect of selecting for increased and decreased size is interesting. The mice developed by selecting for smaller size were active, aggressive, and savage. Those selected for large size were docile and quiet. The mice selected for large size were mostly solid colored, brown, or cinnamon, with a few albino and several dilute. Thus, the genes b and d were retained and s was discarded by selecting for large size. Castle (1936) has reported that the genes b and d accelerate growth in mice as one of their pleiotropic effects, while B, D, and s retard growth, thus making for smaller size.

Size of the litters also changed with selection for small and large size. The mice selected for large size produced 84 per cent more young per litter, and the young at birth were 24 per cent heavier than those produced by mice selected for small size. It is probable that selection for larger size results in a pituitary which is more actively secreting both gonadotropic and growth factors, rather than in the accumulation of more genes for increased ovarian functions.

Post-weaning growth rate in farm animals appears to be more highly heritable than pre-weaning growth rate. It appears that the heritability of post-weaning growth rate is sufficiently high for rapid progress to result from selections based on individual performance. However, during the suckling period, milk production by the dam influences rate of gain of the young. Consequently, selection for more rapid pre-weaning gains is directed in part toward increased milk production and in part toward more rapid gains. Heritability of pre-weaning gains is lower, and therefore progeny-testing will show some advantages. Crossbreeding or the combining of lines will generally be advantageous to commercial producers for obtaining maximum growth during the suckling period. The use of rotational crossing of stock from highly selected closed herds will be most beneficial. This can be done within a breed or between breeds.

Large size at birth is probably of little importance except as it affects survival or future rate of gain. Since selection based on survival at birth and future gains would largely take care of the need for large size at birth, one can see little need for selection directed toward heavier birth weights. It is possible that young of extreme size might have a detrimental influence on delivery. Consequently, young that do well following birth rather than large young are the real need.

Since rate of post-weaning gain and feed efficiency are so closely related, considerable progress in improving feed efficiency can be made by selecting only for rate of gain. This appears to be true for both swine and beef cattle.

EXERCISES

1. In what ways can inheritance influence growth rate?

2. Reciprocal crosses of Shire and Shetland horses yield F_1, which grow at different rates and reach adult body sizes that differ, although the two groups of F_1 should be similar in genotypes. Explain this difference.

3. Discuss the relative environmental and genetic effects on growth during the prenatal, nursing, and post-weaning periods.

24

TWINS

There are two types of twins in animals: monozygotic or identical, in which one egg develops into two individuals; and dizygotic or fraternal, in which the two individuals result from two different fertilized eggs. Monozygotic twins are of the same sex and should be largely of the same genetic constitution, but they may differ considerably in cytoplasmic material. They may differ somewhat in some characteristics, depending upon when separation occurs. If the fertilized egg divides to form two cells which separate, each forming an individual, the twins will be very similar because not only are they alike genetically but their cytoplasm will also be quite similar. If separation into two individuals occurs after several cell divisions have occurred, and there has been considerable cytoplasmic differentiation, the monozygotic twins may differ considerably.

Dizygotic or fraternal twins should occur in the approximate ratio of 1 ♂ ♂ : 2 ♂ ♀ : 1 ♀ ♀. In animals such as cattle, there may be a fusion of the extra-embryonic membranes (the chorion) so that the blood stream of one of the twins is continuous with that of the other twin. When the blood stream of a male twin is continuous with that of the female, the blood from the male carries testosterone which circulates and causes the female reproductive system to develop in the direction of the male. The result is that the female reproductive tract is so modified that it never can become functional after the testosterone influence is removed by birth of the twins. This case of a sterile female twinborn with a male is known as a *freemartin* (Lillie, 1916, 1917 and 1923). Twins are not frequent in cattle and only one-half of the dizygotic twins will be of opposite sex; therefore, freemartins are not common. In the herd at the Oregon station, in which 50 calves are produced each year, only one freemartin has been produced during a period of eight years.

Dizygotic twins should resemble each other to the same degree as litter mates in animals from which litters are produced. Because of the prenatal environmental influences, they may be more similar than full sibs born at different times. Actually, dizygotic twins are a small litter and can vary genetically as much as two full sibs born at different times.

Fig. 133. Littermates may vary as much genetically as other full sibs but they may be more similar in appearance due to uniform environmental conditions. These guinea pigs show marked color variations (genetic) but are quite uniform in size, a portion of which is due to a uniform environment. *(Courtesy Oregon State College.)*

Monozygotic twins should be more similar than dizygotic twins. In both cases, the prenatal environments are the same, but monozygotic twins are also largely of the same genetic constitution. The monozygotic twins may have cytoplasmic differences and there may be some advantage of one over the other in uterine environment. These same differences, as well as genetic differences, can influence dizygotic twins.

Fig. 134. Monozygotic twins may differ due to abnormal developmental conditions. This cow was born without a tail although her identical twin sister has a normal tail. This is an extreme difference which does not have a genetic basis. *(Courtesy Oregon State College.)*

Because of the same genotype of monozygotic twins, they have been studied intensively in the human and in beef cattle to determine the relative effects of heredity and environment on important traits. Hirsch (1930) reported a survey made in 1917 in which 1,339,975 human births were studied. Twin births occurred once in every 93 cases; a little more than 1 per cent of all human births are twins. Only a portion of these births is identical, the others being dizygotic. Monozygotic twins occur about 1 in every 300 births (Snyder, 1951).

Several characteristics have been studied to determine how much influence different environments can have on identical twins. For example, how much influence does educational advantage have on intelligence? Woodworth (1941) showed that the average I. Q. difference between separated identical twins was 7.6 points, whereas the average difference in I. Q. between unseparated identical twins is 3 points. These figures should be compared with the average difference of 15 points in I. Q. of children paired at random in the same community to demonstrate that environmental influence causes a greater difference between separated identical twins than exists between identical twins reared under the same conditions. However, identical twins under different conditions are much more alike in I. Q. than unrelated children of the same community.

Woodworth reported one of the greatest extremes of identical girls: one was raised in a good farming community, went to college, and became a school teacher; the other twin grew up in a backward area and received only two years of formal schooling. However, this less-educated twin was later employed in a large city and became general assistant in a small printing office where she performed many tasks. The I. Q. rating for the less-educated girl was 92 and for the college-trained twin 116, or a difference of 24 points. At first glance, one would assume that environment was much more effective than heredity in affecting intelligence, but it must be remembered that character expressions are the result of both genetics and environment. In this case, the environment differed more than that existing between two randomly selected persons, and consequently the environmental effects were greater.

In the Newman study (Newman, et al, 1937), involving 19 pairs of identical twins raised in separate environments, it was found that the average intra-pair difference in I. Q. was approximately 8 points. The intra-pair difference in I. Q. between identical twins raised together was about 6 points. The difference in I. Q. of like-sexed fraternal (dizygotic) twins raised together was approximately 10 points. These data would indicate that heredity is most important in determining I. Q. However, one must not overlook the difference in 24 points obtained with one set of twins. It has been shown (Snyder, 1951) that the difference in I.Q. between separated monozygotic twins is related to the difference in environments to which the twins are subjected. This shows definitely that environment influences the I. Q.

Dizygotic twins reared in the same household are more similar than those which are separated. Studies of foster children compared with their sibs and parents and with the foster parents indicated a rather large genetic influence on I. Q. Burks (1928) was of the opinion that heredity contributed 75 to 80 per cent in determining I. Q., whereas Woodworth (1941) would have placed equal emphasis on inheritance and environment in determining I. Q.

An interesting case is worthy of note. A young man who was highly trained in biology and sociology suggested to the "city father" of a large city that slums should be cleaned up by education. This young man was employed to hold night classes in the slum area. He taught and worked diligently in the area for a number of years, and he and the city officials pointed proudly to the improvement in the area. However, an elderly resident of the city made a study of who lived in the area prior to and at the end of the educational program. To everyone's surprise, it was found that about 85 per cent of the people who had formerly lived in the area had been replaced by others. It developed that this young teacher was so effective that he moved the slums to another area and moved into this area a group of people who wanted and appreciated greater educational opportunity. The point that should be stressed is the danger in assigning cause and effect in relationships. It may be that some areas have greater opportunities because the more intelligent people of the area created these opportunities, rather than that the greater opportunities raised the intelligence level of the people.

One might consider the situation in this way: Opportunities, no matter how good they are, will not develop a person beyond his inherited capacity to take advantage of these opportunities. Likewise, inherited ability, no matter how great, will not be expressed unless opportunity permits expression of this ability. Whichever is the limiting factor, that also is the most important factor.

FREQUENCY OF TWINNING

Twinning varies with the species, as shown in Table 35.

Table 35. DIZYGOTIC TWINNING PERCENTAGES FOR VARIOUS FARM ANIMALS

Kind of Animal	Percentage Twinning	Reference
Sheep	20 to 50	Numerous
Goats	20 to 50	Numerous
Dairy cattle	1.88	Johansson (1931)
Beef cattle	0.44	Johansson (1931)
Horses	1.50	Uppenborn (1933)

Identical twins also vary with the species. In the nine-banded armadillo the normal litter size is four young, all arising from one fertilized egg. This would be a case of identical or monozygotic quadruplets. In the human, 37 to 42 per cent of the like-sexed twins are identical. However, identical twins occur less frequently in farm animals, and while no reports of identical twins are available in sheep and horses, there is some variation in the reported incidence of identical twins in cattle. Lillie (1923) found only one case of identical twins (two fetuses but only one corpus luteum in the ovary) from his study of slaughter house material on which he did his freemartin studies. It has been estimated that eight identical pairs are to be expected from each 100,000 births. Johansson (1931) has estimated that about 6 per cent of all twin births, or 11.36 per cent of like-sexed twins, are identical. Bonnier and Hansson (1948) have estimated that 8.48 per cent of like-sexed twins in cattle are identical or monozygotic. It has been also estimated that 10.61 per cent of like-sexed twins are identical. The work of several investigators on the frequency of twinning and of identical twins indicates that, of all births, the percentage of twins varies from 1.02 to 4.61; the percentage of identical twins varies from 0.05 to 0.28; and the percentage of identical twins of like-sexed twins varies from 6 to 27.

One of the reasons for variations in reports on the incidence of monozygotic twins may be that the differentiation of mono- and dizygotic twins is not always easy. Certain characteristics have been used for determining the monozygotic or dizygotic nature of twins. No one characteristic can be completely relied upon, but when several are used and the two individuals are quite similar in all respects, the chances are good that the twins are identical. With certain characteristics it is easier to prove that dissimilar twins are not identical than it is to prove that similar twins are identical. Head measurements, body measurements, muzzle prints, color, white markings, whorls, and hair sections have all been used. Johansson and Venge (1951) have found that actual body and head measurements are as valuable as ratios of these measurements. Where error in taking the measurements is not great, the measurement has greater value for diagnosing monozygotic twins. Hair sections are not only very time-consuming but also have low diagnostic value. Muzzle prints, color, and white markings have some value but probably do not equal measurements for diagnosing identical twins.

It seems logical that a study of blood groups would be an infallible method. Certainly this would be true if it were not for the fact that there may be a fusion of the extra-embryonic membranes such that the blood of one twin is continuous with that of the other. This would have the tendency to make like-sexed dizygotic twins appear the same as monozygotic twins as far as blood groups are concerned. Owen, et al (1946), have found that exchanged cells become established in individuals where circulation is continuous. The use of this method along with others should add a great deal because the error from mosaics produced in dizygotic twins by continuous blood streams should not be great (Stormont, 1954).

Since monozygotic twins are alike genetically, they offer a valuable experimental animal for nutritional, physiological, and grazing studies, as well as being very useful in estimating the relative effects of inheritance and environment on production characteristics. It can be seen that when the members of identical twins are each placed under different experimental treatments, the difference between the members of the twin pairs is due to environmental (treatment) effects; whereas, the difference between the individuals within the treatment is largely due to genetic differences. This makes identical twins much more efficient as experimental animals than random samples from a population.

EFFICIENCY OF IDENTICAL TWINS FOR STUDIES

The efficiency of identical twins is the ratio of the variance within pairs of unrelated animals, divided by the variance within pairs of identical twins. The equation used by Stormont for calculating efficiency value is:

$$\text{Efficiency} = \frac{\dfrac{(\text{between-pair variance})}{(\text{within-pair variance})} + 1}{2}$$

By use of this equation, one can determine the relative efficiency of monozygotic twins over random samples for various traits. In some instances there appears to be very little advantage of monozygotic twins over other animals, but in grazing time it has been shown that one pair of monozygotic twins is equal to 72 pairs of randomly selected animals. In certain work, such as grazing studies, where it is desirable to obtain data on small areas, the use of monozygotic twins can be particularly valuable.

Heritability can be estimated from identical twins by use of the following equation:

$$h = \frac{(\text{between-pair variance}) - (\text{within-pair variance})}{(\text{between-pair variance}) + (\text{within-pair variance})}$$

However, this gives heritability in the broad sense and includes in the heritability estimate variance due to additive gene effects, dominance, and epistasis.

It also includes maternal and pre- and post-natal influences which are similar for one set of twins but differ between sets of twins. By use of this method of analysis, Bonnier, et al (1948), calculated the heritability of weight in cattle at 6, 18, and 27 months of age. These estimates of 91, 98, and 94 per cent, respectively, are much higher than heritabilities calculated for heritability in the narrow sense (additive genetic effects only) and indicate either that estimates by other methods may give heritability figures which are too low, or that dominant and epistatic genetic effects and environmental effects due to maternal influences are more important than may be generally recognized.

Winchester (1953) has used identical twins for establishing the energy requirements of beef calves for maintenance and growth. He has postulated from these studies that it takes practically the same feed to produce an animal under continuous growth as it does where growth is interrupted for some time. This is in sharp contrast to unpublished material of Williams and Woods in studies of rats in which they found that restricted food intake prevented the animals from "catching up" with the liberally fed rats.

Some of the most interesting studies of identical twins were done by Bonnier, et al (1948), and Bonnier and Hansson (1948). These workers established the "ceiling concept," which means that there is a maximum, established by inheritance, beyond which one cannot increase production by better feeding, etc. Animals vary a great deal in this maximum ability. Increased feed will increase growth or production only to the point at which the ceiling is reached. This means that feeding on a high level would be necessary to establish the maximum ability of an animal. On the other hand, these investigators reported that feeding less than maximum did not impose undue hardships on the better animals in relation to the less productive ones. This, of course, is relative because the study recognized a "critical" point, below which all animals, regardless of genotype, could be thrown into the same unproductive group.

It has been shown that for certain types of research, monozygotic twins are more useful than randomly chosen animals. In the cases of lower heritabilities due to linkage, dominance, and gene interactions, one might expect monozygotic twins to be particularly useful. However, in highly heritable traits such as rate of gains in beef cattle, one would expect less advantages from the use of monozygotic twins.

Where there was a genetic-environmental interaction of considerable amount, errors from use of monozygotic twins could be made, and the data from larger numbers of randomly selected animals would be more valid for drawing conclusions relative to the population in general.

Hancock (1954) presented a very good summary on the efficiency of mono-

Fig. 135. Identical triplet Holstein bulls. From the results of all known tests for mono-zygosity these three bulls arose from one ovum. Monozygotic twins or triplets are very efficient for certain types of research. *(Courtesy Oregon State College.)*

zygotic twins and on heritability estimates based on such twins.* It is important to note that in data on identical twins from uniformity trials, there may be errors if environmental-hereditary interactions exist. An efficiency value derived from split-twin experiments should indicate the relative efficiency gained by use of these twins in this particular kind of experiment. Where more than two comparisons are to be made, it becomes necessary to use a special experimental design when monozygotic twins are used. By use of incomplete randomized blocks design, one can make direct and indirect comparisons between treatments. The efficiency of monozygotic twins for trials in which several treatments are used is calculated from the formula

$$\frac{N E}{2(N-1)}$$

where $N =$ the number of treatments and $E =$ the efficiency value for twins when used in a two-treatment trial. The efficiency value of monozygotic twins is presented in Table 36.

* The author is grateful to Dr. John Hancock, Ruakura Animal Research Station, Department of Agriculture, Hamilton, New Zealand, and to the New Zealand Department of Agriculture for permission to use directly from the summary in publication No. 63 the material on efficiency of identical twins and the use of monozygotic twins for making heritability estimates.

Table 36. TWIN EFFICIENCY VALUES

Characteristic	Twin Efficiency Value	No. of Sets Used
Milk	22	7
Butterfat	54	7
Butterfat percentage	15	7
Persistency of lactation	4	7
Grazing time	72	6
Distances covered	3	6
Body weights	26	10
Absolute growth rates	13	10
Instantaneous relative growth rate	11	10
Linear body measurements	5–30	10
Red-cell count	4	12
Red-cell volume	8	10
Haemoglobin content	13	10
Body temperature	37	7
Respiration rate	15	7
Sperm concentration	8	12
Total sperm	8	12
Service volume	2	12
Reduction factor	4	12

Hancock (1954) reports material from Carter (1951) on efficiency values of monozygotic twins.

1. The efficiency value determined from a limited sample is only an estimate of a hypothetical population quantity and is therefore subject to considerable sampling variation.

2. The sensitivity of statistical comparison of treatments depends not only on the "error" variance, but also on the "degrees of freedom" available. For example, no test of significance at all would be possible with one split-twin pair.

3. The possibility of real environment $\times$ heredity interaction when different treatments are applied cannot be discounted. This obviously necessitates the use of a reasonable genotypic range of experimental material (certainly more than one set) if dubious extrapolation is to be avoided. Since in a nonrepeated treatment-experiment, the treatment $\times$ heredity interaction is inevitably included in the "error," the estimate of error variation from a uniformity trial may well underestimate the error appropriate to treatment comparisons, with consequent overestimation of E.

4. It is probable that the genetic variability in a sample of monozygotic twins would be greater than that in a sample from a particular herd or farm. This would imply that the numerator used in the formula for E, i.e., between-set variance, is in fact too high, leading again to an overestimate. On the other hand, the fact that such a twin sample is representative of a wide population should justify increased confidence in generalization of experimental results.

5. Problems of wastage also decrease the usefulness of monozygotic twins below the level indicated by the twin efficiency values. If one member of a set of twins dies or becomes useless for experimental purposes, it is obvious that in most cases a co-twin must be excluded.

6. An efficiency value can only be related to a population which is clearly specified—in regard, for example, to age of animals and length of standardized lactation period.

Heritability estimates using monozygotic twins include epistatic and dominance as well as additive effects in the numerator. In addition, one must recognize that maternal as well as genetic effects will tend to create greater similarity between two members of a set of twins than between two randomly selected animals.

Hancock's interpretations of heritability estimates from monozygotic twin data are:

In uniformity trials, if these are not time-repeated, only two sources of variation can be distinguished: between-set differences, and within-set differences. The between-set variance contains not only all genetic effects—additive as well as those due to dominance and epistasis—but also includes any genotype $\times$ environment interaction present. Heritability estimates based on uniformity trials are therefore likely to be too high.

In split-twin experiments it is, on the other hand, possible to distinguish between three sources of variation: between-set variance, treatment variance, and error. The first term contains, as in uniformity trials, all genetic variation and that due to common pre-natal and contemporary environments. The genotype $\times$ environment interactions, however, are included in the error term. If the twin-sets used are all of the same age and have been brought up together, it is possible, in a split-twin experiment, to separate from the hereditary portion of variance all other nongenetic influences except those due to difference in pre-natal environment.

EXERCISES

1. Why are monozygotic twins more alike than dizygotic twins or than like-sex dizygotic twins?

2. Why might one expect dizygotic twins to be more similar than full sibs born at different times?

3. Explain why heritability estimates based on identical twin data may be higher than heritability estimates based on parent-offspring regressions.

4. For what types of traits are monozygotic twins more efficient as experimental animals?

25

INHERITANCE OF DISEASE RESISTANCE

Since disease has been defined as any deviation from the normal, inherited defects can also be considered as diseases, although such defects would differ from the communicable diseases.

There are two types of disease affecting farm animals, both of which may be under genetic control: (1) the type represented by abnormalities of form or function of parts, of which some are under direct genetic control and may be quite simple in inheritance; (2) diseases that are caused by bacterial infections or parasites, which are not inherited directly but for which resistance or susceptibility to these bacterial or parasitological diseases may be inherited. Even in the case of inherited abnormalities of form or function, the expression of the character may be influenced by environmental interactions.

Genetic abnormalities and lethals were discussed in Chap. 8, where it was pointed out that these conditions take a heavy toll from production in farm animals. It certainly is apparent from the large list of these inherited abnormalities that livestock breeders are faced with a huge task of eliminating or reducing the incidence of them because each one must be dealt with individually, since general vigor of the parents selected does not preclude the possibility that they may carry the inheritance for one or several abnormalities.

DIFFICULTIES IN BREEDING FOR DISEASE RESISTANCE

The possibility of breeding resistance into farm animals against bacterial diseases has been given considerable thought. Certainly the control of the bacterial and parasitological diseases is important because they reduce the income derived from the production of livestock. They also may mask the expression of many desirable genes by reducing the general performance of the animals. In addition, death losses from disease may reduce the number from which selection for other traits may be made.

One may wonder why strains of farm animals have not been developed which possess resistance to all bacterial diseases or parasite infestations. Resistance is not general for all diseases, and therefore a strain that is highly resistant to one disease may be quite susceptible to another. This shows that general vigor is not sufficient for resisting a disease. In fact, some of the more vigorous strains of animals, as shown by growth, etc., may be the most susceptible to certain diseases. This means that the problem of developing herds which are resistant to diseases becomes very complex. It also means that resistance to each disease must be developed because resistance is specific for each disease.

One other situation reduces the possibility of developing strains of animals which are resistant to diseases. Unicellular organisms that cause disease in farm animals may mutate to a more virulent form at a faster rate than resistance can be developed by selection. Since resistance to disease is specific for each disease, mutation of the causitive organism may be more rapid than progress of control which is made through selection. These two facts place doubt on the feasibility of attempting to develop strains possessing general

Fig. 136. It may not be possible to breed disease and parasite resistance into our farm animals but a great deal can be done in disease and parasite prevention so that diseases and parasites will not interfere with selection for other traits. A good pasture rotation which provides clean, lush grass is one of the best means of helping to control diseases and parasites. *(Courtesy Oregon State College.)*

disease resistance. What other alternative is available to the breeder? He may employ strict sanitation, which should minimize the chances of introducing a disease, or he may use vaccination to provide immunity from certain diseases. In the case of internal parasites one may use certain drugs in addition to pasture rotation and other sanitation procedures to hold down infestation. External parasites may be controlled by spraying or dipping.

The idea of maintaining complete freedom from disease by sanitation, use of drugs, and vaccination has complications. If a herd or flock is developed under strict sanitary and disease-free conditions, it may be very susceptible when a disease happens to enter the herd or when these animals are sold to a breeder who has a high state of contamination on his farm. One reason is that animals normally develop an acquired immunity from or resistance to some diseases if they are raised where the diseases are prevalent. When animals are raised in a disease-free environment, they develop no acquired resistance.

One other factor needs consideration. The continued use of drugs to reduce the parasite load may lead to the development of strains of parasites which can tolerate high dosages of the drug. The common housefly, for example, can be developed to the point where it will tolerate 200 times the lethal dose of DDT for flies which have been raised for generations without contact with DDT (Johnston, et al, 1954).

A disease such as hog cholera, which can be controlled adequately by vaccination, is not one toward which a selection program for developing resistance should be directed. Also, certain diseases such as Bang's abortion can be controlled by sanitation and calfhood vaccination in cattle, and therefore selection for resistance to this disease would not be justified. These factors bring us to a very important consideration. With animals of considerable value, and particularly where reproductive rate is low, a definite program for the introduction of breeding animals should be set up. Complete isolation of these animals should be made for a period of time to make sure that they do not carry any infectious diseases, either in the active or incubative state. Strict attention should be given to the health of the animals in the herd from which breeding animals are being selected. The purchase and transportation of animals without regard to their health status can result in the scattering of a disease.

In species where the value of each animal or plant is very low, one cannot invest much in the treatment of such organisms for disease or parasite control. Generally, when the value of each individual is low, the rate of reproduction is relatively high. This could be a real case for which breeding for resistance to a certain disease which is not easily controlled by vaccination or sanitation might be quite effective. This may explain why considerable work has been done in poultry in developing strains resistant to certain diseases.

There are species, breed or race, strain or line, and individual differences in resistance to certain diseases (Kozyelka, 1929). For example, Zebu cattle are resistant to foot-and-mouth, anthrax, and tick fever. The F_1 resulting from crossing Zebu $\times$ English breeds of cattle possess resistance approaching that of the Zebu. Nellore cattle are resistant to rinderpest. When the F_1 is produced by crossing Nellore $\times$ English breeds of cattle, they are intermediate in resistance. It would appear that resistance to foot-and-mouth, anthrax, and tick fever shows some dominance, whereas resistance to rinderpest does not.

Several cases of resistance of certain races, breeds, or species to disease have been reported:

1. Zebu cattle to tick (Texas) fever.
2. Japanese cattle to tuberculosis.
3. Yorkshire swine to erysipelas.
4. Algerian sheep to anthrax.
5. Jewish people to tuberculosis.
6. Chinese to syphilis.

There is some evidence for each of these examples, but a word of caution seems advisable. Several years ago the mule-foot swine were reported to be resistant to hog cholera. As a consequence, many hog producers bred for the mule-foot conditions until hog cholera put them out of the hog business. Once it was established that mule-foot hogs were no more resistant than cloven-foot hogs, no justification for breeding mule-foot hogs could be found.

Gowen (1937) has stated that genetic resistance can be observed in nature or increased by selection to diseases caused by bacteria, fungi, Protozoa, helminths, viruses, and chemicals. Experimental work has shown that poultry can be bred to resist fowl typhoid (Lambert and Knox, 1932). In animals like poultry where reproduction is at a high rate and the value of each animal is not great, one could well afford to breed for resistance to some of the diseases which are difficult to control and which as a consequence take a large toll in production. Newcastle disease may be one for which resistance could be developed in poultry so that the poultryman would avoid large losses.

Resistance, in most cases, is not inherited in a simple way but as a complex due to several genes. However, Tyzzer (1917) found that resistance of mice to a spore-bearing bacillus (B. piliformis N.S.P.) was a simple dominant. Where resistance is simple in its inheritance, it would not be difficult to develop a strain that would be pure for the resistance. However, where resistance is controlled by many genes, it might be very difficult to obtain and maintain a highly resistant strain. For some diseases, resistance is relative, i.e., animals may be resistant to one level of infection but may succumb to a greater level of infection. This could mean that a strain which is resistant under one set of conditions might be unable to survive under a different set of conditions.

When resistance is under the control of many genes, one generally finds that a resistant strain shows a higher survival rate when infected than the susceptible strain. However, there will usually be some in the susceptible strain with sufficient resistance to survive and some in the resistant strain which will succumb to the infection. In these situations, death loss from the disease will not be completely eliminated by use of a resistant strain, but death loss may be materially reduced.

Birch (1923) and Rich (1923) have found that some guinea pigs have natural resistance to hog cholera. Rich showed that a lack of blood complement, inherited as a simple recessive, leads to susceptibility. This example of resistance being inherited as a simple dominant is due to a blood complement rather than to general vigor of the animals. However, in the studies of Birch and Rich, the resistant strain (possessing blood complement) showed 80 per cent survival while the susceptible strain (blood complement deficient) showed 23 per cent survival when inoculated with *B. Cholera suis*.

SELECTING FOR DISEASE RESISTANCE

In the plant field, resistance to several diseases has been developed through selection and breeding. Wilt-resistant tomatoes, smut-resistant wheat, oats and corn, mildew- and wilt-resistant cucumbers and melons, blight-resistant potatoes, and mosaic-resistant tobacco have meant great increases in production, particularly in certain areas. In many of these plants, reasonable progress has been made in breeding for resistance because there is not much change in the causative organism. Also, the resistant strains of plants breed remarkably true for resistance. It might be mentioned that the large numbers with which plant breeders work facilitate the breeding of resistant strains. Also, plants can be inbred to rather high levels without losing the lines. Therefore, breeding true for resistance is possible in plants. However, breeding cereal grains for rust resistance has been very difficult. The changes in the rust have been so great that a variety which has resistance may be grown commercially for only a year or two before a more virulent rust comes along and makes it necessary to breed for resistance to this more virulent rust.

Experimental work on disease resistance in poultry and laboratory animals has been much more extensive than that for the large farm animals because it is very expensive to subject beef or dairy cattle to exposure to disease in order to make selections for the more resistant animals. As a consequence, most of the work with large animals has been concerned with disease prevention by sanitation and vaccination rather than by selection for resistance to disease.

In poultry, Carson (1951) showed that resistance to one disease did not result in resistance to other diseases. He had two lines, C and K, which were resistant to leucosis and a third line which was susceptible. These three lines were tested for resistance to several organisms (Table 37).

Table 37. RESISTANCE OF THREE LINES OF CHICKENS TO VARIOUS DISEASES

| Disease | Leucosis-Resistant Lines | | Leucosis-Susceptible Line |
	Line K	Line C	
Protozoa	Susceptible	Susceptible	Resistant
Virus	Resistant	Intermediate	Susceptible
Bronchitis	Resistant	Susceptible	Resistant
Pullorum	Resistant	Susceptible	Resistant and Susceptible
Cell grafts	Resistant	. . . .	Susceptible

This showed that resistance to one disease was independent of resistance to other diseases.

Lambert and Knox (1932) reduced the percentage of mortality caused by fowl pox from 40 to 15 per cent in three generations of selection for resistance. During the same time that resistance was being developed in the resistant line, the death loss in the same susceptible line was 90, 93 and 86 per cent, respectively, for the three years.

Schott (1932) selected mice for resistance to *Salmonella aertrycke* for six generations. During this time death loss was reduced to 25 per cent at the sixth generation. The death loss for the six generations during which selection for resistance was made was 82, 64, 46, 40, 36, 33 and 25 per cent. The original material showed 82 per cent mortality as compared with 25 per cent after selecting for resistance for six generations. A susceptible strain of silver mice showed 100 per cent mortality. When the resistant were crossed with the susceptible, the F_1 showed 78 per cent mortality, regardless of which way the cross was made. This indicated that there was no maternal influence on resistance in this case. Genetic tests indicated that several pairs of genes were involved.

Hetzer (1937) continued the study on resistance of mice to *Salmonella aertrycke*. He found that passive immunity was not a problem in developing resistant mice. Males were generally more susceptible than females. Crosses of resistant $\times$ susceptible gave F_1 with resistance more like that of the resistant parent. This indicated some dominant influence of resistance. Hetzer also obtained some evidence for complementary gene action affecting resistance. This work differed somewhat from that of Schott who found that there was some evidence for maternal influence (cytoplasmic or otherwise). The F_1 mice from a susceptible female were less resistant than F_1 mice from a resistant female. There was no evidence of sex linkage, and the genetic evidence indicated multiple factor inheritance.

One of the interesting studies on resistance was conducted by Irwin (1929), using Wistar rats which had been inbred for 60 generations by full-sib matings. These rats were very susceptible to paratyphoid enteritis, showing 92.5 per cent mortality. A resistant strain, developed by selection, showed 42 per cent mortality. The F_1 produced by crossing the resistant $\times$ susceptible showed 55 per cent mortality, indicating some dominance of the genes causing resistance. Heavier animals in the resistant strain showed greater resistance, but this weight-resistance relation did not exist in the susceptible strain. There appeared to be several genes affecting resistance to this condition.

Stoddard (1938) found evidence for inherited susceptibility to blood poisoning in the human. There were indications of susceptibility showing some dominance.

Nattan-Larrier (1921) attempted to induce genetic resistance to Dourine in horses. Lambert, et al (1939), found evidence for inherited resistance to encephalomyelitis in horses. His study showed that a greater percentage of horses of Nonius breeding were affected by the disease. As yearlings there were 50 per cent of animals of Nonius breeding affected as compared to 11 per cent of animals of other breeding. As foals 73 per cent of the animals of Nonius breeding were affected as compared with 10.5 per cent of the foals of other breeding.

Johnson and Bancroft (1918) have demonstrated that Zebu cattle are resistant to ticks which are the normal organisms for transferring tick fever from one animal to the other. In this situation the animals may show no more resistance to the disease than the English breeds, but they are less susceptible because they are resistant to the ticks which spread the fever.

Much of the evidence indicates that resistance is not related to general vigor as indicated by growth rate, size, etc. One would expect, however, that animals which contract chronic diseases would show a reduction in rate of gain. The diseased condition may reduce vigor, but inherited increased vigor is no assurance of increased resistance to disease. Wright, et al (1921), found no relation of rate of gain, size, etc., to resistance of guinea pigs to tuberculosis. In the human, the smaller and less vigorous races are less affected by tuberculosis than the large, robust races.

Bonsma (1944) found that Africander cattle possess many more tick repellent factors than British breeds. This probably explains why they are less susceptible to heartwater infection. The F_1 produced by mating Africander $\times$ British breeds shows a great deal of the resistance of the Africander cattle. Apparently, the thick skin and type of coat of the Africander interfere with tick infestation.

Cameron, et al (1943), found that resistance to brucellosis in swine is inherited. A resistant strain of Berkshires and a susceptible strain of Poland China were developed in a disease-free environment. It was shown that by breeding the more resistant Poland China pigs, one could develop a strain possessing resistance.

Lush (1950) and others have reported that susceptibility to mastitis in cows is under genetic control, as shown by a heritability estimate of 0.19. Selection against mastitis by culling affected cows and their sisters and daughters could be expected to reduce the incidence of mastitis.

Some recent studies at the Texas station indicate that goats and sheep show genetic resistance to internal parasites. It appears, however, that the genes for parasite resistance are at such a low incidence in sheep that great losses will occur, and therefore it will take a long time to develop strains which are highly resistant.

SUMMARY

In summary, it can be said that breeding programs with farm animals directed toward developing disease and parasite resistance will be very difficult because of four factors:

1. Resistance is not general. It will be necessary to breed for resistance to each specific disease.
2. Resistance to most diseases is controlled by multiple factors. The possibility of developing strains pure for complete resistance to a disease is very low indeed.
3. Mutations may occur in the causative organism, giving it greater virulence. This increased virulence of the disease organism can occur more rapidly than progress can be made by selecting for resistance.
4. Resistance is relative to the amount of exposure. A strain may show a high resistance to one level of infection and be quite highly affected by a larger level of infection.

It appears that selection for resistance in those species having a low value of each individual and a high rate of reproduction will be more feasible than in species in which reproductive rate is low and the value of each individual is high. In the latter species, one may choose to use sanitation, vaccination, and other means of disease prevention and treatment. Where disease can be adequately controlled by sanitation and vaccination, there is little justification for breeding for resistance. The addition of this trait in a selection program would necessarily reduce the amount of selection which can be applied for other important traits.

EXERCISES

1. Is resistance to disease general; that is, are the animals possessing resistance to one disease generally resistant to all diseases or is resistance to each disease independent of resistance to other diseases?

2. Why is it difficult to breed and maintain disease resistance in a population?

3. If it is difficult or impossible to establish and maintain strains possessing disease resistance, what other alternative does the producer have?

4. Why has inheritance to disease resistance been studied more in plants, laboratory animals, and poultry than in the larger farm animals?

26

RESEARCH BY THE REGIONAL SWINE BREEDING LABORATORY

In 1936 the United States Department of Agriculture became interested in the search for superior germ plasm in animals. Meetings were held with directors of state agricultural experimental stations, and research in animal improvement was launched on a regional basis. The concept of doing research on swine improvement in the corn-hog region was a forward step. The Bankhead-Jones Act provided federal funds for cooperative research by the various experimental stations and the Bureau of Animal Industry of the U.S. Department of Agriculture. Five state experimental stations, Iowa, Minnesota, Missouri, Nebraska, and Oklahoma, initiated projects on swine breeding research in 1937, and Dr. W. A. Craft was selected as director of the Regional Swine Breeding Laboratory, with headquarters in Ames, Iowa. Other states initiated projects so that by 1953 there were nine formal projects organized, with some cooperation by other states on an informal basis.

Some work has been done on crossbreeding of swine at the Iowa and the Minnesota stations which indicates that by crossbreeding advantage can be taken of heterosis in commercial swine production. Since the corn-breeding studies had shown such remarkable results from combining inbred lines for obtaining heterosis of yield, particularly from the double crosses, it seemed wise to initiate the development and use of inbred lines of swine. Several stations, such as Oklahoma and Minnesota, had already inbred swine in a limited way. Guinea pigs had been closely inbred by the U.S. Department of Agriculture for several generations, and rats had been closely inbred by the Wistar Institute for many generations. It was apparent from these studies that several inbred lines would be needed because some of them would likely be lost and some might have little value for combining.

Considerable emphasis had to be placed upon the performance of lines as such because of difficulties in carrying on a line in which low fertility, vigor, and livability existed. Many of the lines were developed by mild inbreeding,

345

accompanied by rigid selection. It appears now that in some cases selections were made for the lower homozygosity rather than for superior material within a level of homozygosity. Several lines were established by combining existing lines within a breed, and some lines were established by crossing breeds as a source of foundation stock.

Craft (1953) summarized the research by the swine breeding laboratory. The primary objectives were the development of methods for improving existing pure breeds, the formation of new breeds with combinations of traits to make them superior to the old breeds, and the development of methods such as crossing lines or breeds for using breeds to improve production performance.

The consequences and uses of inbreeding, the effectiveness and best methods of selection for improving productive performance, and physiological problems related to improvement of swine received special attention. Selections were based largely on production and carcass characteristics, such as number and weight of pigs at weaning, growth rate, feed efficiency, and desirability of carcasses. Approximately 100 inbred lines were started within seven breeds, but about one-half of them showed such low performance that they were dropped. These lines were dropped on the basis of their low performance within the line and their low value for combining or for topcrossing onto outbred stock. Two new breeds were developed and crossbred foundations were tested. Litter size and growth rate declined as inbreeding increased, but economy of gains increased with greater inbreeding in some cases.

A study was made to determine how much selection had been practiced and the effectiveness of this selection. The average selection differential for six stations was one-third of a pig more at farrowing, two-thirds of a pig more at weaning, 22 lb. more for litter weight at weaning, and 15 lb. more per pig at 154 days of age. Response to selection varied from station to station. In some cases the response to selection was approximately what would be expected from heritability estimates. In general, however, the effectiveness of selection was less than expected.

Heritability estimates for productive characteristics were determined at different stations by use of different methods and for different lines of breeding. The results of heritability estimates were in remarkable agreement when considered in light of these differences. The estimate of heritability for number of pigs farrowed was about 15 to 17 per cent, but there was a range of 10 to 44 per cent. The heritability of number of pigs weaned ranged from 15 to 32 per cent; for litter weight, 7 to 16 per cent; economy of gains, 25 to 57 per cent (only two estimates); weight at 154 days of age, 17 to 40 per cent; and score, 20 per cent. Sow repeatability for sow productivity was about 16 per cent. Growth rate was more highly heritable following weaning than prior to weaning.

Crosses of inbred lines within a breed showed increases in growth rate as compared with that of noninbred stock of the same breed. When three inbred lines were combined, there was an increase in number of pigs raised per litter over that in noninbred litters. Crosses of inbred lines of one breed with inbred lines of another breed gave generally higher performance than crossing inbred lines within a breed. There seemed to be differences in combining ability of lines and of breeds (Craft, 1953).

Carcass studies showed that yield of the five primal cuts was the best single measure of carcass desirability. Carcasses from some lines were excellent, but carcasses from others were excessively fat. Generally, the cross of lines differing in carcass desirability resulted in F_1 animals that were intermediate in desirability of carcass. The line and breed crosses generally made superior carcasses.

The summary by Craft (1953) appears to be so excellent that the reader is referred to it for a coverage of the research of the Regional Swine Breeding Laboratory prior to 1954.

During the years 1954–1957, inclusive, there have been about 67,000 pigs farrowed and 50,000 raised from 9,500 litters from which data have been obtained in the swine-breeding laboratory. In addition to these data there have been some stations working with farmers from whom data were obtained.

Material reported from the Regional Swine Breeding Laboratory during the past four years has been concerned with: (1) carcass evaluation, (2) selection methods, (3) breeding systems, (4) physiology, (5) interrelations of weights at different ages, and (6) heritability estimates.

CARCASS EVALUATION

The loin area at the tenth and at the last rib were highly correlated; therefore, little increase in accuracy of predicting lean cuts was obtained by taking measurements in more than one place (Kline and Hazel, 1955). There was also no difference in measurement regardless of the side of the carcass from which it was taken. The correlations between loin area and percentage of lean cuts was high, ranging from 0.65 to 0.74.

The specific gravity of the untrimmed right ham was found to be closely associated with the specific gravity of the entire carcass, with a correlation coefficient of 0.86. However, cut-out percentages, chemical composition of the ham, loin lean areas, and fat thickness measures were not so closely predicted by ham specific gravity as by carcass specific gravity. The correlation coefficients obtained between ham specific gravity and the above mentioned items were all highly significant.

In this study, contrary to previous work, carcass cut-out was more closely associated with live probe and backfat thickness than with specific gravity of the ham. However, specific gravity of the untrimmed ham more closely predicted its chemical composition than lean areas of the loin, carcass length, live probe, or backfat thickness (Price, et al, 1957). Results indicated that specific gravity of the ham or carcass was a more reliable indicator of muscling, or actual meatiness, than live probe or backfat thickness. In determining the suitability of specific gravity of three untrimmed cuts, i.e., the ham, loin, and shoulder, as measures of carcass leanness, it was found that the specific gravity of each of the cuts was closely associated with specific gravity of the entire carcass. The correlation coefficients were +0.94, +0.96, +0.92 for the ham, loin and shoulder, respectively, when both cuts from the same carcass were used. However, on a single cut, corresponding values were +0.93, +0.91, and +0.87 (Pearson, et al, 1956).

In another study by Pearson, et al (1956), the fat-lean ratio in cross section of the rough loin at the last rib was investigated as a possible measure of carcass leanness. Correlation coefficients of approximately −0.60 between the fat-lean ratio and several measures of carcass cut-out indicated that the relationship might be high enough to be useful if it were impossible to obtain cut-out information. However, the area of lean at the tenth rib or last rib was only slightly less reliable than the ratio of fat to lean for estimating cut-out values. Consideration of the relationship between either carcass length or dressing percentage and carcass cut-out indicated that major emphasis should be placed on other methods of measuring leanness.

The magnitude of cutting errors was determined by Lasley and Kline (1957) for various carcass traits, using 222 barrow carcasses. Traits investigated were weight of half-carcass, belly, loin, picnic, Boston butt, skinned ham, four lean cuts, and five primal cuts; length from front of first rib to aitch bone; average of four backfat measures; and loin eye area at the tenth and last ribs. The left side averaged heavier, and yielded heavier loin, ham, picnic, lean cuts, and primal cuts, but yielded lighter belly and Boston butt. Failure to divide the carcass into equal halves was partly responsible for these differences. No evidence of bilateral asymmetry was found. These results indicate that biased values are obtained when either right or left side is consistently appraised but not when both are averaged. Greater precision also results when both sides are averaged, especially for loin, picnic, Boston butt, and belly. About one-half the cutting variation for lean cuts reflects lack of precision in cutting the loin. Ham weight is more reliably estimated than is any other wholesale cut or combination of cuts. If only one side is evaluated it is important that it always be the same side. Careful splitting of the carcass is emphasized when only one side is cut.

Two methods have been used for measuring backfat thickness in the live animal. One is by a ruler which is probed into an incision and the other is by the lean meter. Results of Pearson, et al (1957), indicated that there was little difference in the usefulness of the live probe or lean meter in regard to estimating backfat thickness and percentage of either lean or primal cuts. However, the higher relationship for the live probe with both loin lean areas and with fat trim indicated the live probe to be a more reliable measure for estimating carcass leanness. The accuracy of backfat measurement was very high.

The measurement of backfat thickness on the pigs at a live weight of about 210 lb. by an average of six probes was more highly correlated with percentage of primal cuts, carcass index, and ham specific gravity than was backfat thickness measured on the carcass (DePape and Whatley, 1956). The correlations between the thickness of backfat on the carcass and the live hog measurements taken at various ages were all positive and showed a definite upward trend with increasing age. The predictive value of probes taken prior to 112 days of age was very low. The intra-breed and intra-sex correlation of average probe at slaughter weight with average carcass backfat was 0.69.

Zobrisky, et al (1954), drew several conclusions from an intensive study of 207 hog carcasses.*

1. A reasonably accurate estimate of the live hog's value can be determined from the live hog backfat probes or carcass backfat measurements. Yield of fat can be more easily and accurately determined than the yield of lean. Measurements of fat, such as carcass and live hog backfat thickness measurements, give the highest correlations, with the exception of those obtained by automatic and partial correlations. This is possibly due to the well-defined regions present on the carcass and live animal for taking linear measurements related to fatness. Most present linear measurements of fatness measure the subcutaneous fat alone, whereas measurements used to evaluate the lean are, in part, measures of fat, lean, and bone, or some combinations of these three components (for example, the weight of the preferred cuts and the ham index).

2. Internal carcass measurements (for example, the cross-section area of the loin eye) give the highest correlation with the yield of lean.

3. The yield of any one component of the carcass (or live hog) is influenced by several factors. The larger the number of these influencing factors considered in the method of analysis, the more reliable are the results. If the additional variables included in an analysis exceeds four or five, the mathematical manipulation becomes extensive and laborious, the chances of errors accumulate, and a point of impracticality is soon reached. Since this is the case, complexity is counterbalanced by simplicity and a lower degree of exactness.

* The author gratefully acknowledges the University of Missouri for permitting him to use this material.

SELECTION METHODS

Boulware (1954) studied the efficiency and effectiveness of selection of a line of hogs started from a crossbred foundation. He did not observe significant depressing effects of inbreeding at the low level in the herd. Efficiency of selection for an index, in terms of maximum attainable, was 21 per cent for dams and 50 per cent for sires. It appeared that automatic selections were greater than deliberate selections. Productivity declined in spite of selection, but it did not decline so rapidly as could be expected with the increase in inbreeding. It appeared that selection was partially effective in overcoming the depressing effects of inbreeding.

Bernard, et al (1954), has developed a selection index for farm use which should be an aid to farmers in their selection program because it is very simple and involves those traits most concerned with financial return.

$$I = 4.5x_2 + .5x_4$$

Where x_2 = litter size at 154 days of age and x_4 = individual pig weight at 154 days of age.

Dickerson, et al (1954), made a study of selection practiced, and the actual improvement was compared with that expected by using data from the Illinois, Indiana, Iowa, Minnesota, Missouri, Nebraska, Oklahoma, and Wisconsin stations.[*] They point out that the amount of selection applied for litter size, growth rate, and conformation during the development of inbred lines could have been increased by:

1. More strict adherence to an index in which proper weighting of each trait to increase deliberate selection for larger litters is desirable.
2. Keeping more boars so that post-weaning growth rate and conformation can be used in selecting, rather than castrating most of them at weaning.
3. Adjustments of performance records for level of inbreeding of dams and litters and also for age of dam at farrowing.

They have suggested, however, that ineffectiveness of selection resides in the nature of the genetic and environmental variability of the characteristics under selection, and that selection for maximum performance of crosses can be more effective than selection of the individuals within a line on the basis of phenotype.

Dickerson's study was based on 4,521 litters from 38 lines. A complete summary follows:

[*] The author gratefully acknowledges the University of Missouri for permission to quote this information.

1. Young boars sired 74 per cent and gilts produced 60 per cent of the pigs weaned; the remainder were from older tried boars and sows. The generation interval or mean age of parents was 1.22 for sires and 1.44 for dams.

2. Opportunity for culling should have been greater among the 30 boars than among the 27 gilts weaned per line and season, since only 8 per cent of the boars but 33 per cent of the gilts weaned were used to produce litters at one year of age. Older breeders represented 63 per cent of the boars and 48 per cent of the sows used the preceding season.

3. Superiority of young boars and gilts selected was similar for size of the dam's litter at birth (0.66 vs. 0.60 pigs) and at weaning (1.40 vs. 1.16 pigs), but superiority of boars was greater for individual weight at weaning (6.1 lb. vs. 2.8 lb.) and consequently, for litter average weaning pig weight (1.2 lb. vs. 0.60 lb.), for total weaning weight of the dam's litter (26 lb. vs. 20 lb.), for individual weight at 154 days of age (23 lb. vs. 14 lb.), for the index combining dam's productivity with individual weight at 154 days (36 vs. 25 units), and for inbreeding of the individual (−1.6 vs. −1.1 per cent) and its dam (−1.5 vs. −0.9 per cent). Superiority in total score of conformation at market weight was even slightly greater for gilts than for boar pigs (2.7 vs. 2.5 points).

4. Superiority of older boars retained over all boars used the preceding season was slight for dam's litter size, own growth rate, and conformation, but again the less inbred individuals were saved (−0.85 per cent). Older sows that were retained surpassed all sows farrowing the previous season by 0.6 and 1.1 pigs in size of litters farrowed and weaned, by −0.88 per cent inbreeding but by only 2.4 lb. in own 154-day weight and 0.6 points in own score for conformation as a gilt. Selection for the index that combined productivity and growth rate was only one-sixth as great among tried boars as among boar pigs, but was five-sixths as great among tried sows as among gilt pigs. The average selection differential of parents for this index could have been greater if older boars had not been used, and if older sows had represented somewhat less than 40 per cent of all females producing litters.

5. If boar and gilt pigs had been selected at random (i.e., if the numbers taken from each litter had been proportional to numbers available at weaning age), the selection for larger litters automatically would have been nearly as large as that actually obtained. The "automatic" selection was 0.62 for pigs born, 1.15 for pigs weaned, 31 lb. for weight of litter weaned, but −0.21 lb. for litter average weaning weight per pig. Additional "deliberate" selection was nil for numbers farrowed, slight for numbers weaned (0.25 and 0.09 pigs, for boars and gilts), but rather large for litter average pig weight at weaning (2.75 lb. and 1.49 lb., for boars and gilts). Automatic selection for litter size accounted for 27 per cent of the total superiority in the indexes of the boars chosen and for 38 per cent of that in the indexes of the gilts selected.

6. Opportunity for *deliberate* selection among boar and gilt pigs was utilized most fully for growth rate, less for conformation, and least for litter size. Among boar pigs, individual weaning weight received much more, and conformation less, emphasis than did weight at 154 days; but the reverse was true among gilt pigs.

7. Superiority of selected boar pigs in the *average* combination of sow productivity, 154-day weight and conformation score upon which actual choices appeared to have been made, was found to be only 46 per cent as large as if all culling had

been based upon it. This corresponded to choosing boars from the best 48 per cent instead of the best 8 per cent of those weaned. Superiority of gilt pigs selected was 58 per cent of that expected if all culling had been based on the index apparently used, and corresponded to saving the best 61 per cent instead of the best 33 per cent of those weaned. Apparently, about 50 per cent of the gilts and 80 per cent of the boar pigs were culled because of other factors, such as weaning weight, cryptorchids, hernias, post-weaning mortality, discrimination against pigs from younger litters, and reproductive failures. Poorer utilization of opportunity for selection among boars than among gilts was attributed to excessive culling of boars by castration at weaning age, and possibly to earlier ranting of the faster growing boars, with adverse effects on conformation.

8. Linear regression of performance on time within 47 lines at five stations (364 degrees of freedom) averaged −0.15, −0.16 and −0.22 pigs per year in litter size at birth, 21, and 56 days, respectively. Linear yearly change averaged zero for birth weight, −0.19 lb. for 21-day weight, −0.41 lb. for 56-day weight, and −4.0 lb. (four stations) for 154-day weight of individual pigs. Linear rise of calculated inbreeding varied from 2.13 to 3.9 per cent per year.

9. Consequences of the inbreeding rise were estimated from intra-season, paired comparisons of linecrosses with the parent inbred lines. Data for 325 linecrosses and 538 inbred litters representing 99 crosses of 31 lines yielded estimates of change per 10 per cent of inbreeding of litter as follows: −0.20,* −0.35,** and −0.44** pigs in litter size at birth, 21, 56, and 154 days of age, 0.02, 0.08, 0.03, and −3.44** lb. in weight per pig at these ages. Data at one station for linecrossed litters from 63 linecrossed and 50 inbred dams representing the same lines indicated the following changes per 10 per cent higher inbreeding of the *dam:* −0.17, −0.31,** −0.25,* −0.28,* pigs per litter at 0, 21, 56, and 154 days of age; −0.06, −0.11, 0.06, and −0.13 lb. in weight per pig at these ages. Inbreeding rise for a line included effects of inbreeding both of dam and of litter.

10. After removing expected effects of the inbreeding rise, linear change *per year* in performance of the 47 lines averaged −0.03, 0.07, and −0.01 for litter size at 0, 21, and 56 days of age; 0.01, −0.19, −0.47, and −2.8 lb. in weight per pig at 0, 21, 56, and 154 days of age. These average results indicated that selection during development of mildly inbred lines failed to improve measurably the genetic merit of the lines. At only two stations was there a positive average time-trend in total litter weight at 154 days of age after correction for inbreeding effects.

11. Linear regression of performance on inbreeding of litters, between seasons within 46 lines at four stations, indicated rates of inbreeding decline as large or larger than those obtained from the intra-season comparisons of linecrosses with parental inbred lines.

12. Analysis of data from 12 lines during 9 years at the Iowa station showed that line differences in rate of decline with inbreeding of litter were less than expected from sampling error for litter size and for litter weight at 154 days of age, but were highly significant for pig weight at 154 days of age. There was no indication of curvilinear regression on inbreeding.

13. The apparent inability of selection within inbred lines to improve performance of crosses among the lines did not appear to be adequately explained by

* and ** indicate 95 and 99 per cent levels of significance, respectively.

ordinary dominance (between none and complete) and epistasis alone, but could have resulted from heterozygote advantage in net performance for some of the segregating chromosomal units. Small negative genetic correlations between the traits under selection would have been compatible with heterozygote advantage and could have reduced the effectiveness of selection sharply, even though genetic variability were to remain large for individual traits. Larger positive environmental than genetic correlations also could have reduced effectiveness of selection.

14. Effectiveness of selection probably was reduced because most of the selection actually practiced for litter size was automatic (i.e., would have occurred if a random sample of the pigs weaned had been chosen as breeders). Also, selection favored the less inbred pigs and dams, indicating that 8 to 12 per cent of the variance in total performance was due to variation in level of inbreeding between litters within the same line and season; this reduced effectiveness of selection as much as a comparable amount of environmental variation, slowed the calculated rate of inbreeding, and made actual reduction in heterozygosity lag behind that indicated by the calculated inbreeding coefficient.

15. The foregoing results suggest that selection can be made more effective in swine if it is directed toward the improvement of crosses between complementary strains, with selection of individuals or families being based upon performance of test-cross progeny.

BREEDING SYSTEMS

England and Winters (1953) found that genetic diversity of lines was related to heterosis resulting from crossing of the lines. This same relationship of genetic diversity to heterosis applied in continuous crossing. The use of the crossbred female in rotation crosses gave greater heterosis than in criss-cross crossbreeding. The crossbred pigs were more uniform than the inbreds. Pre-weaning characteristics showed greater heterosis from crossing than post-weaning traits. The better performing lines produced better performing crosses, which indicates that the superior genes of the lines are equally effective in the crosses. These investigators conclude that if desirable results are to be realized from swine crosses in obtaining maximum heterosis, three genetic essentials will be necessary:

1. Full use of genetic diversity.
2. Use of high performing lines.
3. Purging of lines for undesirable genes or a rigid selection program for the development of the lines.

Observations were made by Foote, et al (1956), during four years on the age at puberty in gilts in the swine-breeding experimental herd maintained by the Wisconsin Agricultural Experiment Station in cooperation with the Regional Swine Breeding Laboratory. The numbers of gilts used were: in 1950,

150; 1951, 106; 1952, 95; and 1954, 162. The mean age at puberty of the inbred gilts in 1950 was 227.7 days. They were significantly older at puberty than the line-cross gilts (193.5 days). The mean ages at puberty for the gilts representing the four systems of mating in 1951 (inbred, 244.0; two-line cross, 214.5; three-line cross, 198.4; four-line cross, 208.2) differed only in respect to inbreeding and line-crossing, wth no significant difference between the different line crosses.

Bases for predicting the performance of rotation crosses from the performance of single-crosses and of the parent breeds or lines, where the number of lines or breeds did not exceed four, were presented by Carmon, et al (1956). Although these rest on various assumptions, no epistasis is the only assumption that might seriously affect the results. The findings have indicated that rotational breeding offers an even greater advantage to breeders than the crossing of several breeds or lines followed by random mating. These also enable the breeder to predict which breeds or lines and what order of rotation will give maximum performance in the rotational program.

Physiology

Ovulation, prenatal mortality, and litter size were observed for 87 sows, representing five breeding groups, that had previously farrowed two litters (Lasley, 1957). Heritabilities and correlations arising from additively genetic sources, common litter environment, and residual environment were computed. The number of live fetuses was 59 per cent of the number of corpora lutea, and dead fetuses accounted for 5 per cent. Repeatability of litter size was 0.15 between first and second litters, 0.10 between second and third litters, and −0.06 between first and third litters. Heritability of litter size was 0, 8, and 5 per cent for first, second, and third litters, respectively. Heritability of corpora lutea count was 10 per cent. Genetic and environmental correlations were summarized, but none of the genetic parameters was statistically significant.

From a study on serum protein-bound iodine by Gawienowski, et al (1955), the following conclusions are drawn: *

1. The average protein-bound iodine values of Hampshire gilts and barrows was 3.08 mcg. per 100 ml. of serum. The range was 1.2 to 5.4 mcg. per 100 ml.
2. The average daily gains of the young Hampshire swine studied increased as the level of P.B.I. decreased (probability less than 0.01).
3. The body length decreased as the P.B.I. levels in the blood increased (probability less than 0.05).

* The author gratefully acknowledges the American Society of Animal Production for permission to quote freely from the Journal of Animal Science. Reference is made to the author of any material used.

4. Individual pigs with longer left legs also tended to have a higher P.B.I. content in the blood, but the correlation was not statistically significant.

5. The average backfat thickness increased as the P.B.I. level decreased. The linear correlation was not significant, however.

Several studies have been made in which hormones or drugs have been used to stimulate rate of gain and feed efficiency and to improve carcass quality. Pigs injected daily with three different purified growth hormone preparations gained at a slightly, but not significantly, faster rate, consumed significantly less feed per day, and required significantly less feed per unit of gain than did noninjected pigs (Turman and Andrews, 1955). The carcasses of growth-hormone-injected pigs contained significantly more protein and moisture and less fat than did the carcasses of control pigs.

Daily injection of growth hormone in swine resulted in significant increases in blood glucose, slight but not significant increases in blood inorganic phosphorus, and decreased blood nonprotein nitrogen. The anterior pituitary glands of pigs injected daily with growth hormone contained significantly more of the thyrotropic and gonadotropic hormones than did the pituitaries of control pigs.

Methyl testosterone, at a level of 20 mg. per animal daily, or diethylstilbestrol, at a level of 2 mg. per animal daily, was fed both with and without terramycin in a practical ration to growing and fattening pigs in drylot. The oral administration of these hormones did not improve growth rate or feed efficiency (Beeson, et al, 1955). The feeding of stilbestrol produced clear-cut mammary stimulation in both males and females and enlargement and congestion of the vulva in the female. The feeding of testosterone appeared to improve the appearance of the sides and jowls, and masculine characteristics were observed.

Chemical analysis of carcasses showed that the pig receiving testosterone had about 5 per cent less fat and 5 per cent more lean than the controls.

Interrelations of Weights at Different Ages

The interrelations of birth, 56-day, and 154-day weights of pigs at the Nebraska and Indiana stations (Blunn, et al, 1954) showed the following within-litter correlations: birth and weaning weights, 0.53; birth and 154-day weights, 0.40; weaning and 154-day weights, 0.63. Only 40 per cent of the variation in 154-day weight is accounted for by variations in weaning weight. This proves that selecting pigs for large size at weaning would not be an efficient means of improving post-weaning growth rate.

Taylor and Hazel (1955) found that the growth curves of 255 pigs weighed at 134, 144, 154, 164, and 174 days of age were essentially linear over this period. The growth curves varied for particular pigs, each seeming to be a linear function of the weight attained at a given age. A common intercept of —45 days on the age axis and —154 lb. on the weight axis fitted the data for both fast- and slow-growing pigs, assuming linearity of growth over the period from 134 to 174 days.

Several possible methods of adjusting weights to a standard age (154 days) were examined. One of the most accurate and convenient was

$$\text{Adjusted weight} = \frac{(\text{actual weight} + 154)\ (199)}{\text{actual age} + 45} - 154$$

Linear interpolation is also accurate and convenient when two weights on each animal are available.

Heritability Estimates

The results of a ten-year experiment involving ten generations of selection for heavy weights and eight generations of selection for light weights at 154 and 180 days of age in Hampshire swine were presented by Craig, et al (1956). A total of 2,036 pigs from 288 litters in 124 sire groups were included. Rapid and slow lines derived from a sample of the breed and maintained as closed herds became more and more distinct for 154- and 180-day weight as selection continued over the entire period.

Heritability estimates for 154- and 180-day weights of 0.17 and 0.16 were obtained on the basis of line difference produced, as compared with selection pressure exerted. Selection was as effective in separating the lines in later generations as in the first two, indicating the absence of important epistatic deviations from the additive scheme for these traits. Estimates based on regression of offspring on mean of parents and on intra-sire regression of offspring on dam were combined and found to be 0.16 and 0.14 for 154- and 180-day weights, respectively. A less reliable method, based on variance components, gave heritability estimates of 0.18 and 0.44 for 154- and 180-day weights, respectively.

Heritability estimates for birth-, 21-, and 56-day weights of 0.07, 0.05, and 0.03, respectively, were obtained from combined regression values, while estimates of 0.28, 0.30, and 0.24, respectively, were obtained from variance components. Sex differences in weights were analyzed, and boars were found to be significantly heavier than gilts by about 5 per cent at birth and by about 3 per cent at 21, 56, 154, and 180 days of age. Genetic correlations were estimated on the basis of weight differences produced between lines at birth, 21, and 56 days of age by selection based solely on weights at 150, 154, or 180 days of age. It appeared from the size of the genetic correlations and the more reliable heritability estimates obtained in this study that indirect selection for heavy weights at 154 or 180 days of age on the basis of birth-, 21-, or 56-day weights would be approximately 0, 20, or 50 per cent as effective, respectively, as direct selection for heavy 154- or 180-day weights.

Blunn, et al (1953), estimated the heritability of gains from birth to weaning (56 days), from weaning to 112 days of age, and from 112 days to 154 days of age by use of paternal half-sib relationships. Heritability estimates for the three periods at the North Platte station were 22, 51, and 25 per cent, respectively, and for the pigs at the main station (Lincoln) estimates were 2, 35, and 34 per cent, respectively. It was concluded that selections for rate of gain based on records from weaning to 112 days of age would be effective for growth of bone and muscle and would be sufficiently early in life of the pig so that all animals could be kept intact to that age without serious management problems.

EXERCISES

1. What has the research by the Regional Swine Breeding Laboratory revealed about breeding systems and selection methods?

2. Give the heritability estimates for the various production traits of swine. Classify the traits as to low, medium, and high heritability.

3. What heritability estimate for a given trait would be most accurate for any breeder to use? Explain.

27

REGIONAL BEEF CATTLE BREEDING RESEARCH

The program for improvement of beef cattle through the application of breeding methods was initiated in 1946 on a cooperative basis between the state experimental stations and the Bureau of Animal Industry, U.S.D.A. The Research and Marketing Act provided federal funds which were matched by state funds for this program. The Western Regional Beef Cattle Breeding Project was the first to get a program under way on beef cattle, followed by Southern and North Central Regional Projects. The headquarters for the Western Regional Beef Cattle Breeding Project is located at Denver, Colorado. The North Central Regional Beef Breeding Laboratory has its headquarters at Lincoln, Nebraska. The Southern Regional Beef Cattle Breeding Laboratory has its headquarters at Knoxville, Tennessee. The research program in the beef cattle breeding projects was preceded by studies at the U.S. Range Livestock Station, Miles City, Montana, where workers had already shown that most of the productive traits of beef cattle are highly heritable and that much progress could be made by selecting for these traits.

Many of the stations have the services of recently trained men for conducting breeding research. Each station has undertaken the type of research for which it is most capable, and all the work is carefully coordinated with research of the other stations so that duplications of effort are kept at a minimum. One example of this practice is the comprest studies of the Colorado station, dwarfism studies at the California station, blood and endocrine studies at the Oregon station, and blood group studies at the Wyoming station. Each station has helped as much as possible to forward the work of other stations.

The research in the three regions is directed to some extent toward the problems which exist within each region. However, much basic research is being done in all three regions. The work of the western region is presented in some detail because of the author's greater familiarity with it. The reader should realize that much of what is reported for the western region is in many respects

358

similar to the work being done in the other two regions. The principal objective in presenting the material under study in the western region is to show how a large problem is being attacked by coordination of efforts of several states and the federal government.

INHERITED ABNORMALITIES

The endocrine disturbances associated with dwarfism were studied by Carroll, et al (1951), who concluded that the pituitary was deficient in the production of thyrotropins. The California workers recognized six kinds of dwarf beef cattle: (1) common one called "snorter," for which there has been a selective advantage for the carrier; (2) long-headed type; (3) Bulldog type; (4) comprest; (5) synthetic comprest; and (6) proportionate dwarf. Research is now being concentrated on the inheritance of these types to see if they are allelic or due to mutations at different loci. A detailed anatomical and physiological study of dwarfism is being made.

Gregory and his co-workers have shown that the common dwarf condition is a recessive but that the carrier animals show some expression of the character, particularly in contour of the head in the mid-region. A tool, the profilometer (Gregory, et al, 1953), has been developed to differentiate the carrier from a homozygous normal animal. This has been used successfully with horned Hereford bulls two years old and over, and evidence indicates that it may be useful at younger ages.

Pahnish, et al (1952 and 1955), bred dwarfs to dwarfs and dwarfs to carriers and studied physiology of reproduction and survival of dwarf cattle. The dwarf cattle showed low reproductive capacity and poor survival. Some studies by Stonaker (1954) have shown that the proportion of animals carrying the dwarf gene, as measured by the profilometer, is high. Consequently, the two homozygous groups (those not carrying the dwarf gene and the dwarfs) are proportionately too low. It was calculated that with all heterozygous animals mated, the ratio should be 1 homozygous normal:2 heterozygous (carriers) normals:1 dwarf. These data may indicate that more than one type of dwarfism is involved, each being detected in the heterozygous state by the profilometer.

Considerable research on dwarfism has been done at the Colorado station through X-ray of the vertebrae of calves. The blood changes that follow a stress condition imposed upon the animal by insulin injections have recently been related to the dwarf inheritance. The Missouri station first developed this concept, but it has been used by the Colorado station as a diagnostic method for identifying dwarf carriers among normal-appearing beef animals. Colorado experiments showed that the agreement among these three methods (profilometer, X-ray, and insulin) was only moderate. All three methods showed a rather large overlapping in the distribution curves of the known carriers and the group considered to be free of the dwarf gene.

Schoonover and Stratton (1954) made a thorough study of cow head shapes in an attempt to find a measure which could be used to differentiate dwarf-carrying cows from the homozygous normal cows. It appeared that endocrine secretions from the glands of the calf being carried may have influenced the physiology of the cow, and if measures of diagnostic value are to be found, they will be found in young females. At present the physiology of dwarf calves is being compared with normal calves for the purpose of learning more about the physiology of dwarfism and how this knowledge can be used in diagnosing animals that carry the dwarf gene.

The use of chromatography at the Utah station for comparing dwarf and normal animals has shown consistent differences between the two kinds of cattle, and thus it is possible that chromatography may be used to differentiate the dwarf carrier from the homozygous normal animal. Such a method would have tremendous value because it could be applied to females as well as males and could be used early in life before a portion of the calves have been castrated.

Stroble, et al (1954), attempted to relate the differences of blood types in cattle to the inheritance of dwarfism, but they found no relationship.

The number of offspring necessary to test a male for heterozygosity was calculated by Kidwell. Considerable emphasis was placed on the inheritance of abnormal conditions such as female sterility (Kidwell, et al, 1954), dwarfism, and muscular hypertrophy.

Other studies have shown that cancer eye seldom, if ever, occurs in "red-eyed" Herefords (Guilbert, et al, 1948). Apparently the stimulation that starts cancer eye is more effective in the "white-eyed" Herefords. Studies made by the U.S. Range Livestock Station, California and New Mexico, have shown that the tendency to develop cancer eye is under genetic control. Blackwell, et al (1956), found that cancer eye did not occur until after four years of age. There was no difference in incidence between males and females. Heritability was estimated by half-sib correlations to be 0.17 and by intra-sire regression of offspring on dam to be 0.29.

One of the phases of research for which the California station is best known is the study of genetic abnormalities. Sex-limited genetic infertility (Gregory, et al, 1951), cancer eye, prolonged gestation (Gregory, et al, 1951), semi-hairlessness (Kidwell and Guilbert, 1950), dwarfism, and wry or crooked calves (Gregory, 1954) have all been studied at that station.

PHYSIOLOGY

Several studies have been made to determine the physiological differences between fast and slow gaining calves. Calves with higher body temperatures and heart rates (Williams, et al, 1953 and 1954) are the faster gainers and most efficient feed users. It appears that growing animals have higher body temperatures and heart rates but that both characteristics decline with approaching maturity. The concept that the fast gainers and more efficient animals may represent those which at a given weight are still actively growing and physiologically younger than the slower gaining and inefficient animals is suggested by the relationship of gains and efficiency to heart rate and body temperature. It appears that selection for rate and efficiency of gain might result in a postponement in the plateau of growth and in the increase of bone and muscle production perhaps at the expense of fat. Other evidence that tends to show this relationship is the low blood amino acids and the low urinary excretion of urea in the better-doing animals. This indicates that fast-gaining calves have the capacity to use the amino acids of the blood for building body tissues, bone, and muscle. The slow-gaining calves, on the other hand, because of their inability to make maximum use of the blood amino acids, have an accumulation of amino acids in their blood stream. These amino acids are de-aminated, and the nitrogenous fraction is excreted as urea, while the carbonaceous fraction is used for fattening (MacDonald, et al, 1953 and 1956; Price, et al, 1956).

The Wyoming station has made extensive studies on the relation of blood types to rate and efficiency of gains, but no clear-cut association of a blood type with rate and efficiency of gains has been found. The Washington station is studying the relation of rate of gain and feed efficiency to blood protein-bound iodine and to absorption of I^{131} by the thyroid gland. These studies may add a great deal to our knowledge of the relation of thyroid function to rate and efficiency of gains in farm animals.

The adaptation of cattle to high temperatures is receiving considerable attention both from the standpoint of determining the advantages of providing shade and cool water to cattle of the English breeds and from the use of Brahman breeding to give greater heat resistance. It appears (Ittner, et al, 1951 and 1954) that providing shade and cool water might be an effective means of increasing production of those animals which do not have heat-resistance ability. Some of the studies with crossbreeding in which cattle of Brahman breeding are used indicate that these crossbred animals possess hybrid vigor that gives them greater productivity under varied environments in addition to the greater heat tolerance they possess.

Fig. 137. A great deal of the work in a breeding program is done in the laboratory. Here Dr. D. A. Price, now at the Sheep Breeding Laboratory, Dubois, Idaho, is determining serum protein-bound iodine in a study on thyroid function in relation to rate and efficiency of gains. *(Courtesy Oregon State College.)*

RELATION OF TYPE AND CONFORMATION TO PRODUCTION TRAITS

An extensive study has been made for comprest cattle in comparison with the conventional type of cattle (Lucas, et al, 1950; Safley, 1950; Schleicher, et al, 1950; Stonaker, et al, 1950, 1952, and 1952). They found that the comprest cattle reach a market finish at a smaller weight than conventional cattle. Growth rate is lower for the comprest, but when they are fed to the lighter weights and compared in efficiency with conventional cattle, which are on feed until they reach a much larger weight, no difference in efficiency is noted between the two kinds of cattle.

The feed cost of wintering cows appeared to be related to body size so that costs for feed were greater for the conventional animals than for the comprest. Some evidence indicated that production of cows was related to body size. If this were true, it could make feed costs per unit of production about equal for comprest and conventional cattle. However, some fixed costs that are on a per-head basis might put the comprest at a disadvantage. The Colorado researchers made no mention of breeding or calving troubles with comprest cattle, but breeders have reported troubles of both kinds. Whether this is greater with comprest cattle than with the conventional type of cattle is not known, but some cattlemen feel that comprest cattle are shy breeders and have more calving troubles.

Knox and Koger (1946) reported that rangy steers gained more and had a higher dressing percentage than steers of more compact type. The carcass grades were the same for the steers of the different types. It appears that if size is reduced, it will be difficult to develop cattle possessing rapid gaining ability. Therefore, large size cattle, if equal in conformation to smaller cattle, can be expected to have distinct advantages in over-all merit of beef production. It appears that calves of both the small and the conventional types are equal in converting feed or grass into meat on an age-constant basis. However, the small type of cattle gain at a slower rate.

Durham and Knox (1953) studied 424 steers from 68 sires and 59 calves of different types to determine the relationship of scores to rate of gain. Grade at the beginning of the period was negatively associated with subsequent gains. However, faster-gaining calves tended to be higher in grade at the end of the feeding period. Since the feeding was on a time-constant rather than a weight-constant basis, it was likely that the faster-gaining cattle scored higher because they were larger and fatter. Yearling grade was associated with carcass grade but the association was low. The grade at weaning was not related to carcass grade.

MacDonald and Bogart (1954) made an extensive analysis in which they related scores and body measurements to rate and efficiency of gains. There appeared to be little relationship between conformation score at 800-lb. body weight and rate or efficiency of gains made between the weights of 500 and 800 lb. From this we could assume that selection for over-all merit would develop cattle that were rapid and economical gainers and desirable in conformation. However, selection for conformation alone would not be expected to improve cattle for rate and efficiency gains. Neither could selection for rate and efficiency alone be expected to improve cattle for conformation. The analysis concluded that the only body measurements which were related to gains or efficiency were heart girth and chest depth, which showed a negative relationship and body length and rump measurement which were positively related to both rate and efficiency of gains.

The studies of relationships of feeder scores and slaughter scores to percentage of lean and fat in the carcass (Kidwell, et al, 1957) would lead one to conclude that the fatness of the animal influenced the scores very greatly. Higher scores were positively related to fat percentage and negatively related to lean percentage. McCormick and Kidwell (1953) showed that Holstein cattle made as rapid and economical gains as beef breeds but that carcass quality was lower.

Increased Gains and Efficiency by Use of Hormones

The use of stilbestrol for increasing rate and economy of gains showed favorable results (Clegg and Cole, 1954) in that treated steers gained about 0.5 lb. more per head per day and required from 100 to 300 lb. less feed per 100-lb. of gain. Some conditions may have been less favorable than the results first indicate, since the treated animals made carcasses of significantly lower grade. If the spread in price between grades should be great, this difference in carcass grade may absorb much of the difference in gains and efficiency. The experiment also showed that heifers which received the stilbestrol had a tendency for vaginal prolapse and that animals on pasture did not make so favorable a response to stilbestrol as those in the feedlot. However the fact that many of the cattle on feed are now receiving implants of stilbestrol cannot be ignored. Properly used, this hormone material has proved its value for increasing rates of gain and feed efficiency of cattle in the feedlot.

Bulls gain faster than heifers and steers, and steers gain faster than heifers. The injection of testosterone into heifers and steers at the rate of 1 mg. per kilogram of body weight per week increased rate of gain and feed efficiency during the growing period from 500- to 800-lb. body weight. This increase in rate and efficiency of gains occurred without an increase in daily feed intake. The use of methyl androstenediol, injected at the rate of 1 mg. per kilogram of body weight per week, and the feeding of methyl testosterone, failed to increase rate of gain or feed efficiency (Burris, et al, 1954). The injection of testosterone brought about an increase in thyrotropic content of the pituitary, an increased thyroid size, an increase in protein storage, and a decrease in fat storage, particularly in the kidney fat. These same relations are found when younger animals are compared with older ones and when faster-gaining animals are compared with slower-gaining ones.

One question that is of great concern to those who are interested in beef-cattle improvement deals with the response of different genotypes to hormone treatments. For example, if stilbestrol or testosterone causes an increase in rate and efficiency of gains only in those genotypes which do not result in rapid and economical gains, there may be a tendency to substitute hormone treatment for livestock improvement. Animals that are normally rapid and efficient gainers in this case would not be expected to show the same proportional response to hormone treatments as those of the desirable genotypes. However, if the inherently better-gaining cattle respond favorably to hormone treatments, producers can make use of improved cattle in their producing herds and still use hormones to obtain increased feedlot performance.

FACTORS AFFECTING PRODUCTION TRAITS

Stonaker (1951) reported on a herd of cattle that had been bred as a closed herd since 1902 and which possessed considerable merit in spite of the inbreeding, amounting to 60 per cent in some of the animals. This is an exceptional case however. In contrast, the breeding program at Colorado has been based on the formation of many small lines which can be used for linecrossing or for top-crossing with outbred material, but there has been a general decline in vigor associated with inbreeding, particularly in growth rate in early life.

Cows that were inbred in this program have produced less milk than outbred cows. Sex of calf and age of cow were both found to be important in effect on weaning weights. Bull calves were heavier than steers or heifers and steers were heavier than heifers. Two- and three-year-old cows weaned calves weighing less than more mature cows. Burgess, et al (1954), developed correction factors for inbreeding, age of dam, and sex of calf so that records could be adjusted to an equal basis for comparisons. The use of regression analysis was made for developing a correction for age of dam and inbreeding so that all calves could be put on a basis of no inbreeding percentage and on a mature equivalent age basis. Only by use of adjusted records could selection be made intelligently because without adjustments for age of dam and inbreeding, selections would be from older, less inbred cows.

Comparisons of inbred and outbred calves sired by inbred bulls showed that outbreds exceeded the inbreds by 30 per cent in calves raised to weaning, 18 per cent in weaning weight of calves, 14 per cent in yearling grade of bulls, 7 per cent in final weight and 3 per cent in rate of gain. The inbreds required less feed per unit of gain than the outbreds (Stonaker, 1954).

Koger and Knox (1951) showed that steers which gained the most on pasture were the ones making the faster gains in the feedlot. This indicates that genes which affect growth rate will express themselves when feed conditions permit and that selection on the basis of feedlot gains would result in better-doing cattle on the range. Even more important is the fact that selections can be made for better-performing cattle produced under range conditions.

The New Mexico station has demonstrated what can be done by selection for increasing the calf crop and weaning weights of the calves. Some of their results may be attributed to better feed conditions resulting from proper stocking of the range, and some may be attributed to removing the poor-producing cows from the herd, but there is apparently some genetic improvement which has resulted from this selection program. The percentage of calf crop has been increased 20 to 25 per cent, and the weaning weights have been increased by more than 70 lb. per calf in a 20-year selection program.

Koger and Knox (1948) showed that weaning weight of the first or the first and second calf was a good indication of future weanings of calves by a cow. The score of the first calf produced by a cow was not a good indicator of the scores of succeeding calves and was even less indicative than the weights of calves at weaning. However, both rated sufficiently high to make selections effective when based on one or two calves produced by a cow.

The research of Flower, et al (1953), has indicated that the same sire groups which do well when liberally fed also do well under good pasture conditions. This provides a basis for recommending to ranchers that they select for gains or weight adjusted to a common age even if it should be impossible for them to do feed-testing. In this way the rancher can make considerable improvement even when his facilities will not permit the ideal test conditions. To encourage the practice, the Montana station has feed-tested bulls as a service to ranchers, with the provision that the station will be able to obtain the service of outstanding bulls. This has helped to locate some of the better germ plasm but has reduced the research facilities of the station.

Selection has resulted in considerable improvement at the Montana station. The suckling gains of calves from three-year-old heifers has increased from 1.34 lb. per day during the 1943–1946 period to 1.54 lb. per day during the 1947–1950 period. The top performing bulls have sired calves which return $25.00 to $40.00 per animal more than calves sired by the lower performing bulls. This does not reveal the difference which would exist if the lowest performing bulls were used as sires. The differences between sire groups is more important than differences between the bulls within each selected group.

The studies of Kidwell, et al (1954), indicated that calves on a high plane of nutrition gained more rapidly when group-fed than when individually fed, but that no effect of method of feeding was noticed when the plane of nutrition was lower. Kidwell (1954) found that the gains during two winter feeding periods were apparently under a common genetic influence. Gains on pasture were negatively associated with gains during the winter periods.

The Oregon station feed-tests all bulls and heifers and selects on the basis of equal emphasis for suckling gains, feedlot gains, feed efficiency, and conformation score. Recent studies indicated that score for conformation might have been overemphasized in the selection program. Fertility and freedom from defects were considered on an independent culling level. The calves were test-fed from a weight of 500 lb. to a weight of 800 lb.

Early studies (Sawyer, et al, 1948) revealed that weaning weight of the calves was influenced by age and weight of the dam. Larger cows, within an age group, weaned heavier calves. For each 100-lb. difference in cow size, with age held constant, there was a 15-lb. difference in weaning weight of the calf. These results stress the fact that cow size is important if heavy weaning weight of calves is to be obtained.

Fig. 138. Research with small animals speeds up the development of concepts and principles which can be later applied to farm animals. Here Mr. Robert Mason is using mice in a selection experiment to determine which selection method is most effective. (*Courtesy Oregon State College.*)

Some pilot studies have been made on small animals for the purpose of developing concepts which could later be tested on farm animals. Warren and Bogart (1952) selected rats for early and late vaginal opening and then determined the changes in other characteristics which accompanied changes in age at vaginal opening. The heritability of age at vaginal opening was estimated at

17 per cent. The two lines not only diverged in age at time of vaginal opening but also in litter size, weaning weight, and weight of female at time of vaginal opening. The females in which the vagina opened at an early age were more prolific, apparently as a result of greater number of ova shed. The animals that showed vaginal opening at the early age were the ones which gained at a slower rate. It appears from this study that early sexual maturity and prolificacy are negatively related to rate of gain.

Procedure for Feed-Testing

Keith, et al (1952 and 1954), have made a thorough study of the optimum hay to concentrate ratio for feeding calves and yearlings. They have developed a schematic method for determining the feeding of a proper ratio of hay to concentrate. This method takes into consideration various hay and concentrate prices. It is based on the rate and economy of gains made by the cattle at this station when fed different ratios. Their general results have been satisfactory when the animals have been fed ratios ranging from two parts hay:one part concentrate and one part hay:3 parts concentrate. This gives a choice of ratios in this range, depending on relative hay and concentrate prices. The general function of beef cattle is to convert roughage into meat; therefore, a breeder should consider the use of as much roughage as possible in his breeding program.

The Washington station had the misfortune of a disease condition which necessitated the raising of calves away from their dams from birth in order to develop a disease-free herd (Galgan, et al, 1953). This provided an opportunity for studying rate and efficiency of gains from birth without variations in milking ability of the dams involved. Calves from birth to 180 days of age were much more efficient feed users than calves during the post-weaning period of growth. It will be interesting to learn what this study will reveal with regard to the heritability of gains and efficiency from birth. A comparison of pelleted with ground unpelleted rations was made (Foster, et al, 1953). The cattle on the pelleted ration made better use of their feed and had fewer digestive disturbances than those on the unpelleted ground feed, but rate of gains was similar for the two groups.

The Hawaii station is working with ranchers in the improvement of beef cattle on the ranch. The cattle are grazed for the entire year. Selections are made primarily on weight for age and conformation. Even under such a grazing program, progeny performance of different sires is striking. This indicates that a selection program under pasture production systems could be effective.

Three lines of Herefords and one line of Angus at Corvallis and one line at the Union Station (in Northeastern Oregon) are being developed, each from a different source of breeding stock. The feeding at Union is quite different from that at Corvallis, the ratio of hay to concentrate being 2:1 at Corvallis and 1:2 at Union. Cattle gain at about the same rate at the two locations, but those receiving more concentrate are in better condition at the end of the feed test. It has been the objective at the Oregon station to breed for larger cattle because the data have indicated that larger cows produce heavier calves at weaning and that the larger kind of cattle gain more rapidly and efficiently than the smaller kind. In spite of the large size of the Oregon cattle, a grade of choice has not been difficult to obtain at a weight of 800 lb. when the cattle are fed two parts hay to one part of concentrate.

Cattle were developed on two planes of nutrition at the Squaw Butte station, after which they were grazed together in an attempt to determine if it were necessary to full-feed in order to differentiate the faster-gaining from the slower gaining animals. Another objective was to learn whether cattle that do well on feed will be the ones which do better than others on pasture. The studies showed that when cattle were fed at a level that produced an average gain of 1 lb. per head per day, the better gaining animals could be differentiated from the slower gaining ones. Among the cattle on the high plane of nutrition those that gained the most rapidly during the feeding period also gained the fastest on summer range. Also, among the cattle on the low plane of nutrition those that gained the most rapidly on feed test also gained the fastest on summer range. Obviously, the group that was on the lower plane during the winter feeding period gained more on the summer range than those that had been wintered on a higher plane.

Dahmen and Bogart (1952), and Pierce, et al (1954), studied the effects of various factors on rate and economy of gains in the feed-test period. Birth weight was closely related to gains during the feed-test period and showed some relationship to feed efficiency, with the calves that were larger at birth making faster and more economical gains. Gains during the suckling period showed no relationship (in one case a positive relationship) with rate and economy of gains during the feed-test period. From this study it seems apparent that suckling gains can be influenced by the calf's ability to grow rapidly as well as by the dam's milking ability. Calves that gain faster during the suckling period because of increased milk production of the dam can not be expected to show greater gains on test. On the other hand, faster gaining during the suckling period, resulting from inherited increased growth capacity of the calf, should be related to faster gains during the feed-test period.

Calves that gained the fastest during the feed-test period made the most efficient use of their feed. The regression showed that for each change in gains on test of 0.1 lb. per day, there was a change of 23 lb. of feed per 100 lb. of gain. A calf gaining 3.0 lb. per day made 100 lb. of gain on 230 lb. less feed than a calf that gained at the rate of 2.0 lb. per day. This was a material saving and showed the importance of fast-gaining ability of calves.

The Utah station compared feeding for a 140-day period, feeding for a 168-day period, and feeding from 500- to 800-lb. body weight. Rate of gain was not particularly influenced by either method of feeding, as shown by the high correlations between any two of the methods for rate of gain. Feed efficiency results were quite different for the different feeding methods, as shown by the low correlations of feed efficiency between feeding for 140 days and feeding for 168 days, and also for feeding for 168 days and feeding between the weights of 500- and 800-lb. body weight. Feed efficiency declined with increasing size, and therefore the better-doing cattle were penalized when fed for a given period of time, particularly if this were over a rather long feeding period. Over a shorter feeding period this penalty on fast-gaining animals was not so great; consequently the correlation between efficiency in a 140-day feeding period and efficiency between the 500- and 800-lb. body weight is rather high and is much higher than the correlation of efficiency during a 168-day feeding period with efficiency for the period from 500- to 800-lb. body weight.

DETERMINING BODY COMPOSITION IN THE LIVE ANIMAL

There is a need for determining the proportion of fat and lean in the body of the live animal. In addition, it is necessary to know where most of the fat is being stored. Large quantities of subcutaneous or kidney fat are not desired in the carcass because of waste, but heavy muscling with sufficient marbling to give flavor is highly desirable. Three methods of determining the fat and lean of the animal have received attention. The *antipyrine test* measures the amount of body water, from which protein and fat percentages can be estimated. The *electric probe* measures the thickness of the subcutaneous fat layer. The *somascope* measures thickness of the muscle layer.

The antipyrine method has been used with success (Becker, et al, 1952) in determining the amount of fat in the live animal. This technique should prove useful in research and may have value in selection of animals under farm conditions. However, the technique is not simple and some workers have great difficulty in using this test. Measurement of fat thickness in the live animal by the electric probe has not shown a high correlation with grades of live cattle or measurements of fat thickness made on the carcasses by the Colorado workers. However, these investigators are quite interested in the possibilities offered by the somascope.

Genetic Aspects of Production Traits

Knapp and Nordskog (1946) estimated heritabilities by intra-sire correlations for the following: birth weight, 23 per cent; weaning weight, 12 per cent; final feedlot weight, 81 per cent; feedlot gains, 99 per cent; efficiency, 75 per cent. Estimates of heritability by sire-progeny regressions were: birth weight, 42 per cent; weaning weight, 0 per cent; final weight, 69 per cent; daily gain, 46 per cent; and efficiency, 54 per cent. When adjustments were made each year for differences in feeding the sires, the estimates of heritability were: birth weight, 34 per cent; weaning weight, 30 per cent; final weight, 94 per cent; feedlot gains, 97 per cent; and efficiency, 48 per cent. Heritability estimates for scores and carcass characteristics by intra-sire correlations were: weaning score, 53 per cent; slaughter grade, 63 per cent; carcass grade, 84 per cent; dressing percentage, 1 per cent; and area of eye muscle, 69 per cent.

Knapp and Clark (1947) studied the genetic and environmental correlations for gains between three 84-day periods. They found that there was little environmental correlation between the three periods, and that the genetic influence became greater as the feeding period progressed. In 1950 these investigators revised the estimates of heritability of economic characteristics in beef cattle by using more data. By half-sib correlations the estimates were: birth weight, 53 per cent; weaning weight, 28 per cent; weight at 15 months of age, 86 per cent; feedlot gains, 65 per cent; weaning score, 28 per cent; slaughter grade, 45 per cent; carcass grade, 33 per cent; and area of eye muscle, 68 per cent. Estimates of heritability based on regression of offspring on sire were: weight at 15 months, 92 per cent; and feedlot gains, 77 per cent.

Woodward and Clark (1951) found that calves of the same breeding averaged more at one station (Havre) than at another (Miles City) and stressed the importance of standardized procedures in performance-testing of beef cattle. Quesenberry (1950) pointed out a difference of 119 lb. in weaning weight and 211 lb. in final weight between the best and the worst progeny groups. No association between scores and performance characteristics, such as rate and efficiency of gains, was observed. Cows were equally fertile at the various ages, but weaning weights of the calves were higher for the mature cows than for young or very old cows. Differences between sire groups in the tendency to bloat were noted.

Dawson, et al (1947), reported that birth weight was a good indication of what the calf would do during the post-natal growth period. Calves that were heavier at birth reached the 900-lb. (slaughter) weight sooner than calves that were smaller at birth. There was not much association of birth weight with feed efficiency.

Fig. 139. Improvement of beef cattle through breeding is based on the assumption that feeding and management practices will provide an opportunity for the desirable genes to express themselves. Good pasture improvement and utilization practices are essential to the best beef improvement program. *(Courtesy Oregon State College.)*

Knapp, et al (1951), reported that the Line I Herefords at the U.S. Range Livestock Station had been improved by selection for rate of gain and feed efficiency during a 15-year period. The improvement in rate of gain was 0.16 lb. per day, and the feedlot weight at 15 months of age was 66 lb. more.

Shelby, et al (1954), presented the following estimates of heritability for pre- and post-slaughter characteristics in beef cattle: birth weight, 72 per cent; weaning weight, 23 per cent; feedlot gains, 60 per cent; final feedlot weight, 84 per cent; efficiency, 22 per cent; slaughter grade, 42 per cent; shrink, 91 per cent; dressing percentage, 73 per cent; carcass grade, 16 per cent; color of eye muscle, 32 per cent; area of eye muscle, 72 per cent; and thickness of fat, 38 per cent.

Knapp, et al (1951), presented the genetic history of the Line I Herefords at the U.S. Range Livestock Station. One of the most striking relations of performance in sire and offspring groups was presented for final weight of sires and final weight of their steer offspring. A straight-line relation existed, and a change in final weight of sire of 1 lb. was associated with a change in final weight of offspring of 0.52 lb. This could be interpreted as indicating almost 100 per cent heritability of final weight in beef cattle. Final weight means the weight at the end of the feeding period, usually at 15 months of age.

Koger and Knox (1952), by two methods of analysis, estimated the heritability of over-all weaning score as 50 and 30 per cent, lowness score as 46 and 13 per cent, body thickness score as 15 and 10 per cent, and smoothness score as 15 and 18 per cent. These estimates were made from data on Angus cattle. The estimate of heritability of Hereford cattle for grade was 24 per cent by half-sib correlations and 23 per cent by intra-sire regression of offspring on dam. These data could indicate that selection for a low-set type of cattle would be quite effective.

Hitchcock, et al (1955), did a "paper selection" study to see what would have resulted had culling at given levels been practiced. Estimates of heritability for yearling weights of range cattle were 17 and 39 per cent, when determined by two methods. It was suggested from this study that selections should be made within years or that an attempt should be made to standardize the environment from year to year because repeatability of estimates were not significant when years were ignored. Age of dams did not influence yearling weights even though weaning weights were lower for the younger cows. Selection for heavier yearling weights resulted in increased weaning weights and increased mature size of the cows. No effect on conformation or condition resulted from selecting for increased yearling weights.

Brown, et al (1954), found the heritability of calving interval to be practically zero. Repeatability of calving interval was also zero. Heritability esti-

Fig. 140. A great deal of improvement has been made in putting meat on animals in the right places. A great deal of improvement is yet to be made in improving production. It is estimated that a sound improvement program over the nation for 25 years would result in 1.4 times the beef now produced with the same feed. *(Courtesy Oregon State College.)*

mates by Blackwell, which were based on intra-sire and year regressions of offspring on dam, are: weaning weight, 6 per cent; yearling weight, 37 per cent; weaning grade, 26 per cent; yearling grade, 63 per cent; and yearling gain, 24 per cent. The very high heritabilities reported by various workers for production characteristics in beef cattle could suggest that selection of individuals on the basis of performance records would result in the greatest progress. There should be no need for progeny-testing or the formation of inbred lines to be used in converging or topcrossing for characteristics which are so highly heritable.

The value of production-tested bulls for use by ranchers has been emphasized by the Montana breeders. The ranchers are beginning to recognize the importance of production-testing and are willing to pay more for bulls of higher performance. The results of using production-tested bulls have shown the advantage of selecting bulls for performance, since calves sired by superior bulls make more desirable records themselves.

EXERCISES

1. What is the relationship of type in beef cattle to other production traits?
2. Discuss the environmental factors affecting production traits in beef cattle.
3. Give the heritability estimates for the various production traits in beef cattle. Why do these heritability estimates vary?

28

U.S.D.A. SHEEP BREEDING RESEARCH

The U.S. Sheep Experiment Station was established in 1915 and the Western Sheep Breeding Laboratory, a cooperative regional effort of eleven western states and Texas with the U.S. Department of Agriculture, was established in 1937 at Dubois, Idaho. The work of the Western Sheep Breeding Laboratory differs from that of some of the other regional laboratories in greater concentration of the research at the station at Dubois and less at each of the cooperating state stations. However, the collaborators from the state stations are active in guiding the research program. The facilities at Dubois include about 50,000 acres of land owned by the station and some grazing permits on national forest lands. Three major breeds, Rambouillet, Columbia and Targhee, are bred as lines, tester stock, outbreds, controls, and line crosses. About 2,600 ewes of breeding age, 800 replacements, and 600 rams are maintained. The Columbia and Targhee breeds were developed by the U.S. Sheep Experiment Station from crossing Lincoln and Rambouillet, after which breeding and selecting was done in closed flocks. The Columbia is somewhat superior to the Targhee in mutton qualities, while the Targhee is somewhat superior to the Columbia in wool qualities. Both breeds possess most of the desirable traits of the Lincoln and Rambouillet crossbred, which has found such widespread use as a range sheep, and at the same time, by selection and inbreeding, have attained a state of purity which equals or exceeds that of other breeds of sheep.

Sheepmen of the west have been able to use and are using a great deal of general information about sheep which has been developed by this experiment station.

At one time sheep breeders held to the contention that wool covering over the face was important for obtaining maximum wool production. However, it soon became evident that wool production was not increased by wool covering over the face and that lamb production was materially reduced from wool-blind ewes. Terrill (1949) showed that ewes with open faces produced 11.3

per cent more lambs and 11.1 more pounds of lamb per ewe bred than did wool-blind ewes. Ewes with partially covered faces produced more than wool-blind ewes but less than those with open faces. This increase in production of open-face ewes over wool-blind ewes is due to a greater number of lambs born from open-face ewes (46 per cent), higher weaning weights of lambs from those open-face ewes which became pregnant (19 per cent) and greater viability to weaning time of lambs from open-face ewes (9 per cent). Nordby (1947) indicated that the advantage of open-face ewes was approximately $2.00 per ewe per year of productive life.

Face covering is highly heritable (about 56 per cent); therefore, selection for the open-face condition has been very effective. It is necessary to select for open faces by use of a score because this method requires less time than measurements to describe face covering. One interesting point is that, as improvement in face covering was made, the severity of scoring was increased, and this resulted in yearly scores for face covering that did not show the real improvement being made. However, the selection for open faces was so effective that now most sheep have open faces.

Although these exceedingly effective selections were made by use of score, breeders sometimes erred by taking average score for face covering at two different periods as an index of the improvement made. The breeders of fine-wool sheep at one time contended that wrinkles on the body (skin folds) were necessary to give the added surface area required for producing a heavy yield of wool. Some proponents of the desirability of body wrinkles also suggested that fineness and density were related to the amount of body wrinkles. The research at the laboratory showed conclusively that clean fleece yield and length of fiber were greater in the smoother bodied sheep. In addition, smooth-bodied sheep were easier to shear and could be sheared without damage to the animal. It was also found that smooth-bodied sheep produced a clip of uniform fiber length. Selection for smooth-body or the absence of body folds has resulted in great improvement because this trait is also highly heritable.

ENVIRONMENTAL FACTORS AFFECTING PRODUCTION TRAITS

Terrill and Stoehr (1942) found that ewes which were heavier as yearlings (fall weights) weaned more pounds of lamb per ewe during their lifetime. The ewes that were heavier as yearlings weaned a higher percentage of lambs that were heavier at weaning; however, the greatest advantage of the heavier ewes was their ability to wean more lambs. This advantage of heavier ewes was noted in Columbia, Targhee, and Rambouillet sheep. There was no difference in lifetime production between ewes that were singles and those that were twins. Ewes heavier as yearlings also produced heavier fleeces, but staple length was not altered by size. Mature body weight was associated with lower lifetime production. This could be because the unproductive ewes remain in a higher condition and thus weigh more than the productive ewes.

In order to select properly, it becomes necessary to determine the effect that certain environmental influences have on the desired traits so that corrections or adjustments for these environmental effects can be made. Hazel and Terrill (1945) found in Rambouillet sheep that ram lambs were 8.3 lb. heavier at weaning time than ewe lambs. Single lambs of this breed were 9.2 lb. heavier than twins, and twins raised as singles were heavier than twins raised as twins. Mature ewes weaned lambs which were 6.1 lb. heavier than two-year-old ewes. Ewe lambs, singles, and lambs from mature ewes had higher scores for type and condition. Ram lambs had more neck folds and were not so open-faced as ewe lambs. Inbreeding depressed weaning weight, staple length, body type, and condition of lambs at time of weaning. It appeared that environmental influences affected weaning weights more than, and face covering less than, other traits.

Hazel and Terrill (1946) also determined the effect of environmental influences on important traits in Columbia, Corriedale, and Targhee sheep. Ram lambs were 10.8 lb. heavier than ewe lambs at weaning. Mature ewes weaned lambs each weighing 8.7 lb. more than those from two-year-old ewes. Single lambs were each 11.7 lb. heavier than twin lambs at weaning. Ewe lambs, singles, and those from mature ewes scored higher for type and condition and had longer staple length of the fleeces. Age at time of weaning influenced most traits, since a general increase in all traits was associated with increased age of lambs at weaning. Inbreeding depressed weaning weight, type, and condition but had no marked effect on other traits.

Environment also affects yearling traits (Hazel and Terrill, 1946; Terrill, et al, 1947) in Rambouillet, Columbia, and Targhee ewes. In Rambouillets, those traits which were quantitatively measured by objective methods, such as grease and clean fleece weights, body weight, and staple length, were more influenced by environmental factors than those traits which were measured subjectively by scoring, such as type, condition, face covering, and neck folds. Among yearling ewes, those from mature dams and those which were born as singles were heavier, produced longer staple-length fleeces, and produced more grease and clean wool than yearling ewes from two-year-old dams and yearlings which were raised as twins, respectively. Inbreeding depressed the traits concerned with mutton characteristics (body weight, type, and condition) more than the traits concerned with wool characteristics (staple length and grease and clean fleece weights).

Columbia and Targhee yearlings showed marked effects of environmental influences on fleece and body weights. Year of birth, birth type (singles vs. twins), age at shearing, and inbreeding were important factors affecting these traits. Age of dam had very little effect. Face covering and neck folds were not greatly influenced by the environment. Yearlings that were born and raised as singles were 7 lb. heavier than twins raised as twins. Mature ewes produced yearlings weighing 4 lb. more than those produced by two-year-old ewes. Single ewes also produced heavier fleeces and longer staple and scored higher as yearlings for type and condition than did twins. Inbreeding depressed fleece and body weights, staple length, and score for type and condition of yearling Columbia and Targhee sheep. Daughters from mature dams had heavier fleeces and weighed more than daughters from two-year-old ewes.

The effects of various environmental factors on yearling traits of Rambouillet rams (Terrill, et al, 1948) were studied, and it was concluded from the results that yearly variations and inbreeding were most important. Type of birth and age of dam did not influence yearling traits to a very marked degree. Neck folds, body weight, and fleece weight showed large yearly variations. Inbreeding depressed body weight, clean- and grease-fleece weights, and scores for type and condition in yearling Rambouillet rams. Staple length and neck folds were least influenced by environmental factors. Yearling rams exceeded yearling ewes in every trait studied except in score for type and neck folds. Rams were much heavier (131 lb.) than ewes (85 lb.), and rams also sheared much heavier fleeces (12.2 lb.) than ewes (8.4 lb.) at the yearling age. Even at the ages of two and three years, rams showed marked yearly variations and the depressing effects of inbreeding.

Columbia and Targhee yearling rams (Terrill, et al, 1948) also showed marked yearly variations in body weight and in grease and clean fleece weights. Face covering and staple length were least affected by yearly influences. Age of dam did not have so large an influence on yearling traits of Targhee rams as it did on Columbia rams. Singles had heavier yearling weights and sheared heavier fleeces as yearlings than twins. Inbreeding depressed fleece and body weights, staple length, and scores for type and condition. The greatest effect of inbreeding was on body weight, type, and condition of yearling rams. The effects of inbreeding were greater in the Targhee than in the Columbia breed.

The various workers at the Montana station point out that selection of weaning or yearling sheep could be made more effective if adjustments were made for the environmental influences. If this were done, the effect of sex would not be important as long as comparisons of sheep were made within a sex, and comparisons of progeny by different sires could be made more accurate by adjusting all traits to the basis of one sex. The large numbers of sheep produced at the station made the calculation of inbreeding a laborious task. Emik and

Terrill (1949) developed a systematic procedure, based on a numerator relationship chart, for calculating inbreeding coefficients so that records of all sheep could be kept current.

HERITABILITY ESTIMATES OF PRODUCTION TRAITS

The heritability estimates of traits and the genetic and environmental correlations between traits are necessary for the construction of selection indexes. It is more effective to select on an index basis in which all traits are combined into an over-all estimate of an animal's breeding value than it is to select on the basis of independent culling levels. Hazel and Terrill (1945) estimated the heritability of various economic traits for Rambouillet lambs at weaning in inbred lines and topcrosses (Table 38).

Table 38. ESTIMATES OF HERITABILITY FOR WEANING WEIGHT
(HERITABILITIES EXPRESSED AS PER CENT)

Group and Year	Half-Sib Method, Per Cent	Intra-Sire Regression of Offspring on Dam, Per Cent
One sire, Inbred lines		
1941	24	–6
1942	36	34
Topcrosses		
1941	10	33
1942	15	50
Average	27	34

The average heritability obtained for weaning weight was 27 per cent by half-sib correlations and 34 per cent by intra-sire regression of offspring on dam methods of calculations.

Table 39. ESTIMATES OF HERITABILITY FOR STAPLE LENGTH
(HERITABILITIES EXPRESSED IN PER CENT)

Group and Year	Half-Sib Method, Per Cent	Intra-Sire Regression Method, Per Cent
One sire, Inbred lines		
1941	30	41
1942	49	37
Topcrosses		
1941	64	25
1942	49	50
Average	41	39

The average heritability estimate of staple length was 41 per cent by half-sib correlations and 39 per cent by intra-sire regressions of offspring on dams (Table 39). It was pointed out that the maximum yearly gains to be expected from selecting for either weaning weight or staple length alone would be 0.9 lb. of lamb and 0.06 cm. of wool length, respectively. When other traits are also considered in selecting breeding animals, the net yearly gain for weaning weight and staple length will be reduced for each of the traits, depending on the number of additional traits that are incorporated in the selection program.

Estimates of heritability of scores for body type and condition (Hazel and Terrill, 1946) were very low. The average of eight estimates in inbred and top-crosses, made by two methods of estimation, indicated that type was 13 per cent heritable and that condition was 4 per cent heritable. It was pointed out that selection for these traits which are so low in heritability would not be effective by use of the individual's own scores. Progeny tests, the formation of inbred lines for crossing, or the formation of lines possessing a high combining ability by recurrent selection could be expected to result in greater improvement of these traits than individual selections based on scores.

Face covering and neck folds were shown not to be so greatly influenced by environmental factors as weights and scores for type and condition in Rambouillet lambs. Terrill and Hazel (1946) have shown that these traits are relatively more under genetic influences. The average heritability of face covering was 56 per cent. There was a difference between inbred lines in heritability of face covering and neck folds. The average heritability for neck folds was 39 per cent (Table 40).

Table 40. ESTIMATES OF HERITABILITY FOR FACE COVERING
(HERITABILITIES EXPRESSED IN PER CENT)

Group and Year	Half-Sib Method, Per Cent	Intra-Sire Regression Method, Per Cent
One sire, Inbred lines		
1941	62	69
1942	42	72
Topcrosses		
1941	53	69
1942	53	32
Average	51	60

Weaning traits of Columbia, Corriedale, and Targhee sheep were also studied by Hazel and Terrill (1946). The heritability estimates calculated by half-sib correlations and intra-sire regression of offspring on dam were calculated for weaning weight, staple length, and scores for body type, condition, face covering, and neck folds (Table 41). These data show that face covering

Table 41. ESTIMATES OF HERITABILITY FOR SIX WEANING TRAITS IN COLUMBIA, CORRIEDALE, AND TARGHEE SHEEP (HERITABILITIES ARE EXPRESSED IN PER CENT)

Trait	Columbia Half-Sib	Columbia Regres-sion	Corriedale Half-Sib	Corriedale Regres-sion	Targhee Half-Sib	Targhee Regres-sion	All Breeds Average
	Per Cent	Per Cent	Per Cent	Per Cent	Per Cent	Per Cent	Per Cent
Weaning weight	16	21	32	45	8	1	17
Staple length	38	46	5	40	60	49	43
Body type	4	17	28	11	1	7	7
Condition	13	11	34	41	31	16	46
Face covering	44	48	42	42	38	56	46
Neck folds	5	6	1	6	17	15	8

and staple length can be improved rapidly by selection. One reason for the low heritability of neck folds in these sheep is that they are already practically free from neck folds. Body type will not show much response to selection because of its very low heritability and because the desired type may have been already attained.

PHYSIOLOGICAL STUDIES

Some intensive studies have been made on reproduction physiology of range sheep by Terrill (1944), who found that length of gestation was 151 days for Rambouillets, 149.5 days for Corriedales and Targhees, and 148 days for Columbias. Older ewes carried their lambs longer than younger ewes, and those producing singles had slightly longer gestations than those producing twins. Lambs carried for longer periods were gaining in the uterus at about the same rate as those born earlier had gained after birth. Emik and Terrill (1949) found variations due to year, line of breeding, and age of rams in quantity and quality of semen produced. Wiggins, et al (1953), found by different methods of appraising semen that semen volume, estimated motility count, percentage of abnormal sperm heads, percentage of normal sperm, and percentage of live-normal sperm were all related to percentage of ewes lambing. Inbreeding of the ram depressed the percentage of live lambs born and the percentage of lambs weaned, but it did not lower the percentage of ewes lambing. One point to be emphasized is that semen studies related to fertility show lower correlations because investigators used only those rams that produced good semen. A higher correlation most likely could have been obtained if rams of various degrees of fertility had been used in such a study. The development of the penis in rams following birth (Wiggins and Terrill, 1953) was influenced by age of dam, singles vs. twins, and breeds. The Rambouillet ram lambs showed slower penis development than lambs of any other breed studied. Wiggins, et al (1954), studied the effects of year, breed, age of ram, and number of ewes bred per ram on fertility, using a total of 1,109 rams and 31,473 ewes during a period of 15 years, 1936–1950 inclusive. Yearly variations in lambing percentage were evident. In 1946 only 88 per cent of the ewes lambed, while in 1950 as many as 94 per cent lambed. Targhee rams were highest in fertility, followed in order by Corriedales, Rambouillets, and Columbias. Age of ram did not appear to have a relation to fertility. Also, number of ewes bred per ram did not influence fertility until the number exceeded 50, after which there was a slight drop in fertility.

Much effort is being directed toward locating sterile rams prior to breeding so that only rams of high fertility will be used. Since some rams are not willing to mate, thus making semen collections impossible by natural ejaculations, semen collections are made at times by electrical stimulation. Studies are being made on the normal development of reproductive organs in the male and female so that abnormalities of development can be detected and selection applied against any abnormal reproductive condition which is under genetic control. Studies are also being directed toward determining the causes of barrenness in ewes. From the information obtained, changes can be made in the management program, if needed, to improve fertility. Selection against low fertility can be applied in situations which are genetically influenced.

BREEDING METHODS

Inbred lines are being established by different methods so that information may be obtained on best methods for developing inbred lines of sheep. Mild inbreeding with maximum within-line selection on an index basis for over-all merit is used in the development of 11 lines of Rambouillets, 13 lines of Targhees, and 10 lines of Columbias. Four lines of Rambouillets and three lines of Targhees are being developed by recurrent selection of sires on the basis of progeny tests on ewes from another line or test flock. In the four lines of Rambouillets developed by recurrent selection, four sires from each line are tested both on ewes of the other line and test ewes. The one ram of each line with best weanling performance of the progeny produced is used in the line the next year. In the three lines of Targhees, six sires are tested from each line by mating to test ewes, and the best sire of each line, on the basis of his weanling offspring, is used the next year in the line.

In some respects the index basis and progeny-test methods of developing the lines of Rambouillets are comparable to reciprocal recurrent selection in that rams of two lines are tested for combining ability with ewes of the other two lines. However, it is only on the basis of sire performance in progeny tests that selections are made. The Targhees are mated to a tester stock to determine combining ability, which should measure their general combining abilities as a basis for sire selection.

Two lines of Rambouillets are being developed with maximum inbreeding by selecting replacement animals from those with the higher coefficients of inbreeding. Two comparable lines, one-sire herd size, are being developed with selection entirely at random. Four lines of Rambouillets and two lines of Targhees are being developed by mild inbreeding and maximum within-line selection for specific traits. One line of Rambouillets and one line of Targhees are selected only for body weight. One line of each of these two breeds is selected only for type. One line of Rambouillets is selected for clean fleece weight and another line for staple length. Four lines of Rambouillets are being developed by alternate inbreeding for four years and outcrossing for two years. Two are outcrossed to outbred stock, one to stock from the station and one to stock from outside breeding. Two of these lines are outcrossed to inbred stock, one to inbreds from the station and one to inbreds from outside.

Another program initiated is developing a large number of inbred lines from a large sample within each of three breeds by using very small lines and initially intense inbreeding to locate the material that can withstand inbreeding. The inbred lines that contain fewer detrimental genes and show less ill effects from inbreeding will either be enlarged or converged for developing superior lines. In addition to the lines mentioned, selection on an index basis for overall merit is being practiced in a flock where inbreeding is kept low to determine the effectiveness of selection. Also, a genetically stabilized flock has been established as a comparison group to determine the amount of improvement being made by other methods of breeding.

It seems appropriate to discuss what should be expected from some of the breeding methods. Traits that are highly heritable, due largely to additive gene effects, should improve most rapidly by selection within a flock in which inbreeding is kept low. Traits that are influenced by epistatic gene effects, overdominance, or where the desirable of one trait is associated with the undesirable of the other trait, should show marked improvement and greatest heterosis from recurrent or reciprocal recurrent selection for combining ability or from converging inbred lines. Inbred lines developed by selection for one trait only should show greatest heterosis if crossed when there is a situation in which the desirable of one trait is associated with the undesirable of another trait. Where this situation or overdominance influences are operating, selection on the basis of over-all merit should tend to maintain heterozygosity for those traits so that lines developed from such an over-all merit basis of selection would show least heterosis when converged. However, gene drift could separate these lines sufficiently in spite of artificial selection so that considerable heterosis would result. The development of lines by intense inbreeding in the initial stages should lead to line selections in which inbreeding would be used as a tool for locating breeding material relatively free from detrimental genes.

The facilities at the Dubois station do not permit full-scale testing of lines without reducing the lines that can be maintained, although some line-crossing has been done. Average results from line-crossing during a six-year period showed an advantage of the line crosses over straight-line lambs of 5 to 7 per cent for type and condition, 3 to 5 per cent for weaning weight, and 1 to 2 per cent for staple length. Face covering was the same for inbred and line-cross lambs. Inbred ewes raising line-cross lambs weaned from 5 to 12 per cent more lambs and 10 to 19 per cent more pounds of lamb per ewe bred than when they raised inbred lambs, and therefore it appears that the greatest advantage of line-cross sheep will be in ewe productivity. One trait, neck folds, was inferior in line crosses to that in the inbreds. In over-all merit the line-cross sheep showed an advantage of 1.7 per cent.

The selected control group,* in which selection for over-all merit is practiced and inbreeding is held low, is superior to the lines and line crosses in face covering, staple length, and index but is intermediate between inbreds and line crosses in condition and weaning weight. The traits showing advantages in the selected group or line crosses are the more highly heritable traits, while the traits showing advantages of line crosses over the selected control group are the less highly heritable traits. There has been more progress from selection where inbreeding is lowest. It is possible that certain lines may combine to produce a higher level of production than can be obtained by selection in a non-inbred population. It could be expected that selection for combining ability of lines would result in line crosses with greater hybrid vigor for some of the traits but not for the very highly heritable traits.

Terrill (1951) made a study of how much selection pressure had been applied and how effective the selection had been. It was found that selection had been increased for staple length, type, face covering, and weanling index by greater accuracy of selections and by decreasing generation length for sires.

---

* Control and genetically stabilized populations were discussed in Chap. 19.

The expected genetic gain in weanling traits from selection of sires had been far greater than for selection of dams. From 80 to 90 per cent of the expected genetic progress in weanling index had come from selection of sires. Thus, it was concluded that sire selection, as compared with dam selection, was 40 to 70 times more important for staple length, 8 to 12 times as great for face covering, and 4 to 11 times as great for weight. Actual genetic progress made by selection had been slightly less than that calculated as expected improvement. However, the actual improvement had approached the expected improvement except for body weight and fleece weight. These had declined slightly in spite of selection. Over-all index of weanling lambs had increased with selection, but the actual progress had been slightly lower than the calculated expectancy.

One of the major values of an experiment station is to develop ideas, concepts, and methods which can be used by farmers. The combined efforts of the U.S. Sheep Experiment Station and the Western Sheep Breeding Laboratory have contributed greatly in this respect. The greater production of open-faced and smooth-bodied sheep means a great deal to range sheep producers and has resulted in efforts by all sheep producers to breed sheep with these valuable traits. The relative economic importance and heritability of traits as criteria for selection is becoming recognized by sheep breeders. They are now considering the over-all merit as a basis of selection rather than the concentration on only one trait with the expectation that others will improve as selection develops for this one trait. Breeders are recognizing the importance of research findings by experimental stations because these groups of investigators have proved the soundness of new ideas, concepts, and methods by applying them to experiment station sheep flocks. Furthermore, sheep made available to breeders of the west are proving their superiority to others in the hands of the breeders. One reason for this superior performance of the experiment station sheep is that they have been improved through breeding under the same conditions in which range sheep are actually kept. Another and even more important reason is that only the better genetic material is made available to farmers.

Terrill (1953) has determined from the relation between sale price received at public auction for rams and the measures of merit that breeders are willing to pay more for larger rams and those which shear heavier fleeces, those with better type and condition scores, and those with a higher index for over-all merit. This shows that buyers of stud rams attach real importance to production traits.

A great deal of improvement in sheep has been gained in New Mexico. A large amount of credit for the good work done on the ranches in that state is due Professor P. E. Neale of the New Mexico A. and M. College. Unfortunately much of his work has not been published and it is therefore not readily available. Neale has developed a mechanical device for rapidly estimating the clean fleece weight from a sample of wool. In working with sheepmen, Neale has a well-balanced concept of what constitutes desirability in a sheep. Many traits, such as body size, freedom from defects, and ewe productivity, are considered, but the three most important from the standpoint of wool are clean fleece weight, staple length, and size of the sheep. Neale recommends dividing the ewes into four groups according to superiority. The ewes in the group that is the best are mated to the top rams. The next best ewes are mated to the rams that are in the next to best group. Replacements are not necessarily selected from the top group of ewes if good ones are produced in another group. However, most of the replacements come from the two top groups rather than the two bottom groups of breeding sheep.

EXERCISES

1. What is the relationship of body folds and face covering in sheep to wool and lamb production?

2. Discuss the phenotypic and genotypic correlations among production traits of sheep. Of what value is a knowledge of these correlations?

3. Give the heritability estimates for the various productive traits in sheep. Which of these traits would respond the most to mass selection?

29

A COMMERCIAL BREEDING PROGRAM

Much emphasis is generally placed on the breeding of purebred livestock because it is from the purebred herds and flocks that sires are obtained for commercial livestock production. Since most of the farm animals are commercial grade (about 97 per cent) and only a small number is purebred (about 3 per cent), it is appropriate to consider some breeding plans for commercial livestock production.

The objective in the production of meat animals is to produce them as rapidly and as cheaply as possible and to have a quality of meat which will appeal to the consuming public. In some cases, such as lamb, quality of the animal produced is quite important, and the producer is paid for producing better animals. In other cases, such as pigs, quality of animal produced has never meant a great deal in the selling price of the animals. In this latter case, rate and economy of production become of utmost importance in commercial production.

It has been shown that hybrid vigor results in greater livability of the young and in faster gains. It has also been shown that hybrid vigor is expressed in the female by greater fertility and suckling ability. Hybrid vigor can be obtained by crossing lines within a breed or by crossing breeds. There is evidence to show that crossing lines of different breeds results in greater hybrid vigor than that obtained by crossing lines within a breed or by crossing outbred animals of different breeds.

The relative importance of kind of animal produced and color discrimination dictate to some extent how much one may be able to exploit hybrid vigor in livestock production. Color variations and type and conformation are not so important in swine as they are in sheep and beef cattle. Full use of hybrid vigor can be made in swine production, but some restrictions on use of crossing are imposed upon sheep and beef cattle producers. Let us separate swine, sheep, and beef cattle and see what breeding possibilities are available for maximum production of each.

387

SWINE

There are several possibilities available for swine. Grading-up is not likely to be a valuable breeding method because a breeder can start with the better purebred material without great cost. Reproduction is high so that a large herd can be developed from a small herd in a short time.

Crossbreeding by Use of Two Breeds

Crossbreeding will combine two breeds to obtain greater livability and faster gains of the pigs. If the cross is made properly, the strong characteristics of both breeds can be exploited. Some breeds of hogs are known for their large litters raised and the good suckling ability of the sows. Such breeds as the Yorkshire, Landrace, Hamprace, Minnesota No. 1, and some strains of Chester Whites and Hampshires are well known in these respects. Other breeds, such as Poland Chinas and Berkshires, are known for their fast and economical gains.

The mating of sows of high fertility and suckling ability to boars possessing rapid and economical gains will take advantage of the strong characteristics of each of the breeds in the production of market pigs. The hybrid vigor of the pigs gives them a greater chance for survival and a greater rate of gain. This breeding system only partially utilizes the maximum which can be obtained by crossbreeding, because it offers no possibilities for selection other than those obtained in the material crossed.

Crossbreeding by Breed Criss-Crossing

The advantage of hybrid vigor in a crossbred sow can be gained by mating her to a purebred boar. This system makes use of two breeds, with a boar of each breed used in alternate generations. Let us take two breeds such as the Duroc Jersey $\times$ the Poland China. The crossbred (Duroc Jersey $\times$ Poland China) sows would be mated to a Poland China boar. The crossbred sows resulting from this mating would be mated to a Duroc Jersey boar. In the next generation a Poland China boar would be used. Crossbred sows would be retained each generation and mated to a boar of a breed opposite to that of their sire. This is shown diagrammatically as follows:

Duroc Jersey sow $\times$ Poland China boar
$\downarrow$
Crossbred sow $\times$ Poland China boar
$\downarrow$
Crossbred sow $\times$ Duroc Jersey boar
$\downarrow$
Crossbred sow $\times$ Poland China boar

The same boar should not be used for two generations because this would result in inbreeding of the pigs, a result opposed to the objective in this system of breeding.

Boars can be purchased from purebred breeders or they can be raised by keeping a small herd of purebred sows of each of the two breeds used in the crossbreeding program. Inbreeding would result if a breeder bred his own purebreds from these small herds, but this would not be detrimental to the crossbreeding program. In fact, it could have some advantages because the inbred lines of two different breeds would combine and produce hybrid pigs.

It would be difficult for a producer to maintain two small purebred herds for use in the crossbreeding program unless he had a sizeable operation. For the small operator, the purchase of purebred boars rather than the raising of them will be more feasible. The reason for this is that several sows would be needed in each of the small purebred herds to assure the continuation of each of them when inbreeding was practiced. The use of only one or two purebred sows in each of the purebred herds would likely result in loss of the purebred breeding herd through accidental deaths, if for no other reason.

Crossbreeding by Combining Several Breeds

Greater hybrid vigor can be obtained by using more than two breeds of hogs. A system that can be used by both small and large operators is that in which crossbred sows are retained each generation and are bred to a boar of a breed not used in producing the crossbred sow. This is shown diagrammatically as follows:

$$
\begin{array}{c}
\text{Duroc Jersey sow} \times \text{Poland China boar} \\
\downarrow \\
\text{Crossbred sow} \times \text{Hampshire boar} \\
\downarrow \\
\text{Crossbred sow} \times \text{Berkshire boar} \\
\downarrow \\
\text{Crossbred sow} \times \text{Chester White boar} \\
\text{etc.}
\end{array}
$$

In any system of crossbreeding, the use of the bacon breeds as well as the lard breeds is desirable. The bacon breeds are genetically quite different from the breeds of lard hog, and therefore greater heterosis should be expected when they are combined with the lard breeds than when two lard breeds are combined. In addition, the bacon breeds have some valuable carcass characteristics which should add to the value of the hybrid hogs. Carcasses from bacon breeds of hogs contain less fat and have longer loins and leaner bacons.

Combining Inbred Lines within a Breed

When inbred lines of swine are combined, hybrid vigor is related to the genetic divergence of the two lines and to the value of the genetic material possessed by each of the lines used in the line crossing. The combining of two inbred lines to produce commercial pigs does not make full use of hybrid vigor. The crossline pigs will have greater chance of survival and will gain faster than those produced within the line. However, the inbred sows will not show the fertility and suckling ability of outbred sows; therefore, line-cross pigs will not generally equal outbred pigs. If the line-cross sows are retained for breeding, their performance as pig producers will generally exceed that of outbred sows. The use of two lines for alternate breeding onto line-cross sows will result in maintaining considerable hybrid vigor. However, the use of three or more lines on a rotational mating plan will give the optimum heterosis which can be obtained within a breed. Let us show how four lines, 1, 2, 3, and 4, can be used for this system of breeding.

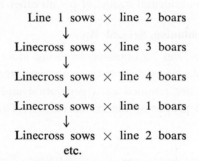

Line 1 sows × line 2 boars
↓
Linecross sows × line 3 boars
↓
Linecross sows × line 4 boars
↓
Linecross sows × line 1 boars
↓
Linecross sows × line 2 boars
etc.

Combining Inbred Lines of Different Breeds

It has been shown that hybrid vigor results when inbred lines are combined and that use of the hybrid female takes advantage of hybrid vigor in sow productivity. It has also been shown that the use of several inbred lines results in greater hybrid vigor than that obtained when only two inbred lines are used, and that cross-breeding of breed crosses also results in hybrid vigor. The use of the crossbred females takes advantage of hybrid vigor as expressed by greater sow productivity of the crossbred. The use of more than two breeds results in greater hybrid vigor than when only two breeds are used. Further, combining inbred lines of different breeds results in greater hybrid vigor than combining lines within a breed or than combining breeds of outbred populations. It appears that maximum hybrid vigor can be obtained by using more than one inbred line within a breed and by using more than two breeds. The use of breeds that differ as much as possible, such as breeds of lard hogs and breeds of bacon hogs, should give greater hybrid vigor when crossed than the crossing of breeds within a swine type.

Some restrictions in use of lines and breeds will be imposed upon the hog producer. One restriction is the size of the operation. A man keeping 10 to 15 brood sows may find it quite difficult to take full advantage of hybrid vigor in this manner. Another restriction may arise from difficulties in obtaining breeding stock from inbred lines or line crosses from the breeds that would give maximum heterosis from crossbreeding. Inbred animals may not be very vigorous and could be looked upon with disfavor by commercial breeders; consequently, line-cross boars may be used more than inbred boars in commercial swine production. Purebred breeders may prefer to release line-cross rather than inbred breeding stock, and commercial breeders may prefer to use line-cross rather than inbred breeding stock. Let us propose a crossbreeding program on the basis of using line-cross breeding stock from three breeds. Since it will not be likely that line-cross sows for the original cross will be purchased, we shall use outbred sows for our initial cross. Let us assume that line-cross material will be available in the Poland China, Landrace, and Hampshire breeds. The breeding program, which should result in great hybrid vigor, is shown diagrammatically as follows:

Outbred Hampshire sows × line-cross Poland boar
↓
Crossbred sows × line-cross Landrace boar
↓
Crossbred sows × line-cross Hampshire boar
↓
Crossbred sows × line-cross Poland boar
etc.

This would mean the purchase of line-cross boars only, because sows would be saved from the pig crop produced. It would be possible to use the crossbred sows and the line-cross boars for several pig crops, saving gilts for the next generation only when the age of the sows indicated the desirability of establishing a new generation. This would reduce the need for line-cross boars and would make it possible to use sows which would produce larger litters than gilts.

If a producer is operating on a large scale, he may want to raise his own inbred breeding stock for crossbreeding. It is likely in this case that he would use only one inbred line within each breed because it would be very difficult to maintain several lines within each of several breeds for crossbreeding purposes. Let us assume that a producer can use three breeds and maintain a line within each of these breeds for supplying boars for crossbreeding. The commercial pigs would be produced from the crossbred sows. Three herds would be maintained, and the purebreds and crossbreds could run together within these three herds. Since it is likely that more than one boar of each breed would be used, the inbreeding of the lines could be held down so that selections would be effective and serious loss of vigor would not result. We may assume that four boars of each breed would be used. A small herd of 8 to 12 purebred sows of each breed could be maintained, and all surplus gilts and barrows could be marketed with the regular commercial hogs. Since pedigree would not be important, a breeder could, if he chose, let the purebred sows run with all four boars, or they could be randomly allotted to the boars if single-boar breeding of the crossbred sows was practiced. This system is outlined as follows:

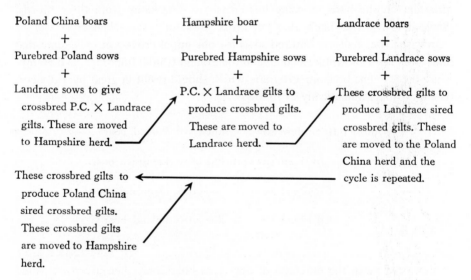

Poland China boars
+
Purebred Poland sows
+
Landrace sows to give crossbred P.C. × Landrace gilts. These are moved to Hampshire herd.

Hampshire boar
+
Purebred Hampshire sows
+
P.C. × Landrace gilts to produce crossbred gilts. These are moved to Landrace herd.

Landrace boars
+
Purebred Landrace sows
+
These crossbred gilts to produce Landrace sired crossbred gilts. These are moved to the Poland China herd and the cycle is repeated.

These crossbred gilts to produce Poland China sired crossbred gilts. These crossbred gilts are moved to Hampshire herd.

The purebred sows in each of the three herds would be used to raise replacement boars for use in crossbreeding. Each of these herds could become highly inbred unless properly controlled. For best results it would be more desirable to use more males than normally required so that inbreeding would not develop rapidly. The crossbred pigs would be marketed, with the exception of gilts to be used. This program could produce crossbred pigs in each herd each year. The entire cycle would be continuously repeated. The commercial pigs would be produced by mating the crossbred sows to the purebred boars of the breed least related to them. The boars would be saved from the small purebred herds for breeding the crossbred and the purebred sows.

SHEEP

Numerous studies show that crossbreeding in sheep can be used to take advantage of the valuable characteristics of the existing breeds in the production of fat lambs. For example, the use of rams of mutton breeds on such range sheep as the Columbia combines the more desirable conformation and ease of fattening of the mutton breeds with the hardiness and range-use characteristics of the Columbia sheep.

In farm flock areas the combination of a breed of ewe that is highly fertile and a good milker with a breed of ram that is of good mutton type and conformation and one that fattens readily makes use of the strong traits of both breeds. The Dorset Horn ewe crossed with Southdown rams serves as an excellent example of this type of crossbreeding. Needless to say, the cross in the opposite direction, i.e., Southdown ewes are mated to Dorset Horn rams, would be extremely undesirable because the strong traits of each breed would be completely wasted by this combination.

Considerable evidence points to the advantage of using crossbred ewes for production of fat lambs. Crossbred ewes are generally very good mothers, if the proper breeds are used in making the cross. What would constitute the proper breeds to use in producing a crossbred ewe for commercial lamb production would depend a great deal on the conditions under which the sheep are produced and the type of lamb production followed. The Lincoln $\times$ Rambouillet crossbred ewe has been proven excellent as a range ewe, and when bred to a ram of a mutton breed such as the Hampshire or Suffolk, produces excellent lambs.

In farm flock production one may find this crossbred Lincoln $\times$ Rambouillet ewe quite satisfactory because she will possess a lot of ruggedness and will be adapted to grass use rather than heavy grain feeding. If she is produced on the dry range, her chances of being disease- and parasite-free are greater than those for ewes raised under farm flock conditions. There is some indication that a more productive crossbred ewe could be produced by crossing the Columbia and Dorset Horn. Both of these have fairly open faces and are white face, and therefore they should not produce sheep possessing any black fibers. The finer wool of the Columbia and the greater fertility of the Dorset Horn will contribute to the value of the crossbred. Such ewes will raise excellent fat lambs when bred to Hampshire, Suffolk, or Southdown rams. If the market is less discriminating, a ram of a larger breed, such as the Hampshire or Suffolk, will yield greater returns to the sheepman because of increased size of the lambs. If the market is discriminating and a good price is offered for the smaller, more compact, and well-finished lambs, the Southdown or Cheviot ram will be ideal.

Very little research has been done on rotation of breeds in a crossbreeding program for sheep. This is a possibility which may be considered, but it is not one which can now be suggested on the basis of experimental evidence. There is no question regarding the value of a crossbred ewe for lamb production. Hybrid vigor in the ewe results in a considerable increase in ewe productivity. There is also no question relative to greater combination possibilities by crossbreeding than by combining families within a breed of sheep. From a study of the strong traits of various breeds, one can plan a crossbreeding program that makes maximum use of the strong traits of breeds. Remember, when two breeds are to be crossed, take advantage of fertility, milking ability, etc., by bringing these traits in through the ewe. The greater compactness, ease of fattening, etc., may be brought into the cross through the ram.

BEEF CATTLE

Beef cattle production differs from swine and sheep production because of the many systems of production in beef cattle. Baby beeves are sometimes produced directly from the cows, or they may be produced by heavy feeding of the calves before and following weaning. Some cattle are roughed through the first winter and fed on pasture the following summer. Some may be sold as grass-fat cattle from pasture without grain feeding. Some may be put on feed as long yearlings following the summer grazing period. A few may be carried over the second winter on roughages and then fattened on grass, or grass and grain, or put into the feedlot as two-year olds in the third winter. The breeding program for commercial beef cattle production will depend somewhat on the production system which is to be followed.

Beef cattle producers are handicapped in a crossbreeding program because of color discrimination at the markets. At one time it was considered that colors differing from those of our major beef breeds either represented scrub or dairy breeding, both of which made less valuable carcasses. Also, the color combinations of the major breeds have been used so much as "trademarks" that most cattle raisers have become "color conscious."

Grading-up

Because of color discrimination and slow rate of reproduction, the most common system of beef cattle production is that of grading-up where females from the breeder's own herd are used for replacements and purebred males of the same breed are used each generation. No doubt this is one of the better methods of approaching the purebred level without purchasing a large number of expensive breeding animals.

Two objectives in a grading-up program can alter the procedure greatly. Some commercial breeders prefer to go every year to the same purebred breeder for bulls because they wish to capitalize on his ability to pursue a sound selection program. One breeder in Wyoming has used bulls from the same herd for 29 years. It so happens that the man from whom he buys bulls has bred his herd without the introduction of new blood since 1902. It follows that this commercial breeder has practically the same genetic constitution in his herd of cattle as exists in the purebred herd. This system of grading-up has much to commend it because of the genetic uniformity which it develops.

A second approach to the grading-up program could be that of maintaining as high a state of hybrid vigor as is possible by staying within a breed. This could be accomplished by securing bulls from three or four different breeders who are using the linebreeding system. The use of these linebred bulls in rotation should maintain a high state of hybrid vigor in the cows and in the calves produced. This would be the nearest approach to hybrid vigor achieved by crossbreeding which could be obtained within a breed.

Crossbreeding

Sufficient research has been done to demonstrate that crossbreeding in beef cattle may be used for making combinations not possible within a breed and for obtaining hybrid vigor in the calves and in the cows used for producing calves. In the farm areas in which baby beef is produced by creep-feeding the calves and marketing them as fat calves at 10 to 12 months of age, milk production of the cows is extremely important. Mating of Holstein or milking Shorthorn cows to Angus bulls could be considered for this purpose. If either of these breeds of cow was to be used for beef production purposes, the calves must be marketed for beef at an early age. If such crossbred calves were carried to older ages, the less desirable conformation resulting from the dairy type of breeding would be allowed to express itself. Some ranch producers are using Shorthorns with better milking ability to cross with Herefords for producing a better milking range cow. There is some debate as to whether this method of infusing higher milking ability into the herd through crossing is to be preferred over selecting for heavier weaning weights of calves within the Hereford breed. It is certainly easier and quicker to obtain better milking by crossing.

A great deal of use has been made of Brahman breeding in hot areas for obtaining heat resistance. Crossbred cows of Brahman × English breeding also possess a great deal of hybrid vigor which makes them good calf producers, particularly in the hot areas.

Crossbreeding by use of the various English breeds of beef cattle has been practiced to a limited extent. The famous "blue roans," resulting from crossing White Shorthorns and Angus, made good feeders and yielded desirable carcasses, but the crossing of these two purebreds, or high grades, to produce a calf with hybrid vigor did not make full use of heterosis. One could combine the two breeds so that advantage would be taken of the strong characteristics of both. Cows from a large, fertile, heavy milking breed mated to bulls of desirable conformation and early maturity result in a crossbred for market which is superior to either of the two breeds.

Greatest advantage from crossbreeding will result from use of crossbred cows for producing calves. It appears that hybrid vigor expresses itself most in those traits related to female productivity and livability of the young in early life. This means that crossbred cows should have a decided advantage in the raising of calves. Colors would be extremely variable if the three major breeds of beef cattle were used in a planned crossbreeding program, but these color variations should not be looked upon with disfavor. If buyers were willing to purchase on the basis of what is inside the hide, the carcass, a planned crossbreeding program would help commercial beef producers to produce more beef with the same feeds and pastures now in use. A suggested program using Shorthorns, Angus, and Herefords is presented as follows:

Shorthorn cows × Hereford bulls
↓
Crossbred cows × Angus bulls
↓
Crossbred cows × Shorthorn bulls
↓
Crossbred cows × Hereford bulls
↓
Crossbred cows × Angus bulls
etc.

The continuous mating of crossbred cows to bulls of the breed least related to them will result in the expression of hybrid vigor in cow productivity and in growth rate of the calf.

EXERCISES

1. Tell how you would exploit hybrid vigor to the fullest possible extent in the commercial production of swine.
2. What traits show the greatest heterosis from crossbreeding?
3. Why has crossbreeding been practiced more extensively in poultry and swine than in dairy and beef cattle?

30

NEW BREEDS OF FARM ANIMALS

A breed of animals is a group of domestic animals, developed and controlled by human intervention, which have distinctive characteristics such as shape and color. A breed, then, may be based entirely on a color "trademark" even though the variations of genetic constitution may be equal to or greater than those in a randomly breeding population in which characteristics of many breeds may be represented. It appears that little genetic significance can be attached to certain breeds; however, some breeds have been selected and inbred sufficiently to make them a fairly distinct genetic group.

Most of the breeds of farm animals, both the old and established and the newer breeds, have resulted from the crossing of existing breeds, strains, etc. However, the crossbred foundation, as such, did not constitute a new breed. It required continuous selection and constructive breeding for a particular set of objectives in order to produce a recognized breed. In fact, all the breeds were developed by inbreeding following the initial crossbreeding. In some cases that was done as a necessity because only a limited number of animals were carried in getting the breed started. In the development of other breeds, a planned inbreeding and selection program was practiced.

Two concepts should be thoroughly understood relative to new breeds of farm animals:

1. Crossbreds of two or more existing breeds do not constitute a new breed. One should recognize this and refrain from purchasing high-priced crossbred animals for breeding purposes when such crossbreds could be produced by anyone. Because of the hybrid vigor which results when breeds are crossed, these crossbreds should be quite superior in themselves, but when intermated, they could produce offspring which would vary a great deal. For example, suppose a Southdown ram had been mated to Dorset Horn ewes to produce a crossbred population. These crossbreds might be quite desirable in growth rate, size, and conformation. They might be given some name such as "Southhorn" and advertised as a breed. However, they would be nothing more than a crossbred group of sheep. If some

397

breeder were to take such a crossbred foundation and select for certain productive traits on a within-flock basis, he could eventually develop a group of sheep which would breed as true as our existing breeds. They could possess merit equal or superior to many of the existing breeds. At this period of development this group of sheep would be considered as a breed.

2. New breeds should not be discriminated against because of their original crossbred foundation. It should be apparent that practically all breeds of farm animals originated from crossing some material which already was in existence. It should be recognized that the breeding systems employed and selection practiced in the development of many of the newer breeds have resulted in a large amount of homozygosity. They may be more homozygous than many of the older breeds of animals. For example, the homozygosity of the Minnesota No. 1 hogs is about 35 per cent, while in some of the older swine breeds the homozygosity will not exceed 15 per cent.

In the development of certain breeds of farm animals, color has been the primary trait which characterizes the breed. Where an animal is used entirely for aesthetic purposes, this emphasis of color is sound; but where production of meat, milk, or work is the primary function of the breed of animal, it is most unfortunate that color should be greatly emphasized. Some of the newer breeds of farm animals have been developed on the basis of selection for productive traits, with color ignored or minimized. From that standpoint, some of the newer breeds are more productive than some of the older breeds that have been selected largely on the basis of color and fancy points.

Some breeds are identified entirely by color to distinguish them from other breeds. The Palomino horse is a breed based on a dilution gene in the heterozygous state acting on chestnut—$bb\ Dd$ genotype. It is apparent that Palominos will not breed true, since the dilution factor must be in the hetero-zygous condition. Chestnut animals that are homozygous for the dilution DD will be "glass-eyed" whites, and those which are dd will be chestnuts. When Palominos are mated they produce 1 "glass-eyed" white:2 Palominos:1 chestnut.

The methods used in the development of a few new breeds of farm animals will be described so that the reader can make clear distinction between a crossbred group of animals and a new breed which has been developed from a crossbred foundation.

RABBITS

One new breed of rabbit, the California (Fig. 141), has been developed by crossing the Himalayan × New Zealand White. Selection has been based on a rabbit of superior meat type, somewhat smaller and more refined than

Fig. 141. A California rabbit. The body is white, and the ears, nose, and feet are black. This breed was developed from first crossing New Zealand White × Himalayan, then interbreeding and selecting. *(Courtesy Oregon State College.)*

the New Zealand but much larger than the Himalayan. The color markings that were adopted for the California rabbits are similar to those of the Himalayan. Selection for these color markings have needlessly reduced the selection which could have been applied for superior meat characteristics because brown, agouti, and other dark markings instead of the desired black often show up.

The California breed of rabbit has become very popular because of its desirable meat qualities and good productive traits. Intense selection, along with some inbreeding, has resulted in as much uniformity in this breed of rabbit as exists in most of the older breeds. However, some color variations are to be found in the California rabbits, one reason for which is that the dark markings are subject to modifications. A breed such as the New Zealand White can show no color variations because the recessive albinism (which must be homozygous) is epistatic to all color genes. It is likely that in the New Zealand White rabbits, color genes are segregating to the same degree as in California rabbits but that their expressions are prevented by the epistatic effects of the albino character.

SWINE

The development of three new breeds of swine will be presented to illustrate the methods which have been used by swine breeders for developing new breeds. The Hamprace was developed cooperatively by the U.S.D.A. at the

U.S. Range Livestock Station, Miles City, and the Montana station by first crossing the Landrace × the Hampshire breeds. Since the white hogs are subject to sunburn, a colored hog was considered more desirable. The belt of the Hampshire hog is influenced by many modifications; consequently, the development of a belted hog would have required intense selection for color markings and this would have reduced the selection that could have been applied to production traits. Consequently, black (nonbelted Hampshire) were used in the original cross and black or red extractions were used for developing the breed. For some time two strains, one black and one red, were maintained, but the solid black color was eventually adopted. The hogs were inbred, since the original crosses were made in 1936 and continuous selection was applied toward improving sow productivity, growth rate, feed efficiency, and carcass merit. A leaner hog with greater body length than is found in the lard breeds was favored by selection. Some of the stock was bred as small lines and some as a large closed herd in which intra-herd selection was practiced. This new breed is noted for its high prolificacy and desirable carcass characteristics.

Sow productivity was shown by an average of 10.6 pigs farrowed, 8.1 pigs raised, and 248.4 lb. as average litter weight at weaning for the years 1939 to 1947 inclusive (Hutton, et al, 1948). Feedlot performance of the Hamprace hogs, from weaning to a weight of 225 lb., has shown a rate of gain of about 1.5 lb. per day and about 375 lb. of feed per 100 lb. of gain. When Hamprace sows were bred to Berkshire boars at the Oregon station, they raised more pigs per litter and the pigs grew more rapidly than when a Hamprace boar was used to sire the pigs. This cross also resulted in pigs that made very good carcasses. The Hamprace breed apparently is more homozygous than some of the older breeds, and when used for crossbreeding, the pigs show more heterosis than when two of the lard breeds are crossed. The inbreeding has been well over 30 per cent for the breed.

The Minnesota No. 1 (Fig. 142) was developed by Dr. L. M. Winters of the University of Minnesota from a crossbred foundation made by crossing Landrace × Tamworth. Again, since a white pig is subject to sunburning, colored pigs were extracted from the crossed material for continuing the breed development. A red or red-and-black spotted hog was considered satisfactory and no particular attention was given to color shades. No inbreeding plan was followed, but the hogs were bred as a closed population. Selection was very rigorous for sow productivity, growth rate, efficiency, and a desirable lean carcass. The relative importance attached to each of these traits was determined in part by the need in the line at the time selections were being made. Dr. Winters has always advocated fertility and livability of pigs, which result

Fig. 142. Minnesota No. 1 sow and a group of pigs. Note the long loins and bacons and the high-functioning mammary systems. *(Courtesy Dr. Ralph Comstock, University of Minnesota. Photograph by Dr. W. A. Craft, Director Regional Swine Breeding Laboratory.)*

in large size of litter at weaning, as a necessity for providing animals which could be selected for other traits. Inbreeding in the Minnesota No. 1 hogs is approximately 35 per cent, and that this homozygosity is greater than that which exists in many of the older breeds of hogs is apparent when the Minnesota No. 1 is crossed with other breeds. The uniform improvement in carcass characteristics which results when this breed is crossed onto other breeds is very striking.

The productivity of the Minnesota No. 1 has been quite satisfactory, as shown by records from 1942 to 1946 inclusive (Winters, et al, 1948). The average number of live pigs per litter was 9.6; average weaning weight per pig, 30 lb.; average weight per pig at 154 days of age, 181 lb.; and feed per 100 lb. of gain on pasture was only 309 pounds.

The Minnesota No. 2 also was developed by Dr. L. M. Winters of Minnesota. He crossed Canadian Yorkshire boars × Poland China sows of Market Lady and Black Star lines. From the segregates in the F_2 and F_3 and some back crosses with the Poland China, the black-and-white spotted pigs were selected. Since the original selection for color to avoid the white hog, which is subject to sunburning, no attention has been given to color. Rigorous selection has been practiced for a meat type of hog which would have high performance in sow productivity, growth rate, and feed efficiency. The crossing of the Yorkshire onto these lines of Poland Chinas was done to retain in the new breed the high rate of gain and feed efficiency of the Poland Chinas and to obtain the high fertility, suckling ability, and leaner carcasses of the York-shires.

The production of the Minnesota No. 2 hogs has been quite satisfactory but perhaps not equal to that of the Minnesota No. 1, either in productive performance or in carcass merit. The production for the period 1942 to 1946 inclusive was indicative of performance of this breed, with the average number of live pigs per litter of 7.9 pigs, the weaning weight per pig of 31 lb., the weight at 154 days of age of 168 lb., and the feed per 100 lb. of gain of 314 lb.

The inbreeding of this breed of hog, which is about 25 per cent, makes them more homozygous than many of the older breeds of hog, and this greater homozygosity is expressed in uniform crossbreds when this breed is crossed with other breeds. The carcasses of hogs of this breed, or of crossbreds when this breed is used in crossing, are more desirable than carcasses from hogs of lard breeds because of a greater proportion of lean in the carcass, longer and better muscled loins, and longer, leaner bacons.

SHEEP

Two breeds of sheep, the Columbia (Fig. 143) and the Targhee, were developed by the U.S. Sheep Experiment Station, Dubois, Idaho. Both breeds resulted from crossing the Lincoln × Rambouillet breeds and inbreeding from the crossbred population. The Targhee has an additional backcross of Ram-

Fig. 143. A Columbia ewe. Note the freedom from face covering and body folds and the presence of desirable mutton type possessed by this breed. *(Courtesy Oregon State College.)*

bouillet breeding and, as a breed today, it shows more fineness of wool and less mutton characteristics than the Columbia.

Inbreeding has not been intense in the development of either breed but selection has been rigorous. The traits concerned with performance of range sheep, such as fertility, growth rate, type and condition of fat lambs, open faces, freedom from body and neck folds, wool yield, and quality, have been considered in selections. The over-all merit of the sheep, as measured by an index which combines the various traits into one figure on the basis of economic importance and heritability of each trait, has been the basis for selection in both breeds in recent years. Both breeds have become uniform, and they are finding greater use on the range for the commercial production of fat and feeder lambs. When ewes of these breeds are mated to rams of mutton breeds, such as Hampshires and Suffolks, they produce very good lambs.

The average weaning weight of Columbia lambs at the station at Dubois for the period 1948 to 1952 inclusive was 77 lb. The breed is practically free from body folds and face covering and has only minor neck folds. Lambs generally score high for mutton conformation and condition, some being fat enough for slaughter and most of the others being superior feeder lambs. The percentage of lambs weaned of the ewes bred is 90 to 95, and the pounds of lamb produced per ewe bred is about 65 lb. per ewe per year. It should be remembered that this breed has been developed under strictly range conditions and that the figures presented are those recorded under range conditions. More feed would have resulted in increased lamb production, but this was not considered because the objective was to develop a breed which would perform well under range conditions.

The average weaning weight of Targhee lambs for the period 1945 to 1949 inclusive was 74 lb. The percentage of lambs weaned of the ewes bred was 84, and the pounds of lamb per ewe bred was 62 lb. per ewe per year. The lambs at weaning showed a lower score for mutton conformation and condition, but they were superior in wool traits to the Columbias. Both breeds are white face.

CATTLE

The Santa Gertrudis breed of cattle was developed at the King Ranch in Texas by mating Shorthorn cows to Brahman bulls of several breeds, including Nellore, Krishna Valley, Guzerat, and Ghur. About 50 Brahmans and Brahman-cross bulls were used on 2,500 Shorthorn cows to produce the crossbred cattle which were intermated and backcrossed. Red segregates were selected for breeding. One very prepotent bull, Monkey, was produced and used in a linebreeding program in which he was mated to his daughters and granddaughters. His outstanding bull descendants, Santa Gertrudis, Tipo, and Cotton were used heavily to concentrate the breeding of Monkey. The breed today is considered to be about three-eighths Brahman and five-eighths Shorthorn. These animals are dark red in color, possess the heat and tick resistance of the Brahman, and are large, productive range cattle. In areas where heat and external parasites such as flies, ticks, and mosquitos are a problem, these cattle are better adapted than cattle of the English breeds.

This is an example of a breed that was developed by combining good qualities of two breeds, which are also of different species, for the purpose of obtaining cattle which could adapt to a particular set of conditions because they were bred and selected under those same conditions. Production under range conditions was considered in the selection program. Inbreeding, which was practiced by linebreeding to Monkey, has created a greater degree of homozygosity in this breed than exists in some of the older breeds of cattle.

The Beefmaster breed of cattle (Fig. 144) was developed by the Lasater

Fig. 144. Beefmaster cow and calf. Calves of this size at weaning, produced under range conditions, contribute to success in commercial beef production. (*Courtesy Tom Lasater, Matheson, Colorado.*)

Ranch by combining the Brahman, Shorthorn, and Hereford. The method used in breeding and selecting to develop this breed differs from that used in ~'... breeds and is one that is based on sound genetic and practical production concepts; therefore, some details of methods used will be presented here.

...he selection now in use with the Beefmaster herd at the Lasater Ranch is one which could be used by any commercial breeder and one which would go a long way toward beef cattle improvement. The Hereford cattle used in one of the crosses that went into the Beefmaster breed had been selected for cow productivity for many years. These Herefords were crossed with Brahmans, which also had undergone several years of rigorous selection. Shorthorn bulls were also crossed with these Brahman cows and again rigorous selection was practiced. These two crossbred groups, the Hereford $\times$ Brahman and the Shorthorn $\times$ Brahman, were then interbred. The first real factor in the success of the Beefmaster breed was the use of breeding material that had already undergone improvement as a result of selection.

Selection in the Beefmaster cattle continues to be entirely for production traits, with color and such superficial traits completely ignored. The six production traits considered are: (1) disposition, (2) fertility, (3) weight for age, (4) conformation, (5) thriftiness, and (6) milk production.

The animals are run on dry range and receive no feed except for an allowance of 2 lb. of alfalfa pellets per animal per day during a winter period of 100 days and a more liberal feeding of bull calves during the first winter. The males and females are first bred as yearlings, and breeding is done in multiple-sire groups so that a slow bull or one that is low in fertility will leave few or no calves in the herd.

The selection of both the males and the females is done each year and is based entirely on performance. Because of the yearly selection, an animal repeatedly risks elimination, which ensures that only those which consistently produce at a high rate will remain in the herd to propagate the next generation. No special treatment is given an animal, so that it is up to the animal to withstand the rigors of the range at all times and thus prove himself. Bull calves are culled to only the upper 30 per cent by weaning time, the remaining 70 per cent being made into steers. At weaning time a few more are made into steers so that about one-fourth of the bull calves are kept beyond weaning age as bulls. These bulls will be selected again in July, at which time only about one-third of the remaining bulls will be kept. Selections at and before weaning are largely on the basis of size and condition, characteristics which reflect milking ability of their dams. The lower 30 per cent of the heifers are culled and removed by the time they are weaned. Some of those that do not grow out well may be removed from the heifer group at breeding time.

The breeding season is 65 days in length with a ratio of 1 young bull run with each ten heifer yearlings and one older bull with 20 cows. Cows are bred separately from the yearlings, and all breeding is done in multiple-sire pastures. When the calves arrive, the cow herd is culled. As soon as an 80 per cent living calf crop is on the ground, this group of cows and calves are kept, while those cows in the 20 per cent group which have lost a calf, do not settle, or calve later are put into the discard group, and they and their calves go to market. This selection procedure applies to the two-year-old heifers as well as the older cows. Some more of the cows will be culled later on the basis of poor calf performance so that eventually only the upper 75 per cent of the original cow herd will be kept. The numbers are held constant by substituting heifers into the herd. Thus, if a breeder had started with a cow herd of 100 bred to calve, this number would have been reduced to 75 by the following winter. Since only 80 per cent of the cows and calves would be retained to weaning, there should be 40 heifers from which to select replacements. Thirty per cent of these heifers, or 12, would be culled by weaning, leaving only 28. This would leave three more to be eliminated by breeding time so that the cow herd would be maintained at 100 animals.

This selection program is one of the most rigorous in existence because selection is made without giving any animal the advantage of special consideration, extra feed, etc. The results of the selection which has been practiced in this Beefmaster herd is reflected in the high cow productivity. At weaning time the 1957 heifer calves averaged 553 lb. and the bull calves averaged 606 lb. The range was very dry because only 7 in. of moisture had been recorded in that area during the 18-month period prior to weaning of the calves. Weaning weights of the 1952 calves were considerably higher, as shown by average weaning weights of heifers of 589 lb. and of bulls of 672 lb. from mature cows and weaning weights of heifers of 497 lb. and of bulls of 614 lb. from two-year-old cows.

It appears that several practices in operation at the Lasater Ranch would be sound for use by many commercial and purebred cattlemen. The limiting of the breeding season to 65 days (or three heat cycles) gives a uniform calf crop and helps to eliminate late calving and low fertility. Mr. Lasater states that only during the first year or two of this procedure is it necessary to eliminate several animals. Soon the herd has very few animals which will be eliminated by a short breeding season. This indicates that late breeders and those of lower fertility are problem animals that should be culled. The keeping of a certain percentage of the young animals on the basis of growth is sound. Also, keeping a percentage of the cows on the basis of production of calves is sound. There is no place for "pets" being kept because of some particular liking for the animal. In commercial operations the use of multiple-sire matings acts as a natural selection tool in reducing the effects of bulls of low fertility because such bulls will leave few or no offspring in the herd.

In summary, one should not consider a group of crossbred animals as a new breed. They can be identified as a new breed only after they have been bred and selected for specific objectives as a closed herd for a sufficient time to give genetic uniformity. At the same time, no stigma should be attached to a breed which has arisen from a crossbred foundation. The only way that new gene combinations can be made is through crossing of existing material. The only methods for fixing the desired traits in a breed are through selection and closed-herd breeding. Thus, crossbreeding allows a greater assortment of genes in the herd base. Selection is used to sort these genes with the hopes of retaining those which contribute most to the objective in mind. Inbreeding produces greater homozygosity and this will lead to greater prepotency of the breed.

In the event that a breeder should decide to develop a breed of farm animals for some specific area, set of conditions, or objective, a sound selection program based on performance should be adopted. Only when large numbers can be handled and only when one can be ruthless in his selections will this type of endeavor be successful.

EXERCISES

1. Upon what two basic genetic principles have most of our breeds of livestock been formed? These principles have been used but may not have been understood by those who used them.

2. Does a crossbred population constitute a new breed? Explain.

3. What is the basis for calling a population of animals a breed?

REFERENCES

Adams, A. E. 1946. Variations in the potency of thyrotropic hormone of the pituitary in animals. Quart. Rev. Biol. 21:1–32.

Anderson, David E., Doyle Chambers, and Jay L. Lush. Studies on bovine ocular squamous carcinoma (cancer eye). III. Inheritance of eyelid pigmentation. J. Animal Sci. 16:1007.

Anderson, D. E., J. L. Lush, and D. Chambers. 1957. Studies on bovine ocular squamous carcinoma (cancer eye). II. Relationship between eyelid pigmentation and occurrence of cancer eye lesions. J. Animal Sci. 16:739.

Anderson, W. A., and C. L. Davis. 1950. Congenital cerebellar hypoplasia in a Holstein-Friesian calf. A.V.M.A. 117:460–461.

Annett, H. E. 1938. A new ear defect in pigs. J. Hered. 21:469–470.

———. 1939. Note on a new recessive lethal in cattle. Genetics 37:301–302.

Asdell, S. A., Ralph Bogart, and G. Sperling. 1941. The influence of age and rate of breeding upon the ability of the female rat to reproduce and raise young. New York Cornell Memoir, 238.

Atkeson, F. W., F. Eldridge, and H. L. Ibsen. 1943. Bowed pasterns in Jersey cattle. J. Hered. 34:25–26.

———. 1944. Prevalence of "wrytail" in cattle. J. Hered. 35:11–14.

———. 1944. Inheritance of an epileptic type character in Brown Swiss cattle. J. Hered. 35:45–48.

Baker, Bryan, Jr., Richard Hollandbeck, H. W. Norton, and A. V. Nalbandov. 1956. Growth hormone content of swine pituitaries in relation to growth rate and age. J. Animal Sci. 15:415–416.

Baker, J. P., R. W. Colby, and C. M. Lyman. 1951. The relationship of feed efficiency to digestion rates of beef cattle. J. Animal Sci. 10:726–732.

Baker, L. N., C. T. Blunn, and M. Plum. 1951. "Dwarfism" in Aberdeen-Angus cattle. J. Hered. 42:141–143.

Baker, L. N., L. C. Ulberg, R. H. Grummer, and L. E. Casida. 1954. Inhibition of heat by progesterone and its effect on subsequent fertility in gilts. J. Animal Sci. 13:656–657.

Baker, M. R. and A. C. Andrews. 1944. The Melanins. I. Studies of the hair pigments of the guinea pig. Genetics 29:104–112.

Bates, R. W., T. Laanes, E. C. MacDowell, and O. Riddle. 1942. Growth in silver dwarf mice, with and without injections of anterior pituitary extracts. Endocrinology. 31:53–58.

Beadle, G. W., and E. G. Tatem. 1945. Biochemical genetics. Chem. Rev. 37:15–96.

409

Beatty, R. A., and M. Fishberg. 1949. Spontaneous and induced triploidy in pre-implantation mouse eggs. Nature. N2. 163:807–808.

———. 1951. Cell number in haploid, diploid and polyploid mouse embryos. J. Exptl. Biol., 28:541–552.

Becker, D. E., E. P. Margerum, C. P. Stroble, Carl Gilbert, and Irene Payne. 1952. Estimation of body fat from measurement *in vive* of body water by use of antipyrine. West. Sec., Proc. Am. Soc. Animal Production. 3:(I)1–6.

Becker, R. B., and P. T. Dix Arnold. 1949. "Bulldog head" cattle. J. Hered. 40:282–286.

Beeson, W. M., F. N. Andrews, T. W. Perry, and Martin Stob. 1955. The effect of orally administered stilbestrol and testosterone on growth and carcass composition of swine. J. Animal Sci. 14:479–480.

Beeson, W. M., C. E. Terrill, and D. W. Bollin. 1944. Some factors affecting the blood phosphorus level of range ewes. J. Animal Sci. 3:175–182.

Bell, A. E. 1953. Recurrent selection compared with hybridization and closed population methods. *Ibid*. 83–93.

———. 1953. A biological evaluation with Drosophila Melanogaster of four methods of selection for the improvement of quantitative characteristics. Proc. 9th Internat. Genet. Cong. 9:851–853.

Bell, A. E., C. H. Moore, B. B. Bohren, and D. C. Warren. 1952. Systems of breeding designed to utilize heterosis in the domestic fowl. Poultry Sci. 31:11–22.

Bell, A. E., C. H. Moore, and D. C. Warren. 1953. Effects of selection on the phenotype and combining ability of inbred lines. Proc. Nat. Poultry Breeders' Roundtable. 67–82.

Berge, S. 1942. Fertility and "pregnancy percentage." (Abs.) J. Dairy Sci. 29:A143–A144.

Berger, J., and J. R. M. Innes. 1948. "Bull-dog" calves (chondrodystrophy, achondro-plasia). Vet. Record 60:57–58.

Bernard, C. S., A. B. Chapman, and R. H. Grummer. 1954. Selection of pigs under farm conditions: kind and amount practiced and a recommended selection index. J. Animal Sci. 13(2):389–404.

Birch, R. R. 1923. Natural and artificial immunity of young pigs to hog cholera. Cornell Vet. 13:159–169.

Black, W. H., and Bradford Knapp, Jr. 1936. A method of measuring performance in beef cattle. Proc. Am. Soc. Animal Production. 29:72–77.

Blackwell, R. L., David E. Anderson and J. H. Knox. 1956. Age incidence and herita-bility of cancer eye in Hereford cattle. J. Animal Sci. 15(4):943–951.

Blunn, C. T. 1945. Yearly differences in growth of Navajo and crossbred ewe lambs. J. Animal Sci. 4(3):306–310.

Blunn, C. T., Guy N. Baker, and L. E. Hanson. 1953. Heritability of gain in different growth periods in swine. J. Animal Sci. 12(1):39–50.

Blunn, C. T., and M. L. Baker. 1949. Heritability of gain in different growth periods in swine. J. Animal Sci. 12:39–50.

Blunn, C. T., and P. W. Gregory. 1935. The embryological basis of size inheritance in the chicken. J. Exptl. Zool. 70(3):397–414.

Blunn, C. T., and E. H. Hughes. 1938. Hydrocephalus in swine. A new lethal defect. J. Hered. 29:203–208.

Blunn, C. T., Everett J. Warwick, and James R. Wiley. 1954. Interrelationships of swine weights at three ages. J. Animal Sci. 13, No. 2:383–388.

Bogart, Ralph. 1953. Rabbit Production. *Ibid*. 745.

Bogart, Ralph, and R. L. Blackwell. 1950. More beef with less feed. Ore. Agr. Expt. Sta. Bull. 488.

Bogart, Ralph, and A. J. Dyer. 1942. The inheritance of dwarfism in sheep. (Abs.) J. Animal Sci. 1:87.

Bogart, Ralph, and H. L. Ibsen. 1937. The relation of hair and skin pigmentation to color inheritance in cattle with some notes on guinea pig hair pigmentation. Genetics 35:31–59.

Bogart, Ralph, and M. E. Muhrer. 1942. The inheritance of a hemophilia-like condition in swine. J. Hered. 33:59–64.

Bonnier, Gert, and A. Hansson. 1948. Identical twin genetics in cattle. (A) The occurrence of identical twins in cattle and their use in research work. J. Hered. 2:(part 1) 1–27.

Bonnier, Gert, A. Hansson, and H. Skjervold. 1948. Studies on monozygous cattle twins. IX. The interplay of heredity and environment on growth and yield. Acta Agr. Suecana. 3:1–57.

Bonsma, J. C. 1944. Hereditary heartwater-resistant character in cattle. Farming in S. Africa. No. 13.

Botkin, M. P., and J. A. Whatley, Jr. 1953. Repeatability of production in range beef cows. J. Animal Sci. 12(3):552–560.

Boulware, R. F. 1954. Efficiency and effectiveness of selection in crossbred swine. J. Animal Sci. 13(1):160–170.

Brandt, G. W. 1941. Achondroplasia in calves. J. Hered. 32:183–186.

Bridges, C. B. 1932. The genetics of sex in Drosophila. Chapter III. Sex and internal secretions. Baltimore: Williams and Wilkens.

Brody, Samuel. 1921. The relation between the age of an animal and the rapidity of its growth. Am. Soc. Animal Production. 33–35.

———. 1926. Time relations of growth. I. Genetic growth constants of animals. J. Gen. Physiol. 8:233–251.

———. 1927. Growth and development. III. Growth rates, their evaluation and significance. Univ. Mo. Agr. Exp. Sta. Res. Bull. 97.

———. 1928. Growth and development. XII. Additional illustrations of the influence of food supply on the velocity constant of growth and on the shape of the growth curve. Univ. Mo. Agr. Exp. Sta. Res. Bull. 116.

———. 1945. Bioenergetics and growth. New York: Reinhold Pub. Corp.

———. 1946. Growth and aging problems in agriculture. Science. 104:307–312.

Brown, Lans O., R. M. Durham, E. Cobb, and J. H. Knox. 1954. An analysis of the components of variance in calving intervals in a range herd of beef cattle. J. Animal Sci. 13:511–516.

Brugman, H. H., and R. Martin. 1954. A portable scale for cattle research. J. Animal Sci. 13:74–80.

Burgess, J. B., Nellie L. Landblom, and H. H. Stonaker. 1954. Weaning weights of Hereford calves as affected by inbreeding, sex and age. J. Animal Sci. 13(4):843–851.

Burks, Barbara. 1928. The 27th Yearbook of the National Society for the Study of Education. Part I. 219. Bloomington, Ill.: Public School Publishing Company.

Burris, Martin J., and Cecil T. Blunn. 1952. Some factors affecting gestation length and birth weight of beef cattle. J. Animal Sci. 11:34–41.

Burris, Martin J., Ralph Bogart, A. W. Oliver, Andrea Overman Mackey, and J. E. Oldfield. 1954. Rate and efficiency of gains in beef cattle. I. The response to injected testosterone. Ore. Agri. Expt. Sta. Tech. Bull. 31.

Burris, Martin J., Hugo Krueger, and Ralph Bogart. 1954. Methyl testosterone in beef cattle. (abs) Am. J. Physiol. 179(3):633.

Bywaters, J. H., and O. S. Willham. 1935. A method of comparing growthiness of pigs weighed at different ages and subjected to different treatments. Proc. Am. Soc. Animal Production. 28:116–119.

Cadmus, W. G. 1949. Sheep records for greater profits. Ore. Agr. Expt. Sta. Cir. 182.

Cameron, H. S., P. W. Gregory, and E. H. Hughes. 1943. Inherited resistance to brucellosis in inbred Berkshire swine. J. Vet. Res. 4:387–389.

Carmichael, J. 1933. "Bull-dog" calf in African cattle. Nature. 131:878.

Carmon, J. L., H. A. Stewart, C. C. Cockerham, and R. E. Comstock. 1956. Prediction equations for rotational crossbreeding. J. Animal Sci. 15:930–936.

Carpenter, K. J. 1953. The concept of an "appetite quotient" for the interpretation of ad libitum feeding experiments. J. Nutrition. 51:435–440.

Carroll, F. D., P. W. Gregory, and W. C. Rollins. 1951. Thyrotropic-hormone deficiency in homozygous dwarf beef cattle. J. Animal Sci. 10:916–921.

———. 1951. Endocrine analysis of homozygous dwarf beef cattle. (Abs.) *Ibid.* 10:1023.

Carson, J. R. 1951. Exposure to disease agents of strains of chickens differing in resistance to leucosis. Poult. Sci. 30:213–230.

Carter, A. 1951. Hancock paper presented at 7th N. Z. Science Congress. Trans. and Proc. Roy. Soc. New Zealand.

Carter, W. H., and W. L. Henning. 1951. The effect of heterosis on birth weight of lambs. (Abs.) J. Animal Sci. 10:1023.

Casida, L. E. and R. O. Murphree. 1942. Fertility and sex ratios in the rabbit from semen treated *in vitro* with lactic acid and sodium bicarbonate. J. of Hered. 33:434–438.

Castle, W. E. 1924. The genetics of multi-nippled sheep. J. Hered. 15:75–85.

———. 1930. The genetics of the domestic rabbit. Cambridge: Harvard Univ. Press.

———. 1933. The linkage relations of yellow fat in rabbits. Nat. Acad. Sci. U.S. 19:947–951.

———. 1934. Yellow fat in sheep. J. Hered. 25:246.

———. 1936. Size inheritance in mice. Am. Naturalist. 70.

———. 1940. Mammalian genetics. Ed. I. Cambridge, Mass.: Harvard Univ.

Castle, W. E., W. H. Gates, and S. C. Reed. 1936. Studies of a size cross in mice. Genetics. 21:66–78.

Castle, W. E., and P. W. Gregory. 1931. Further studies on the embryological basis of size inheritance in the rabbit. J. Exptl. Zool. 59:No. 2.

Chambers, C., J. A. Whatley, and D. Stephens. 1951. Growth of Hereford heifers of different types. Okla. Agr. Expt. Sta. Misc. Publ. MP–22:33–35.

Chapman, A. B., and L. E. Casida. 1937. Analysis of variation in the sexual cycle and some of its component phases with special reference to cattle. J. Agr. Research. 54:417–435.

Christensen, E., and N. O. Christensen. 1952. Congenital hereditary paralysis in calves. A clinical and pathological anatomical investigation. (English Summ.) Norsk. Vet. Tid. 4:861–878.

Clark, T. B., T. D. Runnels, and E. A. Livesay. 1944. Crossbreeding turkeys. 1. Effect on fertility, hatchability and viability of poults. U.S. Egg and Poultry Mag. 50:418–420, 430–431.

Clegg, M. T., and H. H. Cole. 1954. The action of stilbestrol on the growth response in ruminants. J. Animal Sci. 13:108–130.

Colby, R. W., J. H. Ware, J. P. Baker, and C. M. Lyman. 1950. The relationship of various blood constituents to rate of gain in beef cattle (abs.). J. Animal Sci. 9:652.

Cole, C. L. 1942. Hydrocephalus, a lethal in cattle. J. Agr. Research. 65:483–491.

Cole, L. J., E. E. VanLone, and Ivar Johansson. 1934. Albinotic dilution of color in Cattle. J. Hered. 25:145–156.

Comstock, R. E., H. J. Robinson, and P. H. Harvey. 1949. A breeding procedure designed to make maximum use of both general and specific combining ability. Agron. J. 41:360–367.

Craft, W. A., and H. W. Orr. 1924. Thyroid influence in cattle. J. Hered. 15:255–256.

———. 1927. Night blindness in cattle. *Ibid.* 18:215–216.

Craft, W. A., and O. S. Willham. 1936. The role of nutrition in genetic research. Digestion trials with inbred and outbred pigs. Proc. Am. Soc. Animal Production. 29th Annual Meeting. 260–263.

————. 1953. Results of swine breeding research. U.S.D.A. Cir. 916.

Craig, J. V., H. W. Norton, and S. W. Terrill. 1956. A genetic study of weight at five ages in Hampshire swine. J. Animal Sci. 15(1):242–256.

Cranek, L. J., and N. P. Ralston. 1953. Paralyzed hindquarters, a hereditary defect in American Red Danish cattle. (Abs.) J. Animal Sci. 12:892–893.

Crenshaw, W. W., and C. W. Turner. 1954. Estimating the thyrotropin and thyroxine secretion rates of cattle. J. Animal Sci. 13:1017.

Dahmen, J. J., and Ralph Bogart. 1952. Some factors affecting rate and economy of gains in beef cattle. Ore. Agr. Expt. Sta. Tech. Bull. 26.

Dale, D. G., and J. E. Moxley. 1952. Prenatal tendon contracture in a herd of milking Shorthorns. Can. J. Comp. Med. 16:399–404.

Dawson, W. M., R. W. Phillips, and W. H. Black. 1947. Birth weight as a criterion of selection in beef cattle. J. Animal Sci. 6:247–257.

Dawson, W. M., E. H. Vernon, A. H. Baker, and E. J. Warwick. 1954. Selection for increased weights of six-month-old beef calves in a Brahman-Angus population. J. Animal Sci. 13:557–562.

Dawson, W. M., T. S. Yao, and A. C. Cook. 1952. Heritability of growth, beef characters, and body measurements in milking Shorthorn steers. (Abst.) Genetics. 37:575–576.

de Aberle, S. B. 1925. Hereditary anemia in mice and its relation to dominant spotting. Am. Naturalist. 59:327–335.

de Baca, R. C. 1954. Genetic and environmental differences in important economic traits of crossbred sheep in spring lamb production. M.S. Thesis. Ore. State College. 89 pp.

de Baca, R. C., A. C. Warnick, G. H. Hitchcock, and R. Bogart. 1954. Factors associated with the onset of estrus in ewes. Ore. Agr. Expt. Sta. Tech. Bull. 29.

deBeer, G. R., and H. Gruneberg. 1940. A note on pituitary dwarfism in the mouse. Genetics. 39:297–300.

DePape, J. G., and J. A. Whatley, Jr. 1956. Live hog probes at various sites, weights, and ages as indicators of carcass merit. J. Animal Sci. 15:1029–1035.

Detlefson, J. A., and W. W. Yapp. 1920. The inheritance of congenital cataract in cattle. Am. Naturalist. 54:277–280.

Dickerson, G. E. 1947. Composition of hog carcasses as influenced by heritable differences in rate and economy of gains. Iowa Agr. Expt. Sta. Res. Bull. 354.

————. 1955. Genetic slippage in response to selection to multiple objectives. Cold Springs Harbor Symposium on Population. Genetics. 20:213–224.

Dickerson, G. E., C. T. Blunn, A. B. Chapman, R. M. Knottman, J. L. Krider, E. J. Warwick, and J. A. Whatley, Jr. 1954. Evaluation of selection in developing inbred lines of swine. Univ. Mo. Agr. Exp. Sta. Research Bull. 551.

Dickerson, G. E., and J. W. Gowen. 1947. Hereditary obesity and efficient food utilization in mice. Science. 105:496–498.

Dickerson, G. E., and J. C. Grimes. 1947. Effectiveness of selection for efficiency of gain in Duroc swine. J. Animal Sci. 6:265–287.

Donald, H. P., D. W. Deas, and A. L. Wilson. 1952. Genetical analysis of the incidence of Dropsical calves in herds of Ayrshire cattle. Brit. Vet. J. 108:227–245.

Donald, H. P., and J. L. Hancock. 1953. Evidence of gene-controlled sterility in bulls. J. Agr. Sci. 43:178–181.

Donald, H. P., and J. W. McLean. 1935. The growth-rate of lambs in Canterbury. New Zealand J. of Sci. Technol. 17:497–519.

Doolittle, M. H. 1878. United States Coast and Geodetic Survey. Report 115.

Downs, W. H., Jr. 1928. An American "Dexter monster." Anat. Record. 37:365–372.

Dunbar, R. S., Jr., and C. R. Henderson. 1950. Heritability of fertility in dairy cattle. J. Dairy Sci. 33:377.

Durham, R. M., and J. H. Knox. 1953. Correlations between grades and gains of Hereford cattle at different stages of growth and between grades at different times. J. Animal Sci. 12:771–774.

Dwyer, P. S. 1941. The solution of simultaneous equations. Psychometrica. 6:101–129.

Eaton, O. N. 1932. A quarter century of inbreeding in guinea pigs. J. Exptl. Zool. 63:261–290.

———. 1937. A summary of lethal characters in animals and man. J. Hered. 28:320–326.

Eldridge, F. E., and F. W. Atkeson. 1953. Occurrence of hereditary edema in Ayrshires. (Abs.) J. Dairy Sci. 36:598, Pt. 1.

Eldridge, F. E., F. W. Atkeson, and H. L. Ibsen. 1949. Inheritance of a karakul-type curliness in the hair of Ayrshire cattle. J. Hered. 40:205–214.

Eldridge, F. E., W. H. Smith, and W. M. McLeod. 1951. Syndactylism in Holstein-Friesian cattle. J. Hered. 42:241–250.

Elijah, H. D., and C. W. Turner. 1942. The weight and thyrotropic content of the anterior pituitary of swine. Mo. Agr. Expt. Sta. Bull. 357.

Ellis, N. R., W. A. Craft, and J. H. Zeller. 1936. A preliminary study of variations in free-choice intake of the components of a standard ration and breeding as possible factors in the occurrence of lameness in pigs. Proc. Am. Soc. Animal Production. 29:77–81.

Ellis, N. R., and L. L. Madsen. 1941. The relation of diet of swine to development of locomotor incoordination resulting from nerve degeneration. J. Agr. Research. 62:303–316.

Emik, L. O., and C. E. Terrill. 1949. Systematic procedures for calculation of inbreeding coefficients. J. Hered. 40:51–55.

———. 1949. The semen production of rams under range conditions. J. Animal Sci. 8:605.

England, David C., and L. M. Winters. 1953. The effects of genetic diversity and performance of inbred lines *per se* on hybrid vigor in swine. J. Animal Sci. Vol. 12 (No. 4):836–847.

Engle, E. T., R. C. Crafts, and C. E. Zeithaml. 1937. First estrus in rats in relation to age, weight, and length. Proc. Soc. Explt. Biol. and Med. 37:427–432.

Eriksson, I. K. 1946. Hereditary hypoplasia in cattle. J. Hered. 37:38.

Eriksson, Karl. 1943. Hereditary forms of sterility in cattle. Biological and genetical investigations. Lund: Häkan Ohlssons Boktryckeri. 155 pp.

Falconer, D. S., and M. Latyszewski. 1952. The environment in relation to selection for size in mice. Genetics. 51:67–80.

Fincher, M. G., and W. L. Williams. 1926. Arrested development of the Muellerian ducts associated with inbreeding. Cornell Vet. 16:1–19.

Fischberg, M., and R. A. Beatty. 1951. Spontaneous heteroploidy in mouse embryos to mid-term. J. Exptl. Zool. 118:321–325.

———. 1952. Heteroploidy in mammals. II. Induction of triploidy in pre-implantation mouse eggs. J. Genetics. 50:455–470.

Flower, A. E., F. S. Willson, and J. Urick. 1953. Studies on gains of limited-fed steer calves and their subsequent range and full-fed gains. Western Sec., Am. Soc. Animal Production. No. XV:1–4.

Foote, W. C., D. P. Waldorf, A. B. Chapman, H. L. Self, R. H. Grummer, and L. E. Casida. 1956. Age at puberty of gilts produced by different systems of mating. J. Animal Sci. 15:959–969.

Foster, D. E., M. W. Galgan, and M. E. Ensminger. 1953. Pelleted vs. non-pelleted rations for beef cattle. Wash. Agr. Expt. Sta. Cir. 232.

Fordyce, Ely, F. E. Hull, and H. B. Morrison. 1939. Agnathia, a new bovine lethal. J. Hered. 30:105–108.

Fox, D. L. 1936. Structural and chemical aspects of animal coloration. Am. Naturalist. 70:477–493.

Frank, E. R. 1943. Neoplasms of the bovine eye. J. Am. Vet. Med. Assoc. 102:200–203.

Fransen, J. M., and F. N. Andrews. 1954. The physiology of dwarfism in beef cattle. J. Animal Sci. 18:1020.

Freudenberger, C. B. 1932. A comparison of the Wistar albino and the Long-Evans hybrid strain of the Norway rat. Am. J. Anat. 50:293–349.

Gaines, W. L., and J. R. Palfrey. 1931. Length of calving interval and average milk yield. J. Dairy Sci. 14:294–306.

Galgan, M. W., M. E. Ensminger, E. M. Hanks, and F. K. Bracken. 1953. Raising calves from birth on synthetic and reconstituted milk. Wash. Agr. Expt. Sta. Cir 234.

Gawienowski, A., D. T. Mayer, and J. F. Lasley. 1955. The serum protein-bond iodine of swine as a measure of growth potentialities. J. Animal Sci. 14:3–6.

Gerlaugh, Paul, and L. E. Kunkle. 1950. Feedlot performance of steers produced by scientific breeding procedures compared with steers from recognized commercial sources. (Abs.) J. Animal Sci. 9:637.

Giannotti, D. 1954. Cases of congenital hydrocephalus in calves. An. Breeding Abs. 22:915.

Gifford, W. 1930. The mode of inheritance of yearling butterfat production. Mo. Agr. Expt. Sta. Bul. 144.

———. 1949. Importance of high milk production in beef cows overestimated. J. Animal Sci. 8:605–606.

Gilman, J. P. W., and E. W. Stringam. 1953. Hereditary umbilical hernia in Holstein cattle. J. Hered. 44:113–116.

Gilmore, L. O. 1949. The inheritance of functional causes of reproductive inefficiency. A review. J. Dairy Sci. 32:71–91.

———. 1952. Dairy cattle breeding. New York: J. B. Lippincott Co.

Gluecksohn-Schoenheimer, S., R. Segal, and N. Fitch. 1950. Embryological tests of genetic male sterility in the house mouse. J. Exptl. Zool. 113:621–631.

Godglück, G. 1952. Partial congenital hydrocephalus in a calf (Encephalocysto-meniagocele of the bulbi olfactorii). Monatschefte für Veterinärmedizin 7:250–252.

Goldschmidt, R. 1942. Sex-determination in Melandrium and Lymantria. Science n.s. 95:120–121.

Gonzalez, B. M., and V. Villegas. 1928. "Bighead" of horses a heritable disease. J. Hered. 19:159–167.

Goodale, H. D. 1918. Internal factors influencing egg production in the Rhode Island Red breed of domestic fowl. Am. Naturalist. 52:65–94, 209–232, 301–321.

———. 1927. Selecting a herd sire. Mt. Hope Farm publication.

Gordon, Manuel J. 1957. Control of sex ratio in rabbits by electrophoresis of spermatozoa. P.N.A.S. 43; Ph.D. Thesis.

Gowen, J. W. 1936. Inheritance as it affects survival of rats fed a diet deficient in vitamin D. Genetics 21:1–23.

———. 1937. Contribution of genetics to understanding of animal disease. J. Hered. 28:233–240.

Graves, R. R. 1926. Transmitting ability of 23 Holstein-Friesian sires. U.S. Dept. Agr. Bull. 1372.

Greene, H. S. N. 1940. A dwarf mutation in the rabbit, constitutional influence on homozygous and heterozygous individuals. J. Exptl. Med. 71:839–856.

Greene, H. S. N., C. K. Hu, and W. H. Brown. 1934. A lethal dwarf mutation in the rabbit with stigmata of endocrine abnormality. Science 79:487–488.

Gregory, Keith E., Cecil T. Blunn, and Marvel L. Baker. 1950. A study of some of the factors influencing the birth and weaning weights of beef calves. J. Animal Sci. 9:338–346.

Gregory, K. E., and G. E. Dickerson. 1950. Influence of inbreeding and plane of nutrition on rate and economy of gain, digestion and carcass composition of pigs. (Abs.) J. Animal Sci. 9:637.

Gregory, P. W. 1954. An analysis of wry calves in California beef herds. (Abs.) J. Animal Sci. 13:957.

Gregory, P. W., and H. Goss. 1933. Glutathione concentration and hereditary body size. J. Exptl. Zool. 66:155–173.

Gregory, P. W., S. W. Mead and W. M. Regan. 1942. A new type of recessive achondroplasia in cattle. J. Hered. 33:317–322.

————. 1943. A congenital hereditary eye defect of cattle. *Ibid.* 34:125–128.

————. 1951. A genetic analysis of prolonged gestation in cattle. Portugaliae Acta. Biol. Exptl. Series A. R. B. Goldschmidt Volumen:861–882.

Gregory, P. W., S. W. Mead, W. M. Regan, and W. C. Rollins. 1951. Further studies concerning sex-limited genetic infertility in cattle. J. Dairy Sci. 34:1047–1055.

Gregory, P. W., W. M. Regan and S. W. Mead. 1945. Evidence of genes for female sterility in dairy cows. Genetics. 30:506–517.

————. 1945. Evidence of genes for female sterility in dairy cows. Genetics. 30:506–517.

Gregory, P. W., W. C. Rollins, and F. D. Carroll. 1952. Heterozygous expression of the dwarf gene in beef cattle. Southwestern Vet. 5:345–349.

Gregory, P. W., W. C. Rollins, P. S. Pattengale, and F. D. Carroll. 1951. A phenotypic expression of homozygous dwarfism in beef cattle. J. Animal Sci. 10:922–933.

Gregory, P. W., C. B. Roubicek, F. D. Carroll, P. O. Stratton, and N. W. Hilston. 1953. Inheritance of bovine dwarfism and the detection of heterozygotes. Hilgardia. 22:407–450.

Guilbert, H. R., G. H. Hart, K. A. Wagnon, and H. Goss. 1944. The importance of continuous growth in beef cattle. Calif. Agr. Expt. Sta. Bull. 688.

Guilbert, H. R., A. Wahid, K. A. Wagnon, and P. W. Gregory. 1948. Observations on pigmentation of eyelids of Hereford cattle in relation to occurrence of ocular epitheliomas. J. Animal Sci. 7:426–429.

Habel, R. E. 1948. On the inheritance of metatarsal inclination in Ayrshire cattle. Am. J. Vet. Research. 9:131–139.

Hadley, F. B. 1927. Inheritance of epithelial defects in cattle. Am. Soc. Animal Production. 41–43.

Hadley, F. B., and L. J. Cole. 1928. Inherited epithelial defects in cattle. Wisconsin Agri. Expt. Sta. Res. Bull. 86.

Hafez, E. S. E. 1951. The influence of environment and heredity on the breeding season of the ewe. Experientia VII:9, p. 353–354.

Haggqvist, G., and A. Bane. 1950. Studies in triploid rabbits produced by colchicine. Hereditas 36:329–334.

Hale, Fred. 1933. Pigs born without eye balls. J. Hered. 24:105–106.

Hall, H. W., H. C. Dickey and A. O. Shaw. 1948. Selecting a dairy bull. Maine Agri. Expt. Sta. Bul. 461.

Hallqvist, C. 1933. Ein Fall von Lethalfaktorin beim Schwein. Hereditas 18:219–224.

Hammond, John. 1914. On some factors controlling fertility in domestic animals. J. Agr. Sci. 6:263–277.

————. 1921. Further observations on the factors controlling fertility and foetal atrophy. J. Agr. Sci. 11:337–366.

———. 1935. The inheritance of productivity in farm animals. Empire J. Exptl. Agri. 3:1–12.

———. 1940. Farm animals. New York: Longmans, Green & Co. 199 pp.

Hancock, John. 1954. Studies in monozygotic cattle twins. New Zealand (Ruakura) Dept. Agr., An. Res. Div. (Collected Ed.) Pub. No. 63.

Hauser, E. R., G. E. Dickerson, and D. T. Mayer. 1952. Reproductive development and performance of inbred and crossbred boars. Mo. Agr. Expt. Sta. Res. Bull. 503.

Hayden, C. C. 1946. The use of unproved sires. Ohio Agri. Expt. Sta. Special Cir. 73.

Hays, F. A. 1936. Inheritance of sexual maturity in Rhode Island Reds. Proc. 6th World's Poultry Cong. (Leipzig) 6 parts. 2:34–38.

———. 1940. Inheritance of broodiness in Rhode Island Reds. Mass. Agr. Expt. Sta. Bull. 377.

———. 1950. Is fertility in domestic fowl regulated by inheritance? Poultry Sci. 29:171–175.

Hays, F. A., and Ruby Sanborn. 1924. The inheritance of fertility and hatchability in poultry. Mass. Agr. Expt. Sta. Tech. Bull. 6.

———. 1926. Annual persistency in relation to winter and annual egg production. Mass. Agr. Expt. Sta. Tech. Bull. 9.

———. 1932. Types of intensity in Rhode Island Reds. Mass. Agr. Expt. Sta. Bull. 286:1–11.

Hazel, L. N. 1943. The genetic basis of constructing selection indexes. Genetics 28:476–490.

Hazel, L. N., M. L. Baker, and C. F. Reinmiller. 1943. Genetic and environmental correlations between growth rates of pigs at different ages. J. Animal Sci. 2:118–128.

Hazel, L. N., and J. L. Lush. 1942. The efficiency of three methods of selection. J. Hered. 33:393–399.

Hazel, Lanoy N., and Clair E. Terrill. 1943. Heritability of yearling fleece and body traits of range Rambouillet ewes. (Abs.) J. Animal Sci. 2:358–359.

———. 1945. Effects of some environmental factors on weaning traits of range Rambouillet lambs. J. Animal Sci. 4:331–341.

———. 1945. Heritability of weaning weight and staple length in range Rambouillet lambs. *Ibid.* 4:347–358.

———. 1946. Heritability of type and condition in range Rambouillet lambs as evaluated by scoring. *Ibid.* 5:55–61.

———. 1946. Heritability of weaning traits in range Columbia, Corriedale and Targhee lambs. *Ibid.* 5:371–377.

Heape, W. 1899. Note on the fertility of different breeds of sheep, with remarks on the prevalence of abortion and barrenness therein. Proc. Roy. Soc. London. 65:99–111.

———. 1899. Abortion, barrenness and fertility in sheep. J. Roy. Agr. Soc. Engl. 10: Pt. 2:217–248.

Heizer, E. E. 1932. An inherited udder abnormality in cattle. J. Hered. 23:111–114.

Heizer, E. E., and M. C. Hervey. 1937. Impacted molars—a new lethal in cattle. J. Hered. 28:123–128.

Hess, C. W., and M. A. Jull. 1948. A study of the inheritance of feed utilization efficiency in the growing domestic fowl. Poultry Sci. 27:24–39.

Hetzer, H. O. 1937. The genetic basis for resistance and susceptibility to Salmonella aerotrycke in mice. Genetics. 22:264–283.

Hirsch, N. D. 1930. Twins: Heredity and environment. Cambridge: Harvard Univ. Press.

Hitchcock, Glen H., W. A. Sawyer, R. Bogart, and L. D. Calvin. 1955. Rate and efficiency of gains in beef cattle: III. Factors affecting weight and effectiveness of selection for gains in weight. Ore. Agr. Expt. Sta. Tech. Bull. 34.

Hogan, A. G. 1929. Retarded growth and mature size of beef steers. Mo. Agri. Expt. Sta. Res. Bull. 123.

Holzinger, J. H. 1935. The statistical evaluation of nature and nurture. J. Am. Sta. Assoc. 30:274–280.

Hooper, J. J. 1919. Inheritance of Jersey colors. J. Dairy Sci. 2:290–292.

Houck, J. W. 1930. Hydrocephalus in lower animals. Anat. Record 45:83–106.

Hughes, E. H. 1935. Polydactyly in swine. J. Hered. 26:415–418.

Hughes, E. H., and H. Hart. 1934. Defective skulls inherited in swine. J. Hered. 25:111–115.

Hull, F. H. 1945. Recurrent selection for specific combining ability in corn. J. Am. Soc. Agron. 37:134–145.

――――. 1946. Overdominance and corn breeding where hybrid seed is not feasible. J. Am. Soc. Agron. 38:1100–1103.

Hultz, F. S. 1927. Type in beef calves. Wyo. Agr. Exp. Sta. Bull. 153.

Hutt, F. B. 1933. Genetics of the fowl. II. A four-gene autosomal linkage group. Genetics. 18:82–94.

――――. 1934. A hereditary lethal muscle contracture in cattle. J. Hered. 25:41–46.

――――. 1934. Inherited lethal characters in domestic animals. Cornell Vet. 24:1–25.

Hutt, F. B., and J. N. Frost. 1948. Hereditary epithelial defects in Ayrshire cattle. J. of Hered. 39:131–137. No. 5.

Hutt, F. B., and L. Z. Saunders. 1953. Viable genetic hypotrichosis in Guernsey cattle. J. Hered. 44:97–103.

Hutton, R. E., J. R. Quesenberry, J. H. Zeller, and R. L. Davis. 1948. The Hamprace hog. Mont. Agr. Expt. Sta. Bull. 454.

Ibsen, H. L., and R. F. Cox. 1940. Inheritance of horns and scurs in sheep. J. Hered. 31(7):327–336.

Ibsen, H. L. and E. Steigleder. 1917. Evidence for the death *in utero* of homozygous yellow mouse. Am. Naturalist. 51:740–752.

――――. 1933. Cattle inheritance. I. Color. Genetics. 18:441–480.

――――. 1951. Principles of genetics. St. Louis, Mo.: John S. Swift Co., Inc.

Innes, J. R. M., and W. N. MacNaughton. 1950. Inherited cortical cerebellar atrophy in Corriedale lambs in Canada identical with "daft lamb" disease in Britain. Cornell Vet. 40:127–135.

Irwin, M. R. 1929. The inheritance of resistance to Danysz bacillus in the rat. Genetics. 14:337–365.

Ishihara, Marie. 1950. Studies on the undesirable recessive genes in Japanese breed of cattle. Chugoku-Shikoku (Japan) Expt. Sta. Res. Bull. 58.

Ittner, N. R., T. E. Bond, and C. F. Kelly. 1954. Increasing summer gains of livestock with cool water, concentrates, roughage, wire corrals, and adequate shades. J. Animal Sci. 13:867–877.

Ittner, N. R., C. F. Kelly, and H. R. Guilbert. 1951. Water consumption of Hereford and Brahman cattle and the effect of cooled drinking water in a hot climate. J. Animal Sci. 10:742–751.

Jerome, F. N., C. R. Hendeson, and S. C. King. 1956. Heritability, gene interactions and correlations associated with certain traits in the domestic animal fowl. Poultry Sci. 35:995–1013.

Johansson, Ivar. 1931. The sex ratio and multiple births in cattle. Zeit. f. Zucht. Reihe. B24:183–268.

Johansson, Ivar, and O. Venge. 1951. Studies on the value of various morphological characters for the diagnosis of monozygosity of cattle twins. Zeit f. Tierzucht. u. Zucht. 59:(4) 389–424.

———. 1953. A new type of achondroplasia in cattle. J. Hered. 39:75–87.

Johnson, D. W., and L. S. Palmer. 1939. Individual and breed variations in pigs on rations devoid of vitamin D. J. Agr. Research. 58:929–939.

Johnson, L. E. 1940. "Streamlined" pigs. J. Hered. 31(5):239–242.

———. 1945. Fused teats. A hereditary defect in beef cattle. J. Hered. 36:317–320.

Johnson, L. E., and Ted Aegerter. 1952. Are cattlemen interested in production tested sires? Shorthorn World. 37:16.

Johnson, L. E., G. S. Harshfield, and W. McCone. 1950. Dwarfism, an hereditary defect in beef cattle. J. Hered. 41:177–181.

Johnson, T. H., and M. J. Bancroft. 1918. A tick-resistant condition in cattle. Proc. Roy. Soc. Queensland. 30:219–317.

Johnston, E. F., Ralph Bogart, and A. W. Lindquist. 1954. The resistance to DDT by houseflies. J. Hered. 45:177–182.

Johnston, E. F., N. R. Ellis, and C. F. Winchester. 1956. The interaction of temperature and thiouracil feeding upon carcass characteristic and feeding characteristics of pigs. J. Animal Sci. 15:426–427.

Jones, I. R. 1946. Reproductive efficiency. Inheritance is a factor as shown by a survey of two cow families. Hoards Dairyman. 91:921.

Jull, M. A. 1940. Poultry breeding. 2d ed. New York: John Wiley and Sons, Inc. 484 p.

———. 1952. *Ibid*. 398 p.

Karam, H. A., A. B. Chapman, and A. L. Pope. 1953. Selecting lambs under farm flock conditions. J. Animal Sci. 12:148–164.

Keith, T. B. 1930. Relation of size of swine litter to age of dam and to size of succeeding litters. J. Agri. Research. 41:593–600.

Keith, T. B., R. F. Johnson, and W. P. Lehrer, Jr. 1952. The optimum ratio of concentrate to alfalfa hay for fattening steers. Idaho Agr. Expt. Sta. Bull. 290.

———. 1954. Optimum ratio of concentrate to alfalfa hay for steers as affected by protein level and method of feeding. Idaho Agr. Expt. Sta. Res. Bull. 26.

Kelley, T. B. 1937. Studies in fertility of sheep. Australia Council Sci. and Ind. Research Bull. 112. p. 67.

Kelley, T. B., and H. E. B. Shaw. 1939. Observations on the periodicity of estrus in certain Australian Merino ewes and a half-bred group. J. Australia Council Sci. and Ind. Research. 12:18–22.

———. 1943. Fertility in sheep. An experimental study of the periodicity of estrus and non-breeding seasons in Australia. Australia Council Sci. and Ind. Research. Bull. 166.

———. 1946. Studies on the breeding performance of ewes. *Ibid*. Bull. 205:1–28.

Kempster, H. L., and J. E. Parker. 1936. The normal growth of chickens under normal conditions. Mo. Agr. Exp. Sta. Res. Bull. 247.

Kidwell, J. F. 1953. Some growth relations in range Hereford cattle. West. Sec. Proc. Amer. Soc. Animal Production. 4:(I)1–3.

———. 1954. Some growth relations in range cattle. J. Animal Sci. 13:54–60.

Kidwell, J. F., V. R. Bohman, and J. E. Hunter. 1954. Individual and group feeding of experimental beef cattle as influenced by maturity of hay. J. Animal Sci. 13:543–547.

Kidwell, J. F., and H. R. Guilbert. 1950. A recurrence of the semihairless gene in cattle. J. Hered. 41:190–192.

Kidwell, J. F., J. E. Hunter, P. R. Terman, C. E. Shelby, and R. T. Clark. 1957. Relations between conformation scores and production factors in yearling steers. J. Animal Sci. 16(3):1017 (Abst.)

Kidwell, J. F., E. H. Vernon, R. M. Crown, and C. B. Singletary. 1952. Muscular hypertrophy in cattle. J. Hered. 43:62–68.

Kidwell, J. F., L. Walker, and J. A. McCormick. 1954. Hereditary female sterility in Holstein-Friesian cattle. J. Hered. 45:142–145.

King, H. D. 1918. Studies on inbreeding. I. The effect of inbreeding on the growth and variability in body weight of the albino rat. J. Exptl. Zool. 26:1–54.

———. 1919. Studies on inbreeding. IV. A further study of the effects of inbreeding on the growth and variability in body weight of the albino rat. *Ibid.* 29:135–175.

King, J. W. B. 1950. Pygmy, a dwarfing gene in the house mouse. J. Hered. 41:249–252.

King, S. C., and C. R. Henderson. 1954. Variance components analysis in heritability studies. Poultry Sci. 33(1): 147–154.

Kinzelbach, W. 1932. Unter suchungen über atresia ani beim Schweine. Zetchr. f. Indukt. Abstamm. u Vererb. 60:84–124.

Kirkham, W. B. 1917. Embryology of the yellow mouse. Anat. Record. 11:480–481.

Kleiber, M. 1936. Problems involved in breeding for efficiency of food utilization. Proc. Am. Soc. Animal Production. 247–257.

———. 1947. Body size and metabolic rate. Physiol. Revs. 27:511–541.

Kline, E. A., and L. N. Hazel. 1955. Loin area at tenth and last ribs as related to leanness of pork carcass. J. Animal Sci. 14:659–663.

Knapp, Bradford, Jr., and A. L. Baker. 1944. Correlation between rate and efficiency of gains in steers. J. Animal Sci. 3:219–223.

Knapp, Bradford, Jr., A. L. Baker, and R. T. Clark. 1949. Crossbred beef cattle for the Northern Great Plains. U.S.D.A. Cir. 810.

Knapp, Bradford, Jr., and W. H. Black. 1941. Factors influencing rate of gain during the suckling period in beef calves. J. Agr. Research. 62:249–254.

Knapp, Bradford, Jr., R. C. Church and A. E. Flower. 1951. Genetic history of line 1 Hereford cattle at the U.S. Range Livestock Experiment Station, Miles City, Montana. Mont. Agr. Expt. Sta. Bull. 479.

Knapp, B., Jr., and R. T. Clark. 1947. Genetic and environmental correlations between growth rates of beef cattle at different ages. J. Animal Sci. 6:174–181.

———. 1950. Revised estimates of heritability of economic characteristics in beef cattle. J. Animal Sci. 9:582–588.

———. 1951. Genetic and environmental correlations between weaning scores and subsequent gains in the feedlot with record of performance steers. *Ibid.* 10:365–370.

Knapp, Bradford, Jr., M. W. Emmel, and W. F. Ward. 1936. The inheritance of screw tail in cattle. J. Hered. 27:269–271.

Knapp, Bradford, Jr., and A. W. Nordskog. 1946. Heritability of growth and efficiency in beef cattle. J. Animal Sci. 5:62–70.

Knapp, Bradford, Jr., and R. W. Woodward. 1951. Heritability of weights of beef steers by months during the feeding period. (Abs.) J. Animal Sci. 10:1026.

Knox, C. W. 1930. Factors influencing egg production. I. The influence of maturity upon egg production in S.C. White Leghorns. Iowa Agr. Exp. Sta. Res. Bull. 119.

Knox, C. W., M. A. Jull, and J. P. Quinn. 1935. Correlation studies of egg production and possible genetic interpretations. J. Agr. Research. 50(7):573–589.

Knox, J. H., and Marvin Koger. 1946. A comparison of gains and carcasses produced by three types of feeder steers. J. Animal Sci. 5:333–337.

Koch, Robert M. 1951. Size of calves at weaning as a permanent characteristic of range Hereford cows. J. Animal Sci. 10(3):768–775.

Koger, Marvin, and J. H. Knox. 1952. Heritability of grade and type in range beef cattle. J. Animal Sci. 11:361–369.

———. 1951. The correlation between gains made at different periods by cattle. *Ibid.* 10:760–767.

————. 1948. First calves forecast production. New Mex. Agr. Exp. Sta. Bull. 1026.

Kozelka, A. W. 1929. The inheritance of natural immunity to disease. J. Hered. 20:519–530.

Kraus, W. M., S. Brock, and P. Sloane. 1929. Thyroneural dystrophy. Am. J. Med. Sci. 178:548–562.

Krider, J. L., B. W. Fairbanks, W. E. Carroll, and E. Roberts. 1946. Effectiveness of selecting for rapid and for slow growth rate in Hampshire swine. J. Animal Sci. 5:3–15.

Kronacher, C. 1932. Zwillingsforschung beim Rind. Zeit. f. Züchtung. B 25:327–414.

Kunkel, H. O., R. W. Colby, and C. M. Lyman. 1953. The relationship of serum protein-bound iodine levels to rates of gain in beef cattle. J. Animal Sci. 12:3–9.

Lagerlöf, N. 1951. Hereditary forms of sterility in Swedish cattle breeds. Fertility and Sterility. 2:230–242.

Lambert, W. V., and C. W. Knox. 1932. Selection for resistance to fowl typhoid in chickens with reference to inheritance. Iowa Agri. Expt. Sta. Res. Bull. 153.

Lambert, W. V., S. R. Speelman, and E. P. Osborn. 1939. Differences in incidence of encephalomyelitis in horses. J. Hered. 30:349–352.

Lamoreux, W. F., and F. B. Hutt. 1937. Genetic resistance to deficiency of vitamin B in the chick. Genetics. 22:198–199.

————. 1939. Breed differences in resistance to a deficiency of vitamin B in the fowl. J. Agri. Research. 58:307–316.

Landauer, W. 1929. Thyrogenous dwarfism (Myxoedema infantilis) in the domestic fowl. Am. J. Anat. 43:1–44.

————. 1934. Studies on the creeper fowl. VII. The expression of vitamin D deficiency (rickets) in creeper chicks as compared with normal chicks. Am. J. Anat. 55:229–252.

————. 1941. The hatchability of chicken eggs as influenced by environment and heredity. Conn. (Storrs) Agr. Expt. Sta. Bull. 236:1–124.

Lasley, Earl L. 1957. Ovulation, prenatal mortality and litter size in swine. J. Animal Sci. 16(2):339–340.

Lasley, E. L., and E. A. Kline. 1957. Splitting and cutting errors in swine carcass evaluation. J. Animal Sci. 16:485–489.

Lasley, J. F., and Ralph Bogart. 1943. Some factors influencing reproductive efficiency of range cattle under artificial and natural breeding conditions. Mo. Agri. Expt. Sta. Res. Bull. 376.

Legates, J. E. 1954. Genetic variation in service per conception and calving interval in dairy cattle. J. Animal Sci. 13:81–88.

Lerner, I. M. 1944. Lethal and sublethal characters in farm animals. J. Hered. 35:219–224.

————. 1950. Population genetics and animal improvement as illustrated by the inheritance of egg production. Cambridge, England: Cambridge Univ. Press. 342 pp.

Lerner, I. M., and E. R. Dempster. 1951. Attenuation of genetic progress under continued selection in poultry. Heredity. 5:75–94.

Lerner, I. M., and L. W. Taylor. 1936. The relation of pause to rate of egg production. J. Agr. Research. 52(1):39–47.

————. 1937. The measurement of sexual maturity and persistency. Poultry Sci. 16:419–421.

————. 1943. The inheritance of egg production in the domestic fowl. Am. Naturalist. 77:119–132.

Lillie, F. R. 1916. The theory of the free-martin. Science. 43:611–613.

————. 1917. The free-martin. A study of the action of sex hormones in the foetal life of cattle. J. Exptl. Zool. 23:371–451.

————. 1923. Supplementary notes on twins in cattle. Biol. Bull. 44:47–78.

Lindley, C. E. 1951. Observations on midgets in beef cattle. J. Hered. 42:273–275.

Lloyd-Jones, O., and J. M. Evvard. 1916. Inheritance of color and horns in blue-gray cattle. Iowa Agr. Expt. Sta. Res. Bull. 30.

Loje, K. 1930. Letale gener (dodbringende arveanlaeg) hos husdyrene, specielt hos kvaeg af rod dansk malkerace. Tidsskrift for Landokonomi. 1930:517–549.

Long, J. A., and H. M. Evans. 1920. On the attainment of sexual maturity and the character of the first oestrous cycle in the rat. Anat. Record. 18:244–245.

————. 1922. The oestrous cycle in the rat and its associated phenomena. Memoirs of the University of California. 6:1–148.

Lorenz, F. W., and I. Michael Lerner. 1946. Inheritance of sexual maturity in male chickens and turkeys. Poultry Sci. 25(2):188–189.

Lucas, K., F. X. Gassner, H. H. Stonaker, and S. S. Wheeler. 1950. Relationships of thyroid, adrenal, and pituitary characteristics to body development in small and conventional types of fat Hereford steers. Western Sec., Proc. Am. Soc. Animal Production. 1:73–78.

Lush, J. L. 1924. Double ears in Brahma cattle. J. Hered. 15:93–96.

————. 1930. Earlessness in Karakul sheep. *Ibid.* 21:107–112.

————. 1927. "Duck-legged" cattle on Texas ranches. J. of Hered. 21:85–90.

————. 1931. The number of daughters necessary to prove a sire. J. Dairy Sci. 14:209–220.

————. 1933. The bull index problem in the light of modern genetics. J. Dairy Sci. 16:501–523.

————. 1935. Progeny test and individual performances as indicators of an animal's breeding value. J. Dairy Sci. 18:1–19.

————. 1940. Intra-sire correlations or regressions of offspring on dam as a method of estimating heritability of characteristics. Proc. Am. Soc. An. Prod. 33:293–301.

————. 1943. Animal breeding plans. Ames, Iowa. The Iowa State College Press. 437 p.

————. 1945. Animal breeding plans, Third Edition. The Iowa State College Press, Ames, Iowa.

————. 1947. Family merit and individual merit as basis for selection. Amer. Nat. 81:241–261 and 362–379.

————. 1950. Inheritance of susceptibility to mastitis. J. Dairy Sci. 33:121–125.

Lush, J. L., A. L. Anderson, C. C. Culbertson, and W. E. Hammond. 1933. The reliability of some measures of the productiveness of individual brood sows. Proc. Am. Soc. Animal Production, pp. 282–287.

Lush, J. L., and A. E. Molln. 1942. Litter size and weight as permanent characteristics of sows. U.S. Dept. Agr. Tech. Bull. 836.

Lush, J. L., H. W. Norton, III, and Floyd Arnold. 1941. Effects which selection of dams may have on sire indexes. J. Dairy Sci. 24:695–721.

Lush, J. L., P. S. Shearer, and C. C. Culbertson. 1939. Crossbreeding hogs for pork production. Iowa Agri. Expt. Sta. Bull. 380.

Marlowe, T. J., and Doyle Chambers. 1954. Some endocrine aspects of dwarfism in beef cattle. J. Animal Sci. 13:961.

Marshall, F. H. A. 1904. The oestrous cycle and the formation of the corpus luteum in the sheep. (Phil.) Trans. Roy. Soc. (Lond.) Ser. B. 196:47–97.

————. 1904. Fertility in sheep. Trans. Highland and Agr. Soc. Scot. 5 ser. 16 pp. 34–43.

————. 1906. Fertility in Scottish sheep. Proc. Roy. Soc. (Lond.) Ser. B. 77:58–62.

————. 1908. Effects of environment and nutrition upon fertility. Science Progress. 2 parts. 2:369–377.

Marshall, F. H. A., and J. Hammond. 1932. Fertility and animal breeding. Great Britain, Ministry of Agr. and Fisheries. Bull. 39.

Martland, Marjorie, and Robert Robison. 1929. The preparation and use of the bone phosphatase. Biochem. J. 23:2 237–242.

Mayhew, R. L., and C. W. Upp. 1932. Inherited dwarfism in the fowl. A preliminary report of an apparently hereditary condition of dwarfism in the Rhode Island Red fowl suggesting cretinism. J. Hered. 23:269–276.

MacArthur, J. W. 1944. Genetics of body size and related characters. I. Selecting small and large races of the laboratory mouse. Am. Naturalist. 78:142–157.

————. 1944. Genetics of body size and related characters. II. Satellite characters associated with body size in mice. Am. Naturalist. 78:224–237.

MacDonald, M. A., and R. Bogart. 1954. Relationship between rate and efficiency of gain and type in breeding beef cattle. New Zealand J. Sci. and Technol. 36:460–469.

MacDonald, M. A., Hugo Krueger, and Ralph Bogart. 1956. Rate and efficiency of gains in beef cattle. IV. Blood hemoglobin, glucose, urea, amino acid nitrogen, creatinine, and uric acid of growing Hereford and Angus calves. Ore. Agr. Expt. Sta. Tech. Bull. 36.

MacDonald, M. A., R. S. Tether, H. M. Krueger, and R. Bogart. 1953. Differences in blood amino acids and blood glucose in beef cattle. West. Sec., Proc. Am. Soc. Animal Production. Vol. 4. X.

McCormic, J. A., and J. F. Kidwell. 1953. Producing beef from Holstein steers. Nevada Agr. Expt. Sta. Cir. 3.

McMeekan, C. P., and John Hammond. 1940. The relation of environmental conditions to breeding and selection for commercial types in pigs. Empire J. Exptl. Agr. 8:29.

McPhee, H. C., and S. S. Buckley. 1934. Inheritance of cryptorchidism in swine. J. Hered. 25:295–303.

McPhee, H. C., and O. G. Hankins. 1936. Swine—some current breeding problems. U.S.D.A. Yearbook.

McPhee, Hugh C., E. Z. Russel and John Zellar. 1931. An inbreeding experiment with Poland China swine. J. Hered. 22:(12)393–403.

Mead, S. W., P. W. Gregory, and W. M. Regan. 1942. Proportionate dwarfism in Jersey cows. J. Hered. 33:411–416.

————. 1946. A recurrent mutation of dominant achondroplasia in cattle. *Ibid.* 37:183–188.

————. 1949. An hereditary digital anomaly of cattle. J. Hered. 40:151–155.

Melander, Y. 1950. Chromosome behavior of a triploid adult rabbit (as produced by Haggqvist and Bane after colchecine treatment). Hereditas 36:335–341.

Miller, J. E. 1917. Horned horses. J. Hered. 8:303–305.

Mirand, E. A., and C. M. Osborn. 1953. Insulin sensitivity in the hereditary hypopituitary dwarf mouse. Proc. Soc. Exptl. Biol. and Med. 82:746–748.

Mohr, O. L. 1930. Dødbringende arvefaktorer hos husdyr og mennesker. Naturens Verden. 14:1–31.

Mohr, O. L., and C. Wriedt. 1930. Short spine, a new recessive lethal in cattle, with a comparison of the skeletal deformities in short spine and in amputated calves. J. Genetics 22:279–297.

Mollenbach, G. J. 1941. Studies on hereditary dwarfism in mice. IV. On the function of the metabolic active hormones in the anterior pituitary dwarf mouse. Acta path. et microbiol. Scandin., 18:169–185.

Morley, F. H. W. 1950. Selection for economic characters in Merino sheep. Unpublished Ph.D. thesis. Ames, Iowa: Iowa State College Library.

Morrill, E. L. 1945. A new sex-linked defect in cattle. J. Hered. 36:81–82.

Morris, H. P., L. S. Palmer, and C. Kennedy. 1933. Fundamental food requirements for the growth of the rat. VII. An experimental study of inheritance as a factor influencing food utilization in the rat. Minn. Agr. Expt. Sta. Tech. Bull. 92.

Munro, S. S. 1937. Inheritance of egg production in the domestic fowl. II. Increases in production, their extent and characteristics with a discussion of causal factors. Sci. Agr. 17:376–385.

Nattan-Larrier, L. 1921. Essais de transmission hereditaire de la dourine. Bull. Soc. Path. Exot. 14:273–277.

Nelson, R. H., and VenKatachalam, G. 1949. Estimates of the heritability of birth weight and weaning weight of lambs. J. Animal Sci. 8:607–608. (Abs.)

Newman, H. H., F. N. Freeman, and K. J. Holzinger. 1937. Twins. A study of heredity and environment. Chicago: Univ. of Chicago Press.

Nichita, G., N. Tuschak, and Ch. Calcef. 1934. Recherches avitaminosis B in Rhode Island Red hens. Compt. Vet. Soc. Biol. 117:283–286.

Nordby, J. E. 1932. Inheritance of whorls in the hair of swine. J. Hered. 23:397–404.

———. 1933. Congenital melanotic skin tumors in swine. J. of Hered. 24:361–364.

———. 1934. Kinky tail in swine. *Ibid*. 25:171–174.

———. 1943. Improving Rambouillet sheep for western ranges. Nat. Wool Growers 33(3):12–17.

Nordby, J. E., C. E. Terrill, L. N. Hazel, and J. A. Stoehr. 1945. The etiology and inheritance of inequalities in the jaws of sheep. Anat. Record. 92:235–254.

Nordskog, A. W., R. E. Comstock, and L. M. Winters. 1944. Hereditary and environmental factors affecting growth rate in swine. J. Animal Sci. 3:257–272.

———. 1944. The relationship between certain blood components and rate of growth in swine. J. Animal Sci. 3:422–430.

Oestergaard, P. S. 1946. Om Kaelvnings-intervallet (The calving interval). (Abst.) An. Breeding Abst. 14:226.

Olds, D., H. B. Morrison, and D. M. Seath. 1949. Efficiency of natural breeding in dairy cattle. Ky. Agri. Expt. Sta. Bull. 539.

Olds, D., and D. M. Seath. 1950. Predictability of breeding efficiency in dairy cattle. J. Dairy Sci. 33:721–724.

———. 1953. Repeatability, heritability and the effect of level of milk production on the occurrence of first estrus after calving in dairy cattle. J. Animal Sci. 12:10–14.

Olson, M. 1928. Crossbreeding experiment. S. Dak. Agri. Expt. Sta. Ann. Report 14.

Owen, R. D., H. P. Davis, and R. F. Morgan. 1946. Quintuplet calves and erythrocyte mosaicism. J. Hered. 37:291–297.

Pahnish, O. F. 1951. Performance test selects faster gaining cattle. Prog. Agri. in Arizona 3:11–12.

Pahnish, O. F., E. B. Stanley, and C. E. Safley. 1952. A study of homozygous dwarfism in beef cattle. Western Sec., Proc. Am. Soc. Animal Production, 3: Sec. IX:1–5.

———. 1955. The inheritance of a dwarf anomaly in beef cattle. J. Animal Sci. 14(1):200–207.

———. 1955. The history of an experimental herd of dwarf beef cattle. J. Animal Sci. 14:1025–1033.

Palmer, L. S., C. Kennedy, C. E. Caverly, C. Lohn, and P. H. Weswig. 1946. Genetic differences in the bio-chemistry and physiology influencing food utilization for growth in rats. Minn. Agri. Expt. Sta. Tech. Bull. 176.

Pantech Farms. 1950–1953. Investigation of the heritability of gain at Pantech Farms. Texas Technological College Report (mimeo).

Patterson, R. E., J. H. Jones, J. J. Boyles, and R. V. Turnbough. 1949. Performance-testing and progeny-testing of beef breeding stock as an aid to selection. (Abst.) J. Animal Sci. 8:608.

Pearl, R. 1912. The mode of inheritance of fecundity in the domestic fowl. J. Exptl. Zool. 13:153–268.

Pearl, R., J. W. Gowan, and Miner. 1919. Studies in milk secretion VII, Maine Agr. Ext. Bull. 281.

Pearson, A. M., L. J. Bratzler, J. A. Hoefer, J. F. Price, W. T. Magee, and R. J. Deans. 1956. The fat-lean ratio in the rough loin as a tool in evaluation of pork carcasses. J. Animal Sci. 15:896–901.

Pearson, A. M., J. F. Price, J. A. Hoefer, L. J. Bratzler, and W. T. Magee. 1957. A comparison of the live probe and lean meter for predicting various carcass measurements of swine. J. Animal Sci. 16:481–484.

Pierce, Cecil D., H. G. Avery, Martin Burris, and Ralph Bogart. 1954. Rate and efficiency of gains in beef cattle. II. Some factors affecting performance testing. Ore. Agri. Expt. Sta. Tech. Bull. 33.

Pincus, G., and C. H. Waddington. 1939. The effect of mitosis inhibiting treatments on normally fertilized precleavage rabbit eggs. The comparative behavior of mammalian eggs in vivo and in vitro–V. J. Hered. 30:515–518.

Popova-Wassina, E. J. 1931. A naked lamb. J. Hered. 22:91.

Prawochenski, R. 1936. A new lethal factor in the horse (stiff foreleg). J. Hered. 27:411–414.

Price, D. A., M. A. MacDonald, Ralph Bogart, Hugo Krueger, C. E. Shelby, and R. T. Clark. 1956. Correlations of nitrogenous and carbohydrate constituents of the blood and urine with rate and efficiency of gains in beef cattle. Western Sec., Am. Soc. Animal Production. 7:(XLIV)1–9.

Price, J. F., A. M. Pearson, and E. J. Benne. 1957. Specific gravity and chemical composition of the untrimmed ham as related to leanness of pork carcasses. J. Animal Sci. 16:85–92.

Quesenberry, J. R. 1950. Livestock breeding research at the U.S. Range Livestock Expt. Sta. Agr. Information Bull. 18, U.S.D.A.

Rae, A. L. 1950. Genetic variation and covariation in productive characters of New Zealand Romney Marsh sheep. Unpublished Ph.D. Thesis. Ames, Iowa: Iowa State College Library.

Regan, W. M., P. W. Gregory, and S. W. Mead. 1944. Hereditary strabismus in Jersey cattle. J. Hered. 35:233–234.

Regan, W. M., S. W. Mead, and P. W. Gregory. 1935. An inherited skin defect in cattle. J. Hered. 26:357–362.

Reineke, E. P., and C. W. Turner. 1941. Growth response of thyroidectomized goats to artificially formed thyroprotein. Endocrinology. 29:667–673.

Rice, V. A. 1944. A new method for indexing dairy bulls. J. Dairy Sci. 27:921–936.

Rich, F. A. 1923. Concerning blood complement. Vermont Agri. Expt. Sta. Bull. 230.

Riddle, O. 1929. The inheritance of thyroid size and the establishment of thyroid races in ring doves. Am. Naturalist. 63:385–409.

Rhoad, A. O. 1934. Woolly hair in swine. J. Hered. 25:371–375.

———. 1955. Breeding beef cattle for unfavorable environments. Austin, Texas: Univer. of Texas Press.

Roberts, E. 1921. Polydactylism in cattle. J. Hered. 12:84–86.

———. 1940. Effect of lactic acid and sodium bicarbonate on the sex ratio. J. Heredity. 31(12):499–500.

Roberts, E., and W. E. Carroll. 1931. The inheritance of "hairlessness" in swine. J. of Hered. 22:125–132.

————. 1939. A study of hybrid vigor in a cross between Poland China and Duroc Jersey swine. J. Agri. Research. 59:847–854.

————. 1942. Crossbreeding in swine. Univ. of Ill. Bull. 489.

Roberts, J. A. F. 1926. A hereditary lethal deformity in new-born lambs. J. Ministry Agr. (Engl.). 33:795–801.

Robertson, F. W. 1955. Selection responses and the properties of genetic variation. Cold Springs Harbor Symposium on Population. Genetics. 20:166–177.

Robertson, G. L., L. E. Casida, R. H. Grummer, and A. B. Chapman. 1951. Some feeding and management factors affecting age at puberty and related phenomena in Chester White and Poland China gilts. J. Animal Sci. 10:841–866.

Robertson, G. L., R. H. Grummer, L. E. Casida, and A. B. Chapman. 1951. Age at puberty and related phenomena in outbred Chester White and Poland China gilts. J. Animal Sci. 10:647–656.

Rollins, W. C., H. R. Guilbert, and P. W. Gregory. 1952. Genetic and environmental factors affecting preweaning growth in Hereford cattle. Western Sec., Am. Soc. Animal Production. 3:(x)1.

Rommell, George M. 1906. The fecundity of Poland China and Duroc Jersey sows. U.S.D.A. cir. 95.

Romo, A., and R. L. Blackwell. 1954. Phenotypic and genetic correlations between type and weight of range cattle at different periods. Proc. W. Sect. ASAP 5:205–210.

Roubicek, C. B., N. W. Hilston, and S. S. Wheeler. 1951. Progeny studies with Hereford and Shorthorn cattle. Wyo. Agri. Expt. Sta. Bull. 307.

Russell, Elizabeth L. 1939. A quantitative study of genic effects on guinea pig coat colors. Genetics. 24:332–355.

Russell, S. F. 1919. Sheep breeding experiment: Inheritance of characters in sheep. Okla. Agr. Expt. Sta. Bull. 126.

Russell, W. Lawson. 1939. Investigation of the physiological genetics of hair and skin color in the guinea pig by means of the dopa reaction. Genetics. 24:645–667.

Safley, C. E., H. H. Stonaker, and S. S. Wheeler. 1950. A comparison of small and conventional types of Hereford steers as evaluated by body and carcass measurements. Western Sec., Proc. Am. Soc. Animal Production. 1:90–101.

Saunders, L. Z., J. D. Sweet, S. M. Martin, F. H. Fox, and M. G. Fincher. 1952. Hereditary congenital ataxia in Jersey calves. Cornell Vet. 42:559–591.

Sawin, P. B., and R. H. Curran. 1952. Genetic and physiological background of reproduction in the rabbit. I. The problem and its biological significance. J. Exptl. Zool. 120:165–201.

Sawin, P. B., and D. Glick. 1943. Atropenesterase, a genetically determined enzyme in the rabbit. Proc. Nat. Acad. Sci. U.S. 29:55–59.

Sawyer, W. A., Ralph Bogart, and Mohamed M. Oloufa. 1948. Weaning weight of calves as related to age of dam, sex and color. J. Animal Sci. 7(4):514–515.

Schleicher, E. W., H. H. Stonaker, M. H. Hazaleus, and S. S. Wheeler. 1950. Feedlot and carcass characteristics of small and conventional type Hereford steer calves. Western Sec., Am. Soc. Animal Production. 1:68–72.

Schoonover, C. O., and P. O. Stratton. 1954. A study of recessive dwarfism in Hereford females. Western Sec., Proc. Am. Soc. Animal Production. 5:233–238.

Schott, R. G. 1932. The inheritance of resistance to Salmonella aerotrycke in various strains of mice. Genetics. 17:203–229.

Schott, R. G., E. M. Gildow, and R. W. Phillips. 1938. Problems in long-range insemination of livestock. Proc. Am. Soc. Animal Production. p. 241–246.

Serfontein, P. J., and L. F. Payne. 1934. Inheritance of abnormal anatomical condition in the tibial and metatarsal joints. Poultry Sci. 13:61–63.

Shaw, A. O. 1938. A skull defect in cattle. J. Hered. 29:319–320.

Shelby, C. E., R. T. Clark, and R. R. Woodward. 1955. The heritability of some economic characteristics of beef cattle. J. Animal Sci. 14(2):372–385.

Shrode, R. R., and J. L. Lush. 1947. Advances in genetics. New York: Academic Press Inc. 459 pp.

Smith, A. D. B., O. J. Robinson, and D. M. Bryant. 1938. The genetics of the pig. Bib. Gen. 12:1–157.

Smith, P. E., and E. C. MacDowell. 1930. An hereditary anterior-pituitary deficiency in the mouse. Anat. Record. 46:249–257.

————. 1931. The differential effect of hereditary mouse dwarfism on the anterior pituitary hormones. Anat. Record. 50:85–93.

Snedecor, G. W. 1946. Statistical methods, 4th Edition. Iowa State College Press, Ames.

Snell, G. D. 1929. Dwarf, a new Mendelian recessive character of the house mouse. Proc. Natl. Acad. Sci. U.S. 15:733–734.

Snyder, L. H. 1951. The principles of genetics. Boston, Mass.: D. C. Heath and Company.

Sollas, I. B. J. 1914. Note on the offspring of a dwarf bearing strain of guinea pigs. Genetics. 3:201–204.

Sonneborn, T. M. 1951. The role of the genes in cytoplasmic inheritance. Genetics in the 20th Century. New York: The Macmillan Co. pp. 291–314.

Spielman, A., and I. R. Jones. 1939. The reproductive efficiency of dairy cattle. J. Dairy Sci. 22:329–334.

Spriggs, D. N. 1946. White heifer disease. Vet. Record. 58:405–409.

Squiers, C. D., G. E. Dickerson, and D. T. Mayer. 1952. Influence of inbreeding, age, and growth rate of sows on sexual maturity, rate of ovulation, fertilization, and embryonic survival. Mo. Agri. Expt. Sta. Res. Bull. 494.

Stewart, H. A. 1945. The inheritance of prolificacy in swine. J. Animal Sci. 4:359–366.

————. 1945. An appraisal of factors affecting prolificacy in swine. *Ibid.* 4:250–260.

Stoddard, S. E. 1938. Hereditary susceptibility to sepsis. J. Hered. 29:341–342.

Stokes, D. K., Jr., M. F. Futrell, and H. O. Kunkel. 1953. Further studies on the relationship of serum protein-bound iodine levels to rates of gain in beef cattle. J. Animal Sci. 12:897–898.

Stonaker, H. H. 1951. A unique herd of Hereford cattle. J. Hered. 42:207–209.

————. 1954. Observations on reproduction, growth, feed utilization and grades of inbred and outbred Hereford cattle. (Abst.) J. Animal Sci. 13:963.

————. 1954. Dwarfism in beef cattle. Western Sec., Proc. Am. Soc. Animal Production. 5:239–242.

Stonaker, H. H., M. H. Hazaleus, and S. S. Wheeler. 1950. Feed-lot and carcass characteristics of Hereford steers of small and conventional types. (Abs.) J. Animal Sci. 9:639.

————. 1952. Feedlot and carcass characteristics of individually fed comprest and conventional type Hereford steers. J. Animal Sci. 11:17–25.

Stonaker, H. H., J. E. Ingalls, and S. S. Wheeler. 1952. Winter hay consumption of breeding females of large, intermediate, and comprest types Hereford cattle. J. Animal Sci. 11:26–33.

Stonaker, H. H., and J. L. Lush. 1942. Heritability of conformation in Poland China swine as evaluated by scoring. J. Animal Sci. 1:99–105.

Stonaker, H. H., S. S. Wheeler, M. H. Hazaleus, J. E. Ingalls, and E. W. Schleicher. 1950. Beef breeding research in Colorado. Colo. Agr. Expt. Sta. Progress Report.

Stormont, C. 1954. Research with cattle twins. Statistics and mathematics in biology. Ames, Iowa: The Iowa State College Press.

Stroble, C. P., R. W. Mason, and N. W. Hilston. 1954. A study of the immunogenetic behavior of inbred lines of Hereford cattle. (Abst.) J. Animal Sci. 13:963.

Surrarrer, T. C. 1943. Bulldog and hairless calves. J. Hered. 34:175–178.

Taylor, J. M., and L. N. Hazel. 1955. The growth curve of pigs between 134 and 174 days of age. J. Animal Sci. 14:1133–1139.

Taylor, L. W., and I. M. Lerner. 1939. Effect of varying levels of wheat bran on age at sexual maturity. Poultry Sci. 18:323–326.

Terrill, C. E. 1944. More profit in open face ewes. Montana Wool Grower. 18:13–47.

———. 1947. Color on the legs of sheep. Its inheritance in the Columbia and Targhee breeds. J. Hered. 38:89–92.

———. 1949. The relation of face covering to lamb and wool production in range Rambouillet ewes. J. Animal Sci. 8:353–361.

———. 1951. Effectiveness of selection: For economically important traits in sheep. *Ibid.* 10:17–18.

———. 1953. The relation between sale price and merit in Columbia, Targhee, and Rambouillet rams. *Ibid.* 12:419–430.

Terrill, C. E., and L. N. Hazel. 1946. Heritability of face covering and neck folds in range Rambouillet lambs as evaluated by scoring. J. Animal Sci. 5:170–179.

Terrill, C. E., G. M. Sidwell, and L. N. Hazel. 1947. Effects of some environmental factors on yearling traits of Columbia and Targhee ewes. J. Animal Sci. 6:115–122.

———. 1948. Effects of some environmental factors on traits of yearling and mature Rambouillet rams. *Ibid.* 7:311–319.

Terrill, C. E., and J. A. Stoehr. 1942. The importance of body weight in selection of range ewes. J. Animal Sci. 1:221–228.

Tuff, P. 1948. Two new lethal characters in cattle. Skand. Vet.-Tid. 38:379–395.

Turman, E. G., and F. N. Andrews. 1955. Some effects of purified anterior pituitary growth hormone on swine. J. Animal Sci. 14:7–18.

Turner, C. W. 1925. A comparison of Guernsey sires. Mo. Agr. Expt. Sta. Res. Bull. 79.

———. 1939. Hormonic interrelations between reproduction, mammary gland growth and lactation. Growth. 3:323–336.

Tyler, W. J., G. E. Dickerson, and A. B. Chapman. 1946. Influence of inbreeding on growth and production of Holstein-Friesian cattle. (Abst.) J. Animal. Sci. 5:390–391.

Tyzzer, E. E. 1917. A fatal disease of the Japanese waltzing mouse caused by a spore-bearing bacillus (*B. piloformis,* N.S.P.). J. Med. Research. 37:307–338.

Uppenborn, W. 1933. Untersuchungen über die Trächtigkeitsdaner der Stuten. Zeit. f. Zücht. Reihe. B. 28:1–27.

Walther, A. R., J. Prufer, and P. Carstens. 1932. Beitrag zur Kenntnis der Vererbungser-scheinungen beim Schwein. Züchter. 4:178–184.

Walton, A., and J. Hammond. 1938. Maternal effects on growth and conformation in Shire horse and Shetland pony crosses. Royal Soc. Lond. Proc. Series B. 125:311–335.

Ward, R. E., S. I. Bechdel, and N. B. Guerrant. 1940. Carotene and vitamin A in the nutrition of growing dairy cattle. J. Dairy Sci. 23:115–124.

Warnick, A. C., R. H. Grummer, and L. E. Casida. 1949. The nature of reproductive failures in repeat-breeder sows. J. Animal Sci. 8:569–577.

Warren, D. C. 1934. Inheritance of age at sexual maturity in the domestic fowl. Genetics. 19:600–617.

———. 1953. Practical poultry breeding. New York: The Macmillan Co.

Warren, E. P., and Ralph Bogart. 1952. Effect of selection for age at time of puberty on reproductive performance in the rat. Ore. Agr. Expt. Sta. Tech. Bull. 25.

Warren, T. R., and F. W. Atkeson. 1931. Inheritance of hernia in a family of Holstein-Friesian cattle. J. Hered. 22:345–352.

Warwick, B. L. 1931. Breeding experiments with sheep and swine. Ohio. Agr. Expt. Sta. Bull. 480.

Warwick, E. J. 1948. Genetics and animal breeding. Wash. Popular Bull. 189.

Warwick, E. J., A. B. Chapman, and Burr Ross. 1943. Some anomalies in pigs. J. Hered. 34:349–352.

Wassin, B. 1931. Linkage studies in sheep. J. Hered. 22:9–13.

Weaver, L. A., and Ralph Bogart. 1943. Some factors influencing efficient production of sows. Mo. Agr. Expt. Sta. Bull. 461.

————. 1944. Variation in efficiency of hogs. Mo. Agri. Expt. Sta. Cir. 290.

Weber, A. D., and H. L. Ibsen. 1934. The occurrence of the double-muscled character in purebred beef cattle. A.S.A.P. 228–232.

Whatley, J. A., Jr., and E. L. Quaife. 1937. Adjusting weights of pigs to a standard age of 56 days. Proc. Am. Soc. Animal Production. 30:126–130.

Wheeler, S. S. 1944. Results of progeny testing of beef sires. Wyo. An. Prod. Dept. Annual Prog. Report.

White, W. T., and H. L. Ibsen. 1935. Color inheritance in Galloway-Holstein crosses. J. Hered. 26:75–84.

Whiting, P. W. 1943. Multiple alleles in complimentary sex determination of Habrobracon. Genetics. 28:365–382.

Wiggins, E. L., and C. E. Terrill. 1953. Variation in penis development in ram lambs. J. Animal Sci. 12:524–535.

Wiggins, E. L., C. E. Terrill, and L. C. Emik. 1953. The effect of year, breed, age, and number of ewes bred on fertility in range rams. Western Sec., Proc. Am. Soc. Animal Production. 4:XXII, 1–8.

————. 1954. The effect of year, breed, age, and number of ewes bred on fertility in range rams. J. Animal Sci. 13:455–463.

Willey, N. B., O. D. Butler, J. K. Riggs, J. H. Jones, and P. J. Lyerly. 1950. The influence of type on feedlot performance and killing qualities of Hereford steers. (Abst.) J. Animal Sci. 9–641.

Williams, C. M., Hugo Krueger, and Ralph Bogart. 1953. Rectal temperatures of performance tested beef calves. Proceedings of the Am. Soc. An. Prod., Western Sec. 4(6): 1–4.

Williams, C. M., H. Krueger, and R. Bogart. 1954. Heart rates of performance tested beef calves. Western Sec., Proc. Am. Soc. Animal Production. 5:299–304.

Williams, L. G. 1955. Performance in relation to weaning response in production tested beef cattle. M.S. Thesis. Ore. State College, Corvallis.

Willson, Fred S., A. E. Flower, and E. P. Orcutt. 1953. Bull indexing as a selection procedure in the improvement of beef cattle. Mont. Agr. Expt. Sta. Bull. 487.

Willson, Fred S., F. A. Ralston, and A. E. Flower. 1950. Beef cattle improvement through bull indexing. Mont. Agri. Expt. Sta. Cir. 57 (mimeo).

Wilson, J. W. 1940. Development of the Notail sheep. South Dakota Agri. Exp. Sta. Cir. 28.

Wilson, P. T. 1934. A study of twins with special reference to heredity as a factor in determining differences in environment. Human Biol. 6:324–354.

Winchester, C. F. 1953. Energy requirements of beef calves for maintenance and growth. U.S.D.A. Tech. Bull. 1971.

Winge, O. 1934. The experimental alteration of sex chromosomes into autosomes and vice versa, as illustrated by Lebistes. Comp. Rend. des Travaux du Laboratoire Carlsberg. Serie Physiologique. 21:1–49.

Winsor, C. P., and G. L. Clarke. 1940. A statistical study of variation in the catch of plankton nets. J. Marine Research. 3:1–34.

Winter, F. L. 1929. The mean and variability as affected by continuous selection for composition in corn. J. Agr. Research. 39:451–476.

Winters, L. M. 1936. You will find greater profits with crossbred swine. Minn. Agr. Ext. Service. Special Bull. 180.

――――. 1936. Studies of breeding for increased efficiency. A.S.A.P. 263–265.

――――. 1954. Animal Breeding, 5th ed. John Wiley & Sons, Inc. New York. 420 p.

Winters, L. M., R. E. Comstock, R. E. Hodgson, O. M. Kiser, P. S. Jordan, and D. L. Dailey. 1947. Experiments with inbreeding swine and sheep. Minn. Agr. Expt. Sta. Bull. 364.

Winters, L. M., D. L. Dailey, P. S. Jordan, O. M. Kiser, R. E. Hodgson, J. N. Cummings, and C. F. Sierk. 1948. Experiments with inbreeding swine. Minn. Agr. Expt. Sta. Bull. 400.

Winters, L. M., W. W. Green, and R. E. Comstock. 1942. Prenatal development of the bovine. Univ. Minn. Tech. Bull. 151.

Winters, L. M., O. M. Kiser, P. S. Jordan, and W. H. Peters. 1935. A six-year study of crossbreeding swine. Minn. Agr. Expt. Sta. Bull. 320.

Winters, L. M., and H. McMahon. 1933. Efficiency variations in steers. Approved record of performance. Minn. Agr. Expt. Sta. Tech. Bull. 94.

Woodward, R. R., and R. T. Clark. 1950. The repeatability of performance of several Hereford sires as measured by progeny records. J. Animal Sci. 9:588–592.

Woodward, R. R., R. T. Clark, and J. N. Cummings. 1947. Studies on large and small type Hereford cattle. Mont. Agri. Expt. Sta. Bull. 401.

Woodward, R. R., and Bradford Knapp, Jr. 1950. The hereditary aspects of eye cancer in Hereford cattle. J. Animal Sci. 9:571–581.

Woodworth, R. S. 1941. Heredity and environment. N.Y. Social Science Research Council.

Wriedt, C. 1921. Breeding earless sheep. J. Hered. 12:56.

――――. 1924. The "Gromet" pattern in sheep. Another Mendelian character in livestock. J. Hered. 15:125–127.

Wriedt, C., and O. L. Mohr. 1928. Amputated, a recessive lethal in cattle; with a discussion of the bearing of lethal factors on the principles of livestock breeding. J. Genet. 20:187–215.

Wright, S. 1917. Color inheritance in mammals. V. Cattle. J. Hered. 8:521–527.

――――. 1923. Mendelian analysis of the pure breeds of livestock. I. The measurements of inbreeding and relationship. J. Heredity. 14:339–348.

――――. 1931. On evaluation of dairy sires. Amer. Soc. An. Prod. Proc. pp. 71–78.

Wright, S., and O. N. Eaton. 1929. The persistence of differentiation among inbred families of guinea pigs. U.S.D.A. Tech. Bull. 103.

Wright, S., S. D. Lewis, and P. A. Lewis. 1921. Factors in the resistance of guinea pigs to tuberculosis with especial regard to inbreeding and heredity. Am. Naturalist. 55:20–50.

Yamane, J. 1927. Über die "Atresia coli" eine lethale, erbliche Darmmissbildung beim Pferde, und ihre Kombination mit Gehirngliomen. Zeitschr. f. indukt. Abstamm.-u. Vererb. 46:188–207.

Yao, T. S., V. L. Simmons, and R. G. Schott. 1953. Heritability of fur characters and birth weight in Karakul lambs. J. Animal Sci. 12(3):431–439.

Yapp, W. W. 1924. Transmitting ability of dairy sires. Proc. Amer. Soc. An. Prod. 90–92.

Zobrisky, S., D. E. Brady, and J. F. Lasley. 1954. Significant relationships in pork carcass evaluation. (Abs.) J. Animal Sci. 12:904–905.

INDEX